LASERS:
A GUIDE TO THE BOOK LITERATURE

LASERS:
A GUIDE TO THE BOOK LITERATURE

CHARLES BLAIN (EDITOR)

Nova Science Publishers, Inc.
New York

Library of Congress Cataloging-in-Publication Data
Available Upon Request

ISBN 1-59033-225-3.

400 Oser Ave, Suite 1600
Hauppauge, New York 11788-3619
Tele. 631-231-7269 Fax 631-231-8175
e-mail: Novascience@earthlink.net
Web Site: http://www.novapublishers.com

Printed in the United States of America

CONTENTS

PREFACE

Developments in lasers continue to enable progress in many areas such as eye surgery, the recording industry and dozens of others. This book presents citations from the book literature for the last 25 years and groups them for ease of access which is also provided by subject, author and title indexes.

Title Index

#

A

B

C

D

E

F

G

H

I

J

K

L

M

N

O

P

Q

R

S

T

U

V

W

X

BIBLIOGRAPHY

1994 IEEE nonlinear optics: materials, fundamentals and applications: July 25-29, 1994, Hilton Waikoloa Village, Waikoloa, Hawaii: [conference proceedings] / cosponsored by IEEE/Lasers and Electro-Optics Society and Optical Society of America. Published/Created: New York: IEEE, c1994. Related Authors: Lasers and Electro-optics Society (Institute of Electrical and Electronics Engineers) Optical Society of America. Description: x, 471 p.: ill.; 28 cm. ISBN: 0780314743 0780314735 (pbk.) Notes: Includes bibliographical references. Subjects: Nonlinear optics--Congresses. Optical materials--Congresses. Optical materials--Industrial applications--Congresses. LC Classification: QC446.15 .A15 1994 Dewey Class No.: 621.36/9 20

1995 digest of the LEOS summer topical meetings, August 7-11, 1995, at Keystone Resort, Keystone, Colorado. Published/Created: [New York]: Institute of Electrical and Electronics Engineers, c1994. Related Authors: Lasers and Electro-optics Society (Institute of Electrical and Electronics Engineers) Description: 1 v. (various pagings): ill.; 28 cm. ISBN: 078032448X (softbound) 0780324498 (microfiche) Contents: Flat panel display technology -- Technologies for a global information infrastructure / in cooperation with the IEEE Communications Society -- ICs for new age lightwave communications / in cooperation with the IEEE Solid State Circuits Council -- RF optoelectronics / co-sponsored by the IEEE Microwave Theory and Techniques Society. Notes: Cover title. At head of Title - IEEE/LEOS. "IEEE catalog number: 95TH8031." Includes bibliographical references and index. Subjects: Optical communications--Congresses. Laser communication systems--Congresses. Optoelectronic devices--Congresses. Electrooptics--Congresses. LC Classification: TK5103.59 .A14 1994

1998 IEEE/LEOS summer topical meetings: digest, 20-24 July, 1998, Monterey Palza Hotel, Monterey, CA. Published/Created: [New York]: Institute of Electrical and Electronics Engineers, c1998. Related Authors: Institute of Electrical and Electronics Engineers. Lasers and Electro-optics Society (Institute of Electrical and Electronics Engineers) Description: 1 v. (various pagings): ill.; 28 cm. ISBN: 0780349539 (softbound) 0780349547 (microfiche) Partial Contents: Broadband optical networks and technologies. Optical MEMS. Smart pixels. Organic optics and optoelectronics. Notes: Cover title. "IEEE catalog # 98TH8369"--Spine. Includes bibliographical references index. Subjects: Optical communications--Congresses. Optoelectronic devices--Congresses. Multiplexing--Congresses. Broadband communication systems--Congresses. LC Classification: TK5103.59 .A15 1998 Dewey Class No.: 621.382/7 21

2000 Optical data storage conference digest: 14-17 May 2000, Chateau Whistler Resort,

Whistler, British Columbia, Canada / sponsored by IEEE/Lasers and Electro-Optics Society, SPIE, and Optical Society of America. Published/Created: Piscataway, NJ: IEEE Service Center, c2000. Related Authors: Lasers and Electro-optics Society (Institute of Electrical and Electronics Engineers) Society of Photo-optical Instrumentation Engineers. Optical Society of America. Topical Meeting on Optical Data Storage Description: x, 212 p.: ill.; 28 cm. ISBN: 078035950X Notes: IEEE catalog # 00TH8491 Includes bibliographic references and author index. Subjects: Computer storage devices--Congresses. Optical storage devices--Congresses.

A History of the IEEE Lasers and Electro-optics Society / Dean B. Anderson, editor and historian. Published/Created: New York: Institute of Electrical and Electronics Engineers; Piscataway, NJ: Available from IEEE Lasers and Electro-optics Society, c1993. Related Authors: Anderson, Dean B., 1921- Institute of Electrical and Electronics Engineers. Description: 1 v. (various pagings); 28 cm. ISBN: 0780399676 Notes: Includes bibliographical references. Subjects: Lasers and Electro-optics Society (Institute of Electrical and Electronics Engineers)--History. Quantum electronics--Societies, etc.--History. LC Classification: TA1671 .H57 1993 Dewey Class No.: 621.36/6/06073 20

Active and adaptive optical systems: 22-24 July 1991, San Diego, California / Mark A. Ealey, chair/editor; sponsored and published by SPIE--the International Society for Optical Engineering. Published/Created: Bellingham, Wash.: SPIE, c1991. Related Authors: Ealey, Mark A. Society of Photo-optical Instrumentation Engineers. Description: ix, 557 p.: ill.; 28 cm. ISBN: 0819406708 Notes: "Part of a four-conference program ... held at SPIE's 1991 International Symposium on Optical Applied Science and Engineering, 21-26 July 1991"--P. vii. Includes bibliographical references and index. Subjects: Optics, Adaptive--Congresses. Optical detectors--Congresses. Image processing--Congresses. Telescopes--Congresses. Lasers--Congresses. Series: Proceedings of SPIE--the International Society for Optical Engineering; v. 1542. Variant Series: Proceedings / SPIE--the International Society for Optical Engineering; v. 1542 LC Classification: TA1505 .A26 1991 Dewey Class No.: 621.36/7 20

Adriatico Research Conference (1987: Trieste, Italy) Undulator magnets for synchrotron radiation and free electron lasers: Adriatico Research Conference, Trieste, Italy, 23-26 June, 1987: [proceedings] / editors, R. Bonifacio, L. Fonda, C. Pellegrini. Published/Created: Singapore: World Scientific, c1988. Related Authors: Bonifacio, R. Fonda, L. Pellegrini, C. Description: viii, 268 p.: ill.; 23 cm. ISBN: 9971507099 Notes: Includes bibliographical references. Subjects: Wiggler magnets--Congresses. Synchrotron radiation--Congresses. Free electron lasers--Congresses. LC Classification: QC757.92 .A37 1987 Dewey Class No.: 538/.4 20

Advanced high-power lasers: 1-5 November 1999, Osaka, Japan / Marek Osi′nski, Howard T. Powell, Koichi Toyoda, chairs/editors; sponsored by LSJ--the Laser Society of Japan [and] SPIE--the International Society for Optical Engineering; cooperating organizations, Faculty of Engineering and ILE, Osaka University (Japan) ... [et al.]. Published/Created: Bellingham, Wash., USA: SPIE, c2000. Related Authors: Osi′nski, Marek. Powell, Howard T. Toyoda, Koichi. Description: xv, 878 p.: ill.; 28 cm. ISBN: 0819434876 Notes: Includes bibliographical references and index. Subjects: High power lasers--Industrial applications--Congresses. Series: Proceedings of SPIE--the International Society for Optical Engineering; v. 3889. Variant Series: SPIE proceedings series, 0277-786X; v. 3889 LC Classification: TA1673 .A35 2000 Dewey Class No.: 621.36/6 21

Advanced ICFA Beam Dynamics Workshop (19th: 2000: Arcidosso, Italy) Physics of, and science with, the X-ray free-electron laser: 19th Advanced ICFA Beam Dynamics Workshop, Arcidosso, Italy, 10-15 September 2000 / editors, S. Chattopadhyay ... [et al.]. Published/Created: Melville, N.Y.: American Institute of Physics, 2001. Related Authors: Chattopadhyay, Swapan, 1952- Description: x, 236 p.: ill.; 25 cm. ISBN: 0735400229 Notes: Includes bibliographical references and index. Subjects: Free electron lasers--Congresses. Series: AIP conference proceedings; no. 581. Variant Series: AIP conference proceedings; 0094-243X; v. 581 LC Classification: QC689.55.F75 A38 2000 Dewey Class No.: 621.36/6 21

Advanced laser processing of materials: fundamentals and applications: symposium held November 27-30, 1995, Boston, Massachusetts, U.S.A. / editors, Rajiv Singh ... [et al.]. Published/Created: Pittsburgh, Pa.: Materials Research Society, c1996. Related Authors: Singh, R. K. (Rajiv K.) Description: xvii, 674 p.: ill.; 24 cm. ISBN: 1558993002 (alk. paper) Notes: Includes bibliographical references and indexes. Subjects: Lasers--Industrial applications--Materials--Effect of radiation on--Laser ablation--Congresses. Series: Materials Research Society symposia proceedings; v. 397. Variant Series: Materials Research Society symposium proceedings; v. 397 LC Classification: TA1673 .A36 1996 Dewey Class No.: 621.36/6 20

Advanced optical methods for ultrasensitive detection: 6-7 February 1995, San Jose, California / Bryan L. Fearey, chair/editor; sponsored and published by SPIE--the International Society for Optical Engineering. Published/Created: Bellingham, Wash.: SPIE, c1995. Related Authors: Fearey, Bryan L. Society of Photo-optical Instrumentation Engineers. Description: vii, 176 p.: ill.; 28 cm. ISBN: 0819417327 Notes: Includes bibliographical references and index. Subjects: Laser spectroscopy--Surface chemistry--Lasers--Industrial applications--Spectrum analysis--Instruments--Congresses. Series: Proceedings of SPIE--the International Society for Optical Engineering; v. 2385. Variant Series: Proceedings / SPIE--the International Society for Optical Engineering; v. 2385 LC Classification: QC454.L3 A36 1995 Dewey Class No.: 621.36/6 20

Advanced semiconductor lasers and their applications topical meeting. Published/Created: Washington, DC: Optical Society of America, 1999. Description: p.; cm. ISBN: 1557525773 (conference: acid-free paper) Series: OSA technical digest series LC Classification: 9906 BOOK NOT YET IN LC

Advanced semiconductor lasers and their applications: from the Topical Meeting on Advanced Semiconductor Lasers and Their Applications, July 21-23, 1999, Santa Barbara, California / edited by Leo Hollberg and Robert J. Lang; sponsored by Optical Society of America, in cooperation with US Air Force Office of Scientific Research and Electronics Society of IEICE of Japan. Published/Created: Washington, DC: Optical Society of America, 1999. Description: 217 p.; 28 cm. ISBN: 1557526052 Series: Osa trends in optics and photonics series 31

Advanced Solid State Lasers 1998. Edition Information: Conference Edition. Published/Created: Washington, DC: Optical Society of America, 1998. Description: p.; cm. ISBN: 1557525226 (pbk.) Series: 1998 OSA technical digest series LC Classification: 9802 BOOK NOT YET IN LC

Advanced solid state lasers: from the Topical Meeting, January 17-29, 1997, Orlando, Florida / edited by Clifford R. Pollock and Walter R. Bosenberg; sponsored by Optical Society of America in cooperation with IEEE/Lasers and Electro-Optics Society. Published/Created: Washington, DC: Optical Society of America, c1997. Related Authors: Pollock, C. R. (Clifford R.) Bosenberg, Walter R. Optical Society of America. Lasers and Electro-optics Society (Institute of Electrical and Electronics Engineers) Description: xiv, 515 p.: ill.; 28 cm. ISBN: 1557524688 Notes: Includes bibliographical references and indexes. Subjects: Solid-state lasers--Congresses. Series: OSA trends in optics and photonics series; v. 10 LC Classification: TA1705 .A37 1997 Dewey Class No.: 621.36/6 21

Advanced solid state lasers: from the Topical Meeting, January 31-February 2, 1996, San Francisco, California / edited by Stephen A. Payne and Clifford R. Pollock; sponsored by Optical Society of America; cosponsored by IEEE/Lasers and Electro-optics Society. Published/Created: Washington, DC: Optical Society of America, c1996. Related Authors: Payne, Stephen A.. Pollock, C. R. (Clifford R.) Description: 1 v. (unpaged): ill.; 28 cm. ISBN: 1557523703 Notes: Title proper from cover. Title on t.p.: OSA trends in optics and photonics on advanced solid state lasers. Includes bibliographical references and indexes. Subjects: Photonics--Solid-state lasers--Imaging systems in medicine--Diagnostic imaging--Spectrum analysis--Congresses. Series: OSA Trends in optics and photonics; v. 1. Variant Series: Trends in optics and photonics; v. 1 LC Classification: TA1505 .T74 1996 Dewey Class No.: 621.36 21

Advanced solid-state lasers 1999 conference. Published/Created: Washington, DC: Optical Society of America, 1998. Description: p.; cm. ISBN: 1557525668 Series: Osa technical digest series LC Classification: 9812 BOOK NOT YET IN LC

Advanced Solid-State lasers fifteenth topical meeting. Published/Created: Washington, DC: Optical Society of America, 2000. Projected Pub. Date: 0002 Description: p.; cm. ISBN: 1557526273 (conference edition) Series: OSA 2000 conference digest series

Advanced Solid-State Lasers Topical Meeting (1992: Santa Fe, N.M.) Advanced solid-state lasers: summaries of papers presented at the Advanced Solid-State Lasers Topical Meeting, February 17-19, 1992, Santa Fe, New Mexico: technical digest / sponsored by Night Vision & Electro-Optics Directorate, Office of Naval Research, SDIO/Innovative Science and Technology Office for Optical Society of America, IEEE/Lasers and Electro-Optics Society. Edition Information: Conference ed. Published/Created: Washington, DC: Optical Society of America, c1992. Related Authors: United States. Army. Night Vision & Electro-Optics Directorate. United States. Office of Naval Research. Strategic Defense Initiative Organization (U.S.). Innovative Science and Technology Office. Description: xiii, 321 p.: ill.; 28 cm. ISBN: 1557522235 Notes: Includes bibliographical references and index. Subjects: Solid-state lasers--Congresses. LC Classification: TA1705 .A38 1992 Dewey Class No.: 621.36/61 20

Advanced solid-state lasers, January 28-31, 2001, Seattle, Washigton: proceedings volume / editor, Christopher Marshall; sponsored by Optical Society of America; co-sponsored by IEEE/LEOS Lasers and Electro-Optics Scoiety. Published/Created: Washington, DC: Optical Society of America, 2001. Related Authors: Marshall, Christopher (Christopher D.) Optical Society of America. Topical Meeting on Advanced Solid State Lasers (2001: Seattle, Wash.) Description: xvi, 702 p.: ill.; 28 cm. ISBN: 1557526613 Notes: Includes bibliographical references and index. Subjects: Solid-state lasers--Congresses. Series: OSA trends in optics and photonics; v. 50. Variant Series: Trends in optics and photonics series; v. 50 LC Classification: TA1705 .A375 2001 Dewey Class No.: 621.36/61 21

Advanced solid-state lasers. Edition Information: conference ed. Published/Created: Washington, DC: Optical Society of America, 2001. Projected Pub. Date: 0101 Description: p.; cm. ISBN: 1557526605 (conference edition) Series: Osa technical digest series

Advanced solid-state lasers. Edition Information: Conference ed. Published/Created: Washington, DC: Optical Society of America, 1995. Description: p. cm. ISBN: 1557524181 (pbk.) LC Classification: 9604 BOOK NOT YET IN LC

Advanced solid-state lasers. Published/Created: Washington , DC: Optical Society of America, 2002. Projected Pub. Date: 0207 Description: p. cm. ISBN: 1557526974 Series: OSA trends in optics and photonics series; 68

Advanced solid-state lasers. Published/Created: Washington, DC: Optical Society of America, 2002. Projected Pub. Date: 0201 Description: p. cm. ISBN: 1557526966 Series: OSA trends in optics and photonics series

Advanced solid-state lasers: from the topical Meeting on advanced solid state lasers, February 13-16, 2000, Davos, Switzerland / edited by Hagop Injeyan, Ursula Keller, and Christopher Marshall; sponsored by Optical Society of America in cooperation with IEEE/Lasers and Electro-Optics Society and European Physical Society. Published/Created: Washington, DC: Optical Society of America, c2000. Description: xvi, 666 p.: ill.; 28 cm. ISBN: 1557526281 (pbk.) Series: OSA trends in optics and photonics series; 34

Advanced solid-state lasers: OSA Proceedings series. Edition Information: Post Conference ed. Published/Created: Washington, DC: Optical Society of America, 1995. Description: p. cm. ISBN: 155752419X (pbk.) LC Classification: 9604 BOOK NOT YET IN LC

Advanced solid-state lasers: twelfth topical meeting: technical digest, January 27-29, 1997 ... Orlando, Florida / technical cosponsor, IEEE/Lasers and Electro-Optics Society; sponsored by Optical Society of America. Published/Created: Washington, DC: Optical Society of America, c1997. Related Authors: Lasers and Electro-optics Society (Institute of Electrical and Electronics Engineers) Optical Society of America. Description: xiv, 392 p.: ill.; 28 cm. ISBN: 155752467X Notes: Includes bibliographical references and index. Subjects: Solid-state lasers--Congresses. LC Classification: TA1705 .A39 1997 Dewey Class No.: 621.36/61 21

Advanced Workshop on Frontiers in Electronics (1997: Santa Cruz de Tenerife, Spain) 1997 Advanced Workshop on Frontiers in Electronics: WOFE '97 proceedings: Puerto de la Cruz, Tenerife, Spain, 6-11 January 1997 / editors, Gernot S. Pomrenke ... [et al.]; technical co-sponsors, IEEE/EDS and IEEE/LEOS. Published/Created: New York: Institute of Electrical and Electronics Engineers, 1997. Related Authors: Pomrenke, Gernot S. IEEE Electron Devices Society. Lasers and Electro-optics Society (Institute of Electrical and Electronics Engineers) Description: viii, 160 p.: ill.; 28 cm. ISBN: 0780340590 (pbk.) Notes: Includes bibliographical references and index. Subjects: Electronics--Transistors--Optoelectronics--Integrated circuits--Congresses. LC Classification: TK7801 .A37 1997 Dewey Class No.: 621.381 21

Advances in laser and optics research / William T. Lavworth. Published/Created: Huntington, N.Y.: Nova Science Publishers, c2002- Related Authors: Lavworth, William T. Description: v.: ill.; 26 cm. ISBN: 1590330560 (v. 1) Notes: Includes bibliographical references and indexes. Subjects: Lasers. Optics.

Advances in laser interaction with matter and inertial fusion, Madrid, Spain 3-7 June, 1996 / editors, G. Velarde ... [et al.]. Published/Created: Singapore; River Edge, N.J.: World Scientific, c1997. Related Authors: Velarde, G. (Guillermo) European Conference on Laser Interaction with Matter (24th: 1996: Madrid, Spain) Description: xxix, 682 p.: ill.; 23 cm. ISBN: 981023239X Notes: The 24th European Conference on Laser Interaction with Matter (24th ECLIM) was held in Madrid eight years after 19th ECLIM--Pref. Includes bibliographical references and index. Subjects: Laser-plasma interactions--Congresses. Matter--Effect of radiation on--Congresses. Radiation--Congresses. Laser fusion--Congresses. X-ray lasers--Congresses. LC Classification: QC685 .A38 1997 Dewey Class No.: 530.4/46 21

Advances in laser physics / edited by V.S. Letokhov and P. Meystre. Published/Created: Amsterdam, the Netherlands: Harwood Academic, c2000. Related Authors: Letokhov, V. S. Meystre, Pierre. Franken, Peter, 1928-1999. Description: xii, 140 p.: ill.; 24 cm. ISBN: 9058230104 Contents: Introduction / A.M. Prokhorov -- Exploring the universe with atomic clocks / N.F. Ramsey -- Femtosecond pulses at the boundary of a nonlinear dielectric / N. Bloembergen ... [et al.] -- Physics of quantum interference effects in DC-field coupled systems / R.E.W. Pfund, M.D. Lukin and M.O. Scully -- On excitation and Mössbauer-levels of heavy nuclei in a laser-produced plasma / A.A. Papchenko and I.I. Sobelman -- Seventy years of Raman scattering / R.C. Powell and T.T. Basiev -- Excitonic features in semiconductor microcavities / C. Ell ... [et al.] -- Laser resonance photoelectron/photoion microspcopy with subwavelength spatial resolution / V.S. Letokhhov and S.K. Sekatskii -- Nonlinear optics of matter waves / E.V. Goldstein ... [et al.]. Notes: "Dedicated to the memory of Peter Franken"--P. [v]. Includes bibliographical references and index. Subjects: Franken, Peter, 1928-1999. Lasers. Nonlinear optics. Quantum electronics. Lasers in physics. Series: Laser science and technology, 1561-9079; 2nd ser., v. 1 LC Classification: QC689 .A38 2000

Advances in laser remote sensing for terrestrial and oceanographic applications: 21-22 April 1997, Orlando, Florida / Ram Mohan Narayanan, James E. Kalshoven, Jr., chairs/editors; sponsored ... by SPIE--the International Society for Optical Engineering. Published/Created: Bellingham, Wash.: SPIE, c1997. Related Authors: Narayanan, Ram Mohan. Kalshoven, James E. Society of Photo-optical Instrumentation Engineers. Description: vii, 220 p.: ill.; 28 cm. ISBN: 0819424749 Notes: Includes bibliographical references and index. Subjects: Earth sciences--Remote sensing-- Plants, Effect of stress on--Remote sensing-- Oceanography--Remote sensing--Lasers-- Remote sensing--Equipment and supplies--Congresses. Series: Proceedings of SPIE--the International Society for Optical Engineering; v. 3059. Variant Series: SPIE proceedings series, 0277-786X; v. 3059 LC Classification: QE33.2.R4 A28 1997

Advances in mirror technology for synchrotron X-ray and laser applications: 20 July 1998, San Diego, California / Ali M. Khounsary, chair/editor; sponsored ... by SPIE--the International Society for Optical Engineering. Published/Created: Bellingham, Wash.: SPIE, c1998. Related Authors: Khounsary, Ali M. Society of Photo-optical Instrumentation Engineers. Description: vii, 126 p.: ill. (some col.); 28 cm. ISBN: 0819429023 Notes: Includes bibliographical references and index. Subjects: Mirrors--Design and construction--Lasers--Mirrors--Design and construction--Synchrotron radiation--Optical radiometry--Congresses. Series: Proceedings of SPIE--the International Society for Optical Engineering; v. 3447. Variant Series: SPIE proceedings series, 0277-786X; v. 3447 LC Classification: QC385.2.D47 A38 1998 Dewey Class No.: 681/.428 21

Advances in Nd-YAG laser surgery / Stephen N. Joffe, Yanao Oguro editors. Published/Created: New York: Springer-Verlag, c1988. Related Authors: Joffe, Stephen N. Oguro, Yanao. Description: xv, 368 p.: ill.; 28 cm. ISBN: 0387965068: Notes: Includes bibliographies and index. Subjects: Lasers in surgery. Nd-YAG lasers. Laser Surgery. LC Classification: RD73.L3 A38 1988 Dewey Class No.: 617/.05 19

Advances in optical biopsy and optical mammography / edited by Robert R.

Alfano. Published/Created: New York: New York Academy of Sciences, 1998. Related Authors: Alfano, R. R. Description: xii, 203 p.: ill.; 24 cm. ISBN: 1573311251 (cloth: alk. paper) 157331126X (pbk.: alk. paper) Notes: Includes bibliographical references and indexes. Subjects: Biopsy--Spectroscopic imaging--Congresses. Breast--Biopsy--Spectroscopic imaging--Congresses. Optical instruments--Congresses. Diagnostic Imaging--methods--congresses. Diagnostic Imaging--instrumentation--Lasers--diagnostic use--Spectrometry, Fluorescence--methods-- Biopsy--methods--Mammography--methods--congresses. Series: Annals of the New York Academy of Sciences, 0077-8923; v. 838 LC Classification: Q11 .N5 vol. 838 RC78.7.S65 Dewey Class No.: 500 s 616.07/58 21

Advances in vertical cavity surface emitting lasers / edited by Connie J. Chang-Hasnain; sponsored by IEEE/Lasers and Electro-optics Society, Optical Society of America in cooperation with Quantum Electronics Division of the European Physical Optical Society, Japanese Quantum Electronics Joint Group. Published/Created: Washington, DC: Optical Society of America, c1997. Related Authors: Chang-Hasnain, Connie J. Lasers and Electro-optics Society (Institute of Electrical and Electronics Engineers) Optical Society of America. Conference on Lasers and Electro-optics (1997: Baltimore, Md.) Description: ix, 253 p.: ill.; 28 cm. ISBN: 1557525005 Notes: "Featuring articles from CLEO '97, May 18-23, 1997, Baltimore, Maryland." Includes bibliographical references (p. 232-249) and indexes. Subjects: Semiconductor lasers. Series: OSA trends in optics and photonics; v. 15. Variant Series: OSA trends in optics and photonics series, 1094-5695; v. 15 LC Classification: TA1700 .A28 1997 Dewey Class No.: 621.36/6 21

Aerospace Technology Conference & Exposition (1989: Anaheim, Calif.) The use of lasers in manufacturing. Published/Created: Warrendale, PA: Society of Automotive Engineers, c1989. Description: 116 p.: ill.; 28 cm. ISBN: 0898837855 Notes: Compilation of conference proceedings. "SP-704." Includes bibliographical references. Subjects: Lasers--Industrial applications--Congresses. Aerospace industries--Congresses. LC Classification: TL671.28 .A35 1989 Dewey Class No.: 621.36/6 20

Agrawal, G. P. (Govind P.), 1951- Semiconductor lasers / Govind P. Agrawal and Niloy K. Dutta. Edition Information: 2nd ed. Published/Created: New York: Van Nostrand Reinhold, c1993. Related Authors: Dutta, N. K. (Niloy K.), 1953- Agrawal, G. P. (Govind P.), 1951- Long-wavelength semiconductor lasers. Description: xv, 616 p.: ill.; 24 cm. ISBN: 0442011024 Notes: First ed. published 1986 under Long-wavelength semiconductor lasers. Includes bibliographical references and index. Subjects: Semiconductor lasers. LC Classification: TA1700 .A37 1993 Dewey Class No.: 621.36/61 20

Airborne and spaceborne lasers for terrestrial geophysical sensing / Frank Allario, chair/editor; sponsored by SPIE--the International Society for Optical Engineering; cooperating organizations, American Academy of Otolaryngology--Head and Neck Surgery ... [et al.]. Published/Created: Bellingham, Wash., USA: SPIE, c1988. Related Authors: Allario, Frank. Society of Photo-optical Instrumentation Engineers. American Academy of Otolaryngology-Head and Neck Surgery. Description: vi, 165 p.: ill.; 28 cm. ISBN: 0892529245 Notes: "14-15 January 1988, Los Angeles, California." Includes bibliographies and index. Subjects: Remote sensing--Equipment and supplies--Congresses. Lasers--Congresses. Series: Proceedings of SPIE--the International Society for Optical Engineering; v. 889 LC Classification: G70.6 .A35 1988 Dewey Class No.: 621.36/78 20

Airborne laser advanced technology: 13-14 April 1998, Orlando, Florida / Todd D. Steiner, Paul H. Merritt, chairs/editors; sponsored ... by SPIE--the International Society for Optical Engineering. Published/Created: Bellingham, Wash., USA: SPIE, c1998. Related Authors: Steiner, Todd D. Merritt, Paul H. Description: vii, 298 p.: ill.; 28 cm. ISBN: 0819428302 Notes: Includes bibliographical references and index. Subjects: Lasers--Military applications--Congresses. Optics, Adaptive--Congresses. Air defenses--United States--Congresses. Series: Proceedings of SPIE--the International Society for Optical Engineering; v. 3381. Variant Series: SPIE proceedings series; v. 3381 LC Classification: UG486 .A37 1998 Dewey Class No.: 623/.042 21

Alam, Sher. Lasers without inversion and electromagnetically induced transparency / Sher Alam. Published/Created: Bellingham, Wash.: SPIE Optical Engineering Press, [c1999] Description: xiii, 454 p.: ill.; 26 cm. ISBN: 0819430404 Notes: "A publication of SPIE--the International Society for Optical Engineering." Includes bibliographical references and index. Subjects: Lasers. Coherence (Nuclear physics) Coherence (Optics) Electromagnetism. Semiconductors. LC Classification: QC688 .A53 1999 Dewey Class No.: 621.36/6 21

ALT '94 International Conference (1994: Konstanz, Germany) ALT '94 International Conference: laser methods of surface treatment and modification: 5-9 September 1994, Konstanz, Germany / Alexander M. Prokhorov, chair; Vladimir I. Pustovoy, editor; organized by General Physics Institute, Moscow, Russia, Konstanz University, Germany; cosponsored by Russian Ministry of Science ... [et al.]. Published/Created: Bellingham, Wash.: SPIE, c1995. Related Authors: Prokhorov, A. M. (Aleksandr Mikhailovich), 1916- Pustovoy, Vladimir. Institut obshchei fiziki (Rossiiskaia akademiia nauk) Universität Konstanz. Society of Photo-optical Instrumentation Engineers. Description: ix, 250 p.: ill.; 28 cm. ISBN: 0819418552 Notes: Includes bibliographical references and index. Subjects: Surfaces (Technology)--Lasers--Congresses. Series: Proceedings of SPIE--the International Society for Optical Engineering; v. 2498. Variant Series: SPIE proceedings series; v. 2498 LC Classification: TA418.7 .A58 1994 Dewey Class No.: 620/.44 20

Amann, Markus-Christian. Tunable laser diodes / Markus-Christian Amann, Jens Buus. Published/Created: Boston: Artech House, c1998. Related Authors: Buus, Jens. Description: xi, 289 p.: ill.; 24 cm. ISBN: 0890069638 (alk. paper) Notes: Includes bibliographical references and index. Subjects: Tunable lasers. Series: The Artech House optoelectronics library LC Classification: TA1706 .A55 1998 Dewey Class No.: 621.36/6 21

American Conference of Governmental Industrial Hygienists. A guide for control of laser hazards. Edition Information: 4th ed. Published/Created: Cincinnati, Ohio: American Conference of Governmental Industrial Hygienists, 1990. Description: v, 73 p.: ill.; 28 cm. ISBN: 0936712899 Notes: Includes bibliographical references (p. 71-72). Subjects: Lasers--Safety measures. LC Classification: TA1677 .A48 1990 Dewey Class No.: 621.36/6/0289 20

An experimental facility for microwave induced plasma processing of materials [microform] / by D.S. Patil ... [et al.]. Published/Created: Mumbai, India: Bhabha Atomic Research Centre, 1997. Related Authors: Patil, D. S. Description: ia-b, 44 p.: ill.; 29 cm. Notes: At head of Title - Government of India, Atomic Energy Commission. "BARC/1997/E/025." Includes bibliographical references (p. 33). Microfiche. New Delhi: Library of Congress Office; Washington, D.C.: Library of Congress Photoduplication Service, 1998. 1 microfiche. Master microform held by: DLC. Subjects: Microwave plasmas. Lasers in plasma research. LC Classification: Microfiche 98/60436

Anderberg, Bengt. Laser weapons: the dawn of a new military age / Bengt Anderberg and Myron L. Wolbarsht. Published/Created: New York: Plenum Press, c1992. Related Authors: Wolbarsht, Myron. Description: xii, 244 p.: ill.; 22 cm. ISBN: 0306443295: Notes: Includes bibliographical references (p. 231-232) and index. Subjects: Lasers--Military applications. LC Classification: UG486 .A53 1992 Dewey Class No.: 623.4/46 20

Anderson, Donna L. A laser-based continuous miner guidance system / by Donna L. Anderson and John S. Gbruoski. Published/Created: Washington, D.C.: U.S. Dept. of the Interior, Bureau of Mines, 1991. Related Authors: Gbruoski, John S. Description: 14 p.: ill.; 28 cm. Notes: Includes bibliographical references (p. 14). Subjects: Mining machinery--Automatic control--Navigation--Data processing. Optical scanners. Lasers in mining. Series: Information circular (United States. Bureau of Mines); 9288. Variant Series: Information circular; 9288 LC Classification: TN295 .U4 no. 9288 TN345 Dewey Class No.: 622 s 622 20

Anderson, Donna L. Position and heading determination of a continuous mining machine using an angular position-sensing system / by Donna L. Anderson. Published/Created: Pgh. [Pittsburgh], PA: U.S. Dept. of the Interior, Bureau of Mines, [1989] Description: 8 p.: ill.; 28 cm. Subjects: Mining machinery--Automatic control--Data processing. Lasers in mining. Series: Information circular (United States. Bureau of Mines); 9222. Variant Series: Information circular; 9222 LC Classification: TN295 .U4 no. 9222 TN345 Dewey Class No.: 622 s 622/.028 20

Anderson, Donna L. Underground test results of a laser-based tram control system for a continuous miner / by Donna Lynne Anderson. Published/Created: Washington, D.C.: U.S. Dept. of the Interior, Bureau of Mines, 1992. Description: 10 p.: Ill.; 28 cm. Notes: Supt. of Docs. no.: I 28.23:9440. Includes bibliographical references (p. 10). Subjects: Mining machinery--Automatic control. Mine railroads--Automatic control. Lasers in navigation. Series: Report of investigations (United States. Bureau of Mines); 9440. Variant Series: Report of investigations; 9440 LC Classification: TN23 .U43 TN345 Dewey Class No.: 622 s 622 20

Andrews, David L. Lasers in chemistry / David L. Andrews. Edition Information: 3rd ed. Published/Created: Berlin; New York: Springer-Verlag, 1997. Description: xiv, 232 p.: ill.; 24 cm. ISBN: 3540619828 (softcover: alk. paper) Notes: Includes bibliographical references (p. [221]-222) and index. Subjects: Lasers in chemistry. Laser spectroscopy. Laser photochemistry. LC Classification: QD63.L3 A53 1997 Dewey Class No.: 542/.8 21

Andrews, David L. Lasers in chemistry / David L. Andrews. Edition Information: 2nd ed. Published/Created: Berlin; New York: Springer-Verlag, c1990. Description: xii, 188 p.: ill.; 24 cm. ISBN: 3540517774 (Springer-Verlag Berlin: alk. paper) 0387517774 (Springer-Verlag New York: alk. paper) Notes: Includes bibliographical references (p. [179]) and index. Subjects: Lasers in chemistry. Laser spectroscopy. Laser photochemistry. LC Classification: QD63.L3 A53 1990 Dewey Class No.: 542 20

Arter, W. Flow simulations for a glow discharge laser / W. Arter, D.F. Fletcher, A.C. Selden. Published/Created: Abingdon, Oxfordshire: Culham Laboratory, United Kingdom Atomic Energy Authority; London: H.M.S.O., [distributor], c1988. Related Authors: Fletcher, D. F. Selden, A. C. Description: 13, [6] p.: ill.; 30 cm. ISBN: 0853111723 Notes: "November 1988." "CLM-R288." Includes bibliographical references (p. 12). Subjects: Gas lasers. Gas flow--Mathematical models. LC Classification: TA1695 .A77 1988 Dewey Class No.: 621.36/63 20

Asia-Pacific Conference on Communications (5th: 1999: Beijing, China) Proceedings

APCC/OECC'99: Fifth Asia-Pacific Conference on Communications and Fourth Optoelectronics and Communications Conference: [joint conference held] October 18-22, 1999, Friendship Hotel, Beijing China / co-sponsored by China Institute of Communications, IEEE ComSoc/LEOS (Technical), Optical Society of America (Technical); organized by China Institute of Communications, Beijing University of Posts & Telecommunications; [edited by Jintong Lin, Junichi Yoshida]. Edition Information: 1st ed. Published/Created: Beijing: Pub. House, BUPT; 1999. Related Authors: Lin, Jintong. Yoshida, Jun'ichi, 1948- Lasers and Electro-optics Society (Institute of Electrical and Electronics Engineers) Optical Society of America. Optoelectronics and Communications Conference (4th: 1999: Beijing, China) Description: 2 v. (1718 p.): ill.; 29 cm. ISBN: 7563504028 Notes: Includes bibliographical references and index. Subjects: Telecommunication--Data transmission systems--Computer networks--Optical communications--Optoelectronic devices--Congresses. LC Classification: TK5101.A1 A86 1999 Dewey Class No.: 621.382 21

Atlas of cutaneous laser surgery / editor, David B. Apfelberg. Published/Created: New York: Raven Press, c1992. Related Authors: Apfelberg, David B. Description: xii, 483 p.: ill. (some col.); 29 cm. ISBN: 0881677647 Notes: Includes bibliographical references (p. 463-473) and index. Subjects: Lasers--Therapeutic use--Atlases. Skin--Surgery--Atlases. Laser Surgery--atlases. Skin--surgery--atlases. LC Classification: RL120.L37 A85 1992 Dewey Class No.: 617.4/77059 20

Atomic spectra and collisions in external fields / edited by K.T. Taylor, M.H. Nayfeh, and C.W. Clark. Published/Created: New York: Plenum Press, c1988. Related Authors: Taylor, K. T. Nayfeh, Munir H. (Munir Hasan) Clark, C. W. (Charles W.), 1952- Description: xiv, 457 p.: ill.; 26 cm. ISBN: 0306431475 Notes: "Proceedings based on a satellite meeting of the Fifteenth International Conference on the Physics of Electronic and Atomic Collisions, entitled: Atomic Spectra and Collisions in External Fields 2, held July 30-31, 1987, at Royal Holloway and Bedford New College, in Egham, Surrey, United Kingdom"--T.p. verso. Includes bibliographies and index. Subjects: Nuclear excitation--Electric fields--Magnetic fields--Photoionization--Multiphoton processes--Lasers--Congresses. Series: Physics of atoms and molecules LC Classification: QC794.6.E9 A863 1988 Dewey Class No.: 539.7 19

Azar, Dimitri T. Excimer laser phototherapeutic keratectomy / Dimitri T. Azar, Roger F. Steinert, Walter J. Stark. Edition Information: 1st ed. Published/Created: Baltimore, Md., USA: Williams & Wilkns, c1997. Related Authors: Steinert, Roger F. Stark, Walter J. Description: x, 214 p.: ill. (some col.); 29 cm. ISBN: 0683303465 Notes: Includes bibliographical references and index. Subjects: Eye--Laser surgery. Eximer lasers. Keratectomy, Photorefractive, Excimer Laser--methods. LC Classification: RE86 .A93 1997 Dewey Class No.: 617.7/19 21

Ball, Kay, RN. Lasers: the perioperative challenge / Kay A. Ball. Edition Information: 2nd ed. Published/Created: St. Louis: Mosby, c1995. Description: xiii, 434 p.: ill. (some col.); 24 cm. ISBN: 081510524X (pbk.) Notes: Inclusdes bibliographical references and index. Subjects: Lasers in surgery. Lasers in medicine. LC Classification: RD73.L3 B35 1995 Dewey Class No.: 617/.05 20

Ball, Kay, RN. Lasers: the perioperative challenge / Kay Ball. Published/Created: St. Louis: Mosby, 1990. Description: x, 262 p.: ill.; 24 cm. Cancelled ISBN: 1801601231 Notes: Includes bibliographical references and index. Subjects: Lasers in surgery. Lasers in medicine. Laser Surgery. Lasers. LC Classification: RD73.L3 B35 1990 Dewey Class No.: 617/.05 20

Basiev, T. T. Room temperature tunable color center lasers / T.T. Basiev and S.B. Mirov.

Published/Created: Chur, Switzerland; New York: Harwood Academic Publishers, c1994. Related Authors: Mirov, S. B. Description: viii, 158 p.: ill.; 23 cm. ISBN: 3718653494 Notes: Includes bibliographical references (p. 137-151) and index. Subjects: Tunable lasers. Ionic crystals. Color centers. Series: Laser science and technology LC Classification: TA1706 .B37 1993 Dewey Class No.: 621.36/6 20

Bäuerle, D. (Dieter), 1940- Laser processing and chemistry / Dieter Bäuerle. Edition Information: 3rd rev. enlarged ed. Published/Created: Berlin; New York: Springer, c2000. Description: xx, 788 p.: ill.; 24 cm. ISBN: 3540668918 (alk. paper) Notes: Includes bibliographical references and index. Subjects: Lasers--Industrial applications. Surfaces (Technology)--Effect of radiation on. Materials--Effect of radiation on. Laser photochemistry. Laser-plasma interactions. Materials processing. LC Classification: TA1677 .B39 2000 Dewey Class No.: 660/.293/028 21

Bäuerle, D. (Dieter), 1940- Laser processing and chemistry / Dieter Bäuerle. Edition Information: 2nd ed. Published/Created: Berlin; New York: Springer, c1996. Related Authors: Bäuerle, D. (Dieter), 1940- Chemical processing with lasers. Description: xx, 649 p.: ill. (some col.); 25 cm. ISBN: 354060541X (hardcover: alk. paper) Notes: Rev. ed. of: Chemical processing with lasers. c1986. Includes bibliographical references (p. [589]-639) and index. Subjects: Lasers--Industrial applications. Surfaces (Technology)--Effect of radiation on. Materials--Effect of radiation on. Laser photochemistry. LC Classification: TA1677 .B39 1996 Dewey Class No.: 660/.293/028 20

Baxter, G. David. Therapeutic lasers: theory and practice / G. David Baxter; with contributions by Costas Diamantopoulos, Sharon O'Kane, T. Dolores Shields; foreword by Jim Allen. Published/Created: Edinburgh; New York: Churchill Livingstone, 1994. Related Authors: Diamantopoulos, Costas. Description: x, 259 p.: ill.; 24 cm. ISBN: 0443043930 Notes: Includes bibliographical references and index. Subjects: Lasers in medicine. Lasers--therapeutic use. LC Classification: R857.L37 B38 1994 Dewey Class No.: 610/.28 20

Beach, David P. Applications of lasers and laser systems / David Beach, Allen Shotwell, Paul Essue. Published/Created: Englewood Cliffs, N.J.: PTR Prentice Hall, c1993. Related Authors: Shotwell, Allen. Essue, Paul. Description: xii, 271 p.: ill.; 24 cm. ISBN: 0130419303 Notes: Includes bibliographical references and index. Subjects: Lasers. LC Classification: TA1675 .B42 1993 Dewey Class No.: 621.36/6 20

Beiser, Leo. Laser scanning notebook / by Leo Beiser. Published/Created: Bellingham, Wash.: SPIE Optical Engineering Press, c1992. Description: 1 v. (unpaged): ill.; 28 cm. ISBN: 0819411574 Notes: Cover title. Includes bibliographical references. Subjects: Optical scanners. Lasers. LC Classification: TK7882.S3 B46 1992

Bergquist, Carl J. Howard W. Sams laser design toolkit / by Carl Bergquist. Published/Created: Indianapolis, IN: Prompt Publications, c1999. Description: viii, 223 p.: ill.; 24 cm. ISBN: 079061183X Subjects: Lasers--Amateurs' manuals. LC Classification: TK9921 .B47 1999 Dewey Class No.: 621.36/6 21

Bespalov, V. I. (Viktor Ivanovich) Nonlinear optics and adaptive laser systems / V.I. Besplov and G.A. Pasmanik; translated from Russian by Gia Tsitsuashvily. Published/Created: Commack, N.Y.: Nova Science Publishers, c1994. Related Authors: Pasmanik, G. A. (kGerman Aronovich) Description: x, 143 p.: ill.; 25 cm. ISBN: 1560721219 Notes: Translation of: Nelineinaia optika i adaptivnye lazernye sistemy. Includes bibliographical references (p. [135]-138) and index. Subjects: Nonlinear optics. Lasers. LC Classification: QC446.2 .B4713 1994 Dewey Class No.: 621.36/6 20

Billings, Charlene W. Lasers: the new technology of light / Charlene W. Billings. Published/Created: New York: Facts on File, c1992. Description: ix, 118 p.: ill.; 24 cm. ISBN: 0816026300 (alk. paper) Summary: Explains what lasers are and how they work and examines their various uses. Notes: Includes bibliographical references (p. 112-113) and index. Subjects: Lasers--Juvenile literature. Lasers. Series: Facts on File science sourcebooks LC Classification: TA1682 .B55 1992 Dewey Class No.: 621.36/6 20

Binational USA-USSR Symposium on Laser Optics of Condensed Matter (3rd: 1987: Leningrad, R.S.F.S.R.) Laser optics of condensed matter / edited by Joseph L. Birman, Herman Z. Cummins, and A.A. Kaplyanskii. Published/Created: New York: Plenum Press, c1988. Related Authors: Birman, Joseph Leon, 1927- Cummins, Herman Z., 1933- Kaplianskii, A. A. Description: xiv, 564 p.: ill.; 26 cm. ISBN: 0306428164 Notes: "Proceedings of the Third Binational USA-USSR Symposium on Laser Optics of Condensed Matter, held June 1-6, 1987, in Leningrad, USSR"--T.p. verso. Includes bibliographies and index. Subjects: Condensed matter--Optical properties--Lasers--Congresses. LC Classification: QC173.4.C65 B56 1987 Dewey Class No.: 530.4/1 19

Binational USA-USSR Symposium on Laser Optics of Condensed Matter (4th: 1990: Irvine, Calif.) Laser optics of condensed matter. Volume 2, The physics of optical phenomena and their use as probes of matter / edited by Elsa Garmire, Alexei A. Maradudin, and Karl K. Rebane. Published/Created: New York: Plenum Press, c1991. Related Authors: Garmire, E. Maradudin, A. A. Rebane, Karl Karlovich, 1926- Description: xvi, 447 p.: ill.; 26 cm. ISBN: 0306438208 Notes: "Proceedings of the Fourth Binational USA-USSR Symposium on Laser Optics of Condensed Matter, held January 23-27, 1990, in Irvine, California"--T.p. verso. Includes bibliographical references and indexes. Subjects: Condensed matter--Optical properties--Lasers--Congresses. LC Classification: QC173.4.C65 B56 1990 Dewey Class No.: 530.4/12 20

Biomedical applications of free-electron lasers: 22 January 2000, San Jose, California / Glenn S. Edwards, John C. Sutherland, chairs/editors; sponsored by AFOSR--U.S. Air Force Office of Scientific Research, SPIE--the International Society for Optical Engineering, [and] IBOS--International Biomedical Optics Society. Published/Created: Bellingham, Wash., USA: SPIE, c2000. Related Authors: Edwards, Glenn S. Sutherland, John C. (John Clark), 1940- United States. Air Force. Office of Scientific Research. Society of Photo-optical Instrumentation Engineers. International Biomedical Optics Society. Description: vii, 118 p.: ill.; 28 cm. ISBN: 0819435414 Notes: Includes bibliographical references and index. Subjects: Free electron lasers--Congresses. Lasers in medicine--Congresses. Series: Progress in biomedical optics and imaging, 1605-7422; vol. 1, no. 19 Proceedings of SPIE--the International Society for Optical Engineering; v. 3925. Variant Series: Proceedings of SPIE; v. 3925 LC Classification: R857.L37 B557 2000 Dewey Class No.: 610/.28 21

Biomedical optical instrumentation and laser-assisted biotechnology / edited by A.M. Verga Scheggi ... [et al.]. Published/Created: Boston: Kluwer Academic, c1996. Related Authors: Verga Scheggi, A. M. (Anna Maria) Description: xxviii, 407 p.: ill.; 25 cm. ISBN: 0792341724 (alk. paper) Notes: Includes bibliographical references and index. Subjects: Optical instruments. Biomedical engineering. Lasers in biology. Biotechnology--Instruments. Series: NATO ASI series. Series E, Applied sciences; no. 325 LC Classification: R857.O6 B57 1996 Dewey Class No.: 610/.28 20

Biomedical optical spectroscopy and diagnostics / edited by Eva M. Sevick-Muraca and Joseph A. Izatt. Therapeutic laser applications / edited by Marwood N.

Ediger. Published/Created: Washington, DC: Optical Society of America, 1998. Related Authors: Sevick-Muraca, Eva M. Izatt, Joseph A. Ediger, Marwood N., 1958- Description: x, 352 p.: ill.; 28 cm. ISBN: 1557525471 Notes: Includes bibliographical references (p. 330-348) and indexes. Subjects: Spectroscopic imaging. Lasers in medicine. Series: OSA trends in optics and photonics; v. 22. Variant Series: OSA trends in optics and photonics series, 1094-5695; v. 22 LC Classification: RC78.7.S65 B548 1999 Dewey Class No.: 610/.28 21

Biomedical optics and lasers: diagnostics and treatment: 16-18 September 1998, Beijing, China / Junheng Li, James A. Harrington, chairs/editors; sponsored by SPIE--the International Society for Optical Engineering, COS--Chinese Optical Society, [and] COEMA--China Optics & Optoelectronic Manufacturers Association; cooperating organizations, National Natural Science Foundation of China ... [et al.]. Published/Created: Bellingham, Wash., USA: SPIE, c1998. Related Authors: Li, Chün-heng. Harrington, James A., 1942- Description: vii, 242 p.: ill.; 28 cm. ISBN: 0819430099 Notes: Includes bibliographical references and index. Subjects: Optoelectronic devices--Lasers in medicine--Diagnostic imaging--Congresses. Series: Proceedings of SPIE--the International Society for Optical Engineering; v. 3548. Variant Series: SPIE proceedings series, 0277-786X; v. 3548 LC Classification: R857.B54 B532 1998 Dewey Class No.: 610/.28 21

Biomedical sensing, imaging, and tracking technologies I: 29-31 January 1996, San Jose, California / Robert A. Lieberman, Halina Podbielska, Tuan Vo-Dinh, chairs/editors; sponsored and published by SPIE--the International Society for Optical Engineering. Published/Created: Bellingham, Wash. USA: SPIE, c1996. Related Authors: Lieberman, Robert A. Podbielska, Halina. Vo-Dinh, Tuan. Description: vii, 384 p.: ill.; 28 cm. ISBN: 0819420506 Notes: Includes bibliographical references and index. Subjects: Biosensors--Lasers in medicine--Optical fibers in medicine--Diagnostic imaging--Congresses. Series: Proceedings of SPIE--the International Society for Optical Engineering; v. 2676. Variant Series: SPIE proceedings series, 0277-786X; v. 2676 LC Classification: R857.B54 B533 1996 Dewey Class No.: 610/.28 21

Biomedicine / V. Stefan, editor-in-chief. Edition Information: 2nd ed. Published/Created: La Jolla, CA: Stefan University Press, 2002. Projected Pub. Date: 0202 Related Authors: Stefan, V. Description: p. cm. ISBN: 1889545252 Notes: Includes bibliographical references and index. Subjects: Cancer--Photochemotherapy. Lasers in medicine. Series: The Stefan University Press series on frontiers in biomedical science and technology LC Classification: RC271.P43 B55 2002 Dewey Class No.: 616.99/40631 21

Biomonitoring and endoscopy technologies: 5-6 July 2000, Amsterdam, Netherlands / Israel Gannot ... [et al.], chairs/editors; sponsored by EOS--the European Optical Society, SPIE--the International Society for Optical Engineering, [and] ELA--European Laser Association; cooperating organizations, NMLA--Netherland Medical Laser Association ... [et al.]. Published/Created: Bellingham, Wash., USA: SPIE, c2001. Description: vii, 270 p.: ill.; 28 cm. ISBN: 0819438146 Notes: Includes bibliographical references and index. Subjects: Endoscopy--Biomonitoring--Diagnostic imaging--Lasers in medicine--Congresses. Series: Progress in biomedical optics and imaging, 1605-7422; vol. 1, no. 29 Proceedings of SPIE--the International Society for Optical Engineering; v. 4158. Variant Series: SPIE proceedings series; v. 4158 LC Classification: RC78.7.E5 B545 2001 Dewey Class No.: 610/.28 21

Biophotonics instrumentation and analysis: 28-29 November 2001, Singapore / Arthur E.T. Chiou, Halina Podbielska, Steven L. Jacques, chairs/editors; sponsored ... by

SPIE--the International Society for Optical Engineering [and] Nanyang Technological University (Singapore). Published/Created: Bellingham, Wash., USA: SPIE, c2001. Related Authors: Chiou, Arthur E. T. Podbielska, Halina. Jacques, Steven L. Description: ix, 158 p.: ill.; 28 cm. ISBN: 0819443271 Notes: Includes bibliographical references and index. Subjects: Imaging systems in medicine--Lasers in medicine--Photonics--Optical tomography--Congresses. Series: Proceedings of SPIE--the International Society for Optical Engineering; v. 4597. Variant Series: SPIE proceedings series; v. 4597 LC Classification: R857.O6 B58 2001 Dewey Class No.: 616.07/54 21

Biophotonics international. Published/Created: Pittsfield, MA: Laurin Pub. Co., Description: v.: ill.; 28 cm. Began with v. 2, no. 1 (Jan.-Feb. 1995). Current Frequency: Bimonthly Continues: Biophotonics ISSN: 1081-8693 Cancel/Invalid LCCN: sn 95001697 CODEN: BIINFH Notes: Description based on: Vol. 2, no. 3 (May-June 1995); title from cover. SERBIB/SERLOC merged record Subjects: Imaging systems in medicine--Imaging systems in biology--Lasers in medicine--Lasers in biology--. Photonics--Diagnostic Imaging--Lasers--Light--Technology, Medical--Periodicals. LC Classification: R857.O6 B54 Dewey Class No.: 610/.28/05 20

Bioptics: optics in biomedicine and environmental sciences: proceedings of an intensive course held 17-25 March 1991, Porto, Portugal / Anna Maria Scheggi, Olivério D. Soares, editors; sponsored by Commission of the European Communities (DG XII-SCIENCE) ... [et al.]; cosponsored by Faculdade de Ciências da Universidade do Porto, Portugal ... [et al.]. Published/Created: Bellingham, Wash.: SPIE--the International Society for Optical Engineering in cooperation with European Optical Society [and] Universidade do Porto, c1992. Related Authors: Verga Scheggi, A.M. (Anna Maria) Soares, O.D.D. (Olivério D.D.) Description: 398 p.: ill.; 27 cm. ISBN: 081940652X Subjects: Lasers in medicine--Lasers in biology--Optics--Congresses. Series: Proceedings of SPIE--the International Society for Optical Engineering; v. 1524. Variant Series: SPIE proceedings series; v. 1524 LC Classification: R857.L37 B57 1992 Dewey Class No.: 610/.28 20

Bjarklev, Anders. Optical fiber amplifiers: design and system applications / Anders Bjarklev. Published/Created: Boston: Artech House, c1993. Description: xiv, 392 p.: ill.; 24 cm. ISBN: 0890066590: Notes: Includes bibliographical references and index. Subjects: Lasers. Optical amplifiers. Fiber optics. Optical communications. Series: The Artech House optoelectronics library LC Classification: TA1677 .B54 1993 Dewey Class No.: 621.382/75 20

Blue laser and light emitting diodes / editors A. Yoshikawa ... [et al.]. Published/Created: Tokyo: Ohmsha; Amsterdam; Washington, DC: IOS Press, 1996. Related Authors: Yoshikawa, A. (Akihiko) Chiba Daigaku. Description: xviii, 580 p.: ill.; 31 cm. ISBN: 4274900967 (Ohmsha, Ltd.) 9051992696 (IOS Press) Notes: International Symposium on Blue Laser and Light Emitting Diodes sponsored by Chiba University. Subjects: Semiconductor lasers--Light emitting diodes--Gallium nitride--Congresses. Blue light--Industrial applications--Congresses. LC Classification: TA1700 .B58 1996 Dewey Class No.: 621.36/6 21

Blue lasers: lighting up new markets in displays, optical storage, medical devices, and more: a report / from Technical Insights. Published/Created: New York: John Wiley, c2000. Related Authors: Technical Insights, Inc. Description: 116 p.: ill.; 28 cm. ISBN: 0471418439 Notes: Includes bibliographical references (p. 109-116). Subjects: Semiconductor lasers. Light emitting diodes. Gallium nitride. Blue light. Series: Technical insights; R-278 LC Classification: *

Boekhoff, P. M. (Patti Marlene), 1957- Lasers / by P.M. Boekhoff and Stuart A. Kallen.

Published/Created: San Diego, CA: Kidhaven Press, 2002. Related Authors: Kallen, Stuart A., 1955- Description: 48 p.: ill.; 24 cm. ISBN: 0737709448 (hardback: alk. paper) Notes: Includes bibliographical references and index. Subjects: Lasers--Juvenile literature. Lasers. Series: The kidhaven science library LC Classification: TA1682 .B64 2002 Dewey Class No.: 621.36/6 21

Borshch, A. A. Refractive nonlinearity of wide-band semiconductors and applications / A.A. Borshch, M. Brodin, and V. Volkov. Published/Created: Chur; New York: Harwood Academic Publishers, c1990. Related Authors: Brodin, M. S. (Mikhail Semenovich), 1931- Volkov, V. Description: xiv, 141 p.: ill.; 24 cm. ISBN: 3718649713 Notes: Includes bibliographical references p. (133-140). Subjects: Semiconductor lasers. Semiconductors--Optical properties. Series: Laser science and technology , 0899-2711; v. 9 LC Classification: TA1700 .B67 1990 Dewey Class No.: 621.36/6 20

Bose-Einstein condensates and atom lasers / edited by Sergio Martellucci ... [et al.]. Published/Created: New York: Kluwer Academic/Plenum Publishers, 2000. Related Authors: Martellucci, S. Description: ix, 325 p.: ill.; 26 cm. ISBN: 0306464713 Notes: "Proceedings of the 27th Course of the International School of Quantum Electronics on Bose-Einstein Condensates and Atom Lasers, held October 19-24, 1999, in Erice, Sicily, Italy"--T.p. verso. Includes bibliographical references and index. Subjects: Bose-Einstein condensation--Congresses. Quantum optics--Congresses. Lasers--Congresses. LC Classification: QC175.47.B65 B66 2000 Dewey Class No.: 530.4/2 21

Bradley, Eugene B. Molecules and molecular lasers for electrical engineers / Eugene B. Bradley. Published/Created: New York: Hemisphere Pub. Corp., c1990. Description: xii, 127 p.: ill.; 24 cm. ISBN: 0891167889: Notes: Includes bibliographical references and index. Subjects: Molecular gas lasers. Series: Series in electrical engineering LC Classification: TA1695 .B73 1990 Dewey Class No.: 621.36/63 20

Brandt, Fredric. Age-less: the definitive guide to botox, collagen, lasers, peels, and other solutions for flawless skin / Fredric Brandt with Patricia Reynoso. Edition Information: 1st ed. Published/Created: New York: Morrow, c2002. Projected Pub. Date: 0210 Related Authors: Reynoso, Patricia. Description: p. cm. ISBN: 0060516259 (hbk.: alk. paper) Subjects: Skin--Care and hygiene. Beauty, Personal. Botulinum toxin--Therapeutic use. Skin--Laser surgery. Collagen--Therapeutic use. Chemical peel. LC Classification: RL87 .B665 2002 Dewey Class No.: 646.7/26 21

Brau, Charles A., 1938- Free-electron lasers / Charles A. Brau. Published/Created: Boston: Academic Press, c1990. Description: xi, 420 p.: ill.; 23 cm. ISBN: 0121260003 (pbk.: alk. paper) 0120145960 (alk. paper) Notes: Includes bibliographical references. Subjects: Free electron lasers. Series: Advances in electronics and electron physics. Supplement; 22 LC Classification: TA1693 .B74 1990 Dewey Class No.: 621.36/6 20

Broad, William J. Teller's war: the top-secret story behind the Star Wars deception / William J. Broad. Published/Created: New York: Simon & Schuster, c1992. Description: 350 p.: ill.; 24 cm. ISBN: 0671701061: Notes: Includes bibliographical references (p. 323-332) and index. Subjects: Teller, Edward, 1908- Lawrence Livermore Laboratory--History. Lasers--Military applications--Research--United States--X-ray lasers--History. Strategic Defense Initiative--History. LC Classification: UG486 .B76 1992 Dewey Class No.: 623.4/46/072073 20

Bromberg, Joan Lisa. The laser in America, 1950-1970 / Joan Lisa Bromberg. Published/Created: Cambridge, Mass.: MIT Press, c1991. Description: xiv, 310 p.: ill.; 24 cm. ISBN: 0262023180 (hc) Notes:

Includes bibliographical references (p. [249]-298) and index. Subjects: Lasers--History--20th century. LC Classification: TA1677 .B76 1992 Dewey Class No.: 621.36/6 20

Brooks, Philip, 1963- How things work / by Philip Brooks. Edition Information: 1st ed. Published/Created: New York: Kingfisher, 2002. Projected Pub. Date: 0209 Description: p. cm. ISBN: 0753454904 Summary: Answers questions about how things work, such as car engines, toilets, and lasers. Notes: Includes index. Subjects: Technology--Miscellanea--Juvenile literature. Technology--Miscellanea. Series: Questions and answers (New York, N.Y.) Variant Series: Questions and answers LC Classification: T48 .B853 2002 Dewey Class No.: 600 21

Bryan, Jenny. Medical technology / Jenny Bryan. Published/Created: New York: Bookwright Press, 1991. Description: 46 p.: ill. (some col.); 26 cm. ISBN: 053118398X Summary: Discusses the latest advances in medical science and technology that have enabled physicians to effectively treat illnesses and injuries. Includes lasers, kidney machines, transplants, and genetic engineering. Notes: Includes bibliographical references and index. Subjects: Medical technology--Juvenile literature. Medical technology. Series: Technology in action LC Classification: R855.4 .B79 1991 Dewey Class No.: 610/.28 20

Bunkin, A. F. (Aleksei Fedorovich) Laser remote sensing of the ocean: methods and applications / Alexey Bunkin, Konstantin Voliak. Published/Created: New York: John Wiley, c2001. Related Authors: Voliak, K. I. Description: x, 244 p.: ill.; 25 cm. ISBN: 0471389277 (cloth: alk. paper) Notes: Includes bibliographical references (p. 221-230) and index. Subjects: Oceanography--Remote sensing. Optical radar. Series: Wiley series in lasers and applications LC Classification: GC10.4.R4 V65 2001 Dewey Class No.: 551.46/0028 21

Bunkin, F. V. Lasers in acoustics / F.V. Bunkin, Al. A. Kolomensky, V.G. Mikhalevich. Published/Created: Chur; New York: Harwood Academic Publishers, c1991. Related Authors: Kolomensky, Al. A. Mikhalevich, V. G. Description: xvii, 177 p.: ill.; 23 cm. ISBN: 3718650614 Notes: Includes bibliographical references (p. 163-173) and index. Subjects: Acoustooptics. Sound-waves. Condensed matter--Effect of radiation on. Laser beams. Series: Laser science and technology, 0899-2711; v. 12 LC Classification: QC220.5 .B86 1990 Dewey Class No.: 620.2 20

Buus, Jens. Single frequency semiconductor lasers / Jens Buus. Published/Created: Bellingham, Wash., USA: SPIE Optical Engineering Press, c1991. Description: x, 110 p.: ill.; 26 cm. ISBN: 0819405353 Notes: Includes bibliographical references (p. 106-110). Subjects: Semiconductor lasers. Series: Tutorial texts in optical engineering; v. TT 5 LC Classification: TA1700 .B88 1991 Dewey Class No.: 621.36/6 20

Cardiovascular laser therapy / editors, Jeffrey M. Isner, Richard H. Clarke. Published/Created: New York: Raven Press, c1989. Related Authors: Isner, Jeffrey M. Clarke, Richard H. Description: xiii, 300 p., [24] p. of plates: ill. (some col.); 25 cm. ISBN: 0881674842 Notes: Includes bibliographies and index. Subjects: Cardiovascular system--Diseases--Treatment. Lasers in medicine. Cardiovascular system--Laser surgery. Cardiovascular system--Effect of radiation on. Lasers--Therapeutic use. Lasers--Diagnostic use. Cardiovascular Diseases--therapy. Lasers--therapeutic use. LC Classification: RC669 .C287 1989 Dewey Class No.: 617/.41059 19

Carlson, Nils William. Monolithic diode-laser arrays / Nils W. Carlson. Published/Created: Berlin; New York: Springer-Verlag, c1994. Description: xii, 396 p.: ill.; 25 cm. ISBN: 3540579109 (Berlin: acid-free paper) 0387579109 (New York: acid-free paper) Notes: Includes bibliographical references (p. [339]-387) and index. Subjects: Semiconductor lasers. Series: Springer series in electronics and photonics; v. 33 LC Classification: TA1700 .C36 1994 Dewey Class No.: 621.36/61 20

Carroll, John E. Distributed feedback semiconductor lasers / John Carroll, James Whiteaway & Dick Plumb. Published/Created: London, UK: The Institution of Electrical Engineers: SPIE Optical Engineering Press, c1998. Related Authors: Whiteaway, James. Plumb, Dick. Description: xxv, 412 p.: ill.; 25 cm. ISBN: 0852969171 (IEE) 0819426601 (SPIE) Notes: Includes bibliographical references and index. Subjects: Semiconductor lasers. Diodes, Semiconductor--Mathematical models. Series: IEE Circuits, devices and systems series; 10 SPIE Press Monograph; PM52 Variant Series: SPIE Press Monograph; v. PM52 LC Classification: TA1700 .C367 1998 Dewey Class No.: 621.36/6 21

Catheter-based sensing and imaging technology: 17-18 January 1989, Los Angeles, California / Alan I. West, chair/editor; sponsored by SPIE--the International Society for Optical Engineering; cooperating organizations, American Academy of Dermatology ... [et al.]. Published/Created: Bellingham, Wash., USA: SPIE, c1989. Related Authors: West, Alan I. Description: viii, 229 p.: ill.; 28 cm. ISBN: 081940103X Notes: Papers of one of a six part program held at the Symposium on Medical Applications of Lasers and Optics. Includes bibliographical references. Subjects: Imaging systems in medicine--Congresses. Biosensors--Congresses. Catheters--Congresses. Diagnostic imaging--Congresses Series: Proceedings of SPIE--the International Society of Optical Engineering; v. 1068. Variant Series: Proceedings / SPIE--the International Society for Optical Engineering; 1068 LC Classification: R857.O6 C37 1989 Dewey Class No.: 616.07/54 20

CCAST (World Laboratory) Symposium/Workshop (1995: Beijing, China) Development and applications of free electron lasers / edited by Jia-er Chen ... [et al.]. Published/Created: Amsterdam: Gordon and Breach Science Publishers, c1997. Related Authors: Chen, Jia-er. Description: xiii, 154 p.: ill.; 24 cm. ISBN: 9056995022 Notes: Proceedings of the CCAST (World Laboratory) Symposium/Workshop held at China Center of Advanced Science and Technology (World Laboratory), Beijing, People's Republic of China, May 29-June 3, 1995. Includes bibliographical references and index. Subjects: Free electron lasers--Congresses. Free electron lasers--Industrial applications--Congresses. Series: CCAST (World Laboratory) Symposium/Workshop. China Center of Advanced Science and Technology (World Laboratory) Symposium/Workshop proceedings; v. 12. Variant Series: China Center of Advanced Science and Technology (World Laboratory) Symposium/Workshop proceedings, 0894-2536; v. 12 LC Classification: TA1693 .C33 1995 Dewey Class No.: 621.36/6 21

CERN Accelerator School (1996: Grenoble, France) CAS, CERN Accelerator School: synchrotron radiation and free electron lasers: proceedings, President Hotel, Grenoble, France, 22-27 April 1996 / editor, S. Turner. Published/Created: Geneva: CERN, European Organization for Nuclear Research, 1998. Related Authors: Turner, S. (Stuart), 1935- European Organization for Nuclear Research. Description: xi, 387 p.: ill.; 30 cm. ISBN: 9290831316 Notes: "3 August 1998." Includes bibliographical references. Subjects: Synchrotron radiation--Congresses. Beam dynamics--Congresses. Free electron lasers--Congresses. Series: CERN (Series); 98-04. Variant Series: CERN, 0007-8328; 98-04 LC Classification: QC793.5.E627 C38 1996 Dewey Class No.: 539.7/35 21

CERN Accelerator School (4th: 1989: Chester College) Synchrotron radiation and free electron lasers: proceedings, Chester

College, Chester, United Kingdom, 6-13 April, 1989 / CERN Accelerator School; editor, S. Turner. Published/Created: Geneva: CERN European Organization for Nuclear Research, 1990. Related Authors: Turner, S. (Stuart), 1935- Description: xii, 482 p.: ill.; 30 cm. ISBN: 9290830220 Notes: Includes bibliographical references. Subjects: Synchrotron radiation--Congresses. Free electron lasers--Congresses. Series: CERN (Series); 90-03. Variant Series: CERN, 0007-8328; 90-03 LC Classification: QC770 .E82 1990, no. 3 QC793.5.E627 Dewey Class No.: 539.7 s 539.7/35 20

Chaos in optics: 14-16 July 1993, San Diego, California / Rajarshi Roy, chair/editor; sponsored and published by SPIE--the International Society for Optical Engineering. Published/Created: Bellingham, Wash., USA: SPIE, c1993. Related Authors: Roy, Rajashari. Society of Photo-optical Instrumentation Engineers. Description: ix, 370 p.: ill.; 28 cm. ISBN: 0819412880 (pbk.) Notes: Includes bibliographical references and author index. Subjects: Chaotic behavior in systems--Congresses. Nonlinear optics--Congresses. Semiconductor lasers--Congresses. Neural networks (Computer science)--Congresses. Series: Proceedings of SPIE--the International Society for Optical Engineering; v. 2039. Variant Series: Proceedings / SPIE--the International Society for Optical Engineering; v. 2039 LC Classification: QC446.3.C45 C48 1993 Dewey Class No.: 621.36/9 20

Charged particle detection, diagnostics, and imaging: 30 July-2 August 2001, San Diego, USA / Olivier Delage, Eric Munro, John A. Rouse, chairs/editors; sponsored ... by SPIE--the International Society for Optical Engineering. Published/Created: Bellingham, Wash.: SPIE, c2001. Related Authors: Delage, Olivier. Munro, Eric. Rouse, John A. Society of Photo-optical Instrumentation Engineers. Description: ix, 236 p.: ill.; 28 cm. ISBN: 0819442240 Notes: Includes bibliographical references and index. Subjects: Pellet fusion--Congresses. Lasers in controlled fusion--Congresses. Particle beams--Congresses. Laser-plasma interactions--Congresses. Plasma confinement--Congresses. Electron optics--Congresses. Series: Proceedings of SPIE--the International Society for Optical Engineering; v. 4510. Variant Series: SPIE proceedings series, 0277-786X; v. 4510 LC Classification: QC791.775.P44 C48 2001 Dewey Class No.: 621.48/4 21

Chemical lasers / N.G. Basov ... [et al.; English by Sergei G. Kittell]. Published/Created: Berlin; New York: Springer-Verlag, c1990. Related Authors: Basov, N. G. (Nikolai Gennadievich), 1922- Description: x, 370 p.: ill.; 24 cm. ISBN: 3540161856 (Berlin) 0387161856 (New York) Notes: Includes bibliographical references (p. [347]-368) and index. Subjects: Chemical lasers. LC Classification: TA1690 .C47 1990 Dewey Class No.: 621.36/64 20

Childs, Stacy J. The laser-assisted transurethral resection of the prostate (TURP) / Stacy J. Childs. Published/Created: Baltimore: Williams & Wilkins, 1993. Description: ix, 81 p.: ill. (some col.); 19 cm. ISBN: 0683015400 Notes: Includes bibliographical references (p. 80-81). Subjects: Prostatectomy, Transurethral. Prostate--Laser surgery. Prostatectomy--methods. Laser Surgery--methods. Lasers. LC Classification: RD587 .C49 1993 Dewey Class No.: 617.4/63 20

Chow, W. W. (Weng W.), 1948- Semiconductor-laser fundamentals: physics of the gain materials / Weng W. Chow, Stephan W. Koch. Published/Created: Berlin; New York: Springer, c1999. Related Authors: Koch, S. W. (Stephan W.) Description: x, 245 p.: ill.; 24 cm. ISBN: 3540641661 (hc: acid-free paper) Notes: Includes bibliographical references (p. [235]-240) and index. Subjects: Semiconductor lasers. LC Classification: QC689.55.S45 C45 1999 Dewey Class No.: 621.36/6 21

Chow, W. W. (Weng W.), 1948- Semiconductor-laser physics / Weng W. Chow, Stephan W. Koch, Murray Sargent

III. Published/Created: Berlin; New York: Springer-Verlag, c1994. Related Authors: Koch, S. W. (Stephan W.) Sargent, Murray. Description: xii, 497 p.: ill.; 25 cm. ISBN: 3540576142 (Berlin: acid-free paper) 0387576142 (New York: acid-free paper) Notes: Includes bibliographical references and index. Subjects: Semiconductor lasers. LC Classification: QC689.55.S45 C48 1994 Dewey Class No.: 621.36/61 20

Circular-grating light-emitting sources: 6 February 1995, San Jose, California / S. Iraj Najafi, Nasser Peyghambarian, Mahmoud Fallahi, chairs/editors; sponsored and published by SPIE--the International Society for Optical Engineering. Published/Created: Bellingham, Wash.: SPIE, c1995. Related Authors: Najafi, S. Iraj. Peyghambarian, Nasser, 1954- Fallahi, Mahmoud. Society of Photo-optical Instrumentation Engineers. Description: v, 154 p.: ill.; 28 cm. ISBN: 0819417459 Notes: Includes bibliographical references and index. Subjects: Semiconductor lasers--Congresses. Light emitting diodes--Congresses. Diffraction gratings--Congresses. Series: Proceedings of SPIE--the International Society for Optical Engineering; v. 2398. Variant Series: Proceedings /SPIE--the International Society for Optical Engineering; v. 2398 LC Classification: TA1700 .C57 1995

CLEO/Pacific Rim 2001: the 4th Pacific Rim Conference on Lasers and Electro-optics: Nippon Convention Center, Makuhari Messe, Chiba, Japan, 15-19 July, 2001: co-located with InterOpto2001 / sponsored by Japan Society of Applied Physics ... [et al.]. Published/Created: Piscataway, NJ: IEEE, c2001. Description: 2 v.; 22 cm. ISBN: 0780367383

CLEO/Pacific Rim'99: the Pacific Rim Conference on Lasers and Electro-Optics, August 30-September 3, 1999, Renaissance Seoul Hotel, Korea: technical digest / sponsored by Optical Society of Korea ... [et al.]. Published/Created: [New York]?: Institute of Electrical and Electronics Engineers; Piscataway, NJ: IEEE Service Center, c1999. Description: 117 p.; 30 cm. ISBN: 0780356616

Clinical lasers and diagnostics: 6-8 July 2000, Amsterdam, Netherlands / Patrick A. Brouwer, chair/editor; sponsored by EOS--the European Optical Society, SPIE--the International Society for Optical Engineering, [and] ELA--European Laser Association; cooperating organizations, NMLA--Netherlands Medical Laser Association ... [et al.]. Published/Created: Bellingham, Wash., USA: SPIE, c2001. Related Authors: Brouwer, Patrick A. Society of Photo-optical Instrumentation Engineers. European Optical Society. European Laser Association. Netherlands Medical Laser Association. Description: x, 356 p.: ill.; 28 cm. ISBN: 081943812X Notes: Includes bibliographical references and index. Subjects: Diagnostic imaging--Congresses. Lasers in medicine--Congresses. Series: Progress in biomedical optics and imaging, 1605-7422; vol. 1, no. 28 Proceedings of SPIE--the International Society for Optical Engineering; v. 4156. Variant Series: Proceedings of SPIE; v. 4156 LC Classification: RC78.7.D53 C5665 2001 Dewey Class No.: 616.07/54 21

CO2 lasers and applications II: 12-14 March 1990, the Hague, the Netherlands: proceedings, ECO3, the congress of EPS--European Physical Society, EUROPTICA--the European Federation for Applied Optics, SPIE--the International Society for Optical Engineering / Hans Opower, chair/editor; cooperating organizations, ANRT--Association nationale de la recherche technique ... [et al.]. Published/Created: Bellingham, Wash., USA: SPIE, c1990. Related Authors: Opower, Hans. European Physical Society. European Federation for Applied Optics. Society of Photo-optical Instrumentation Engineers. Association nationale de la recherche technique. European Congress on Optics (3rd: 1990: Hague, Netherlands) Description: ix, 469 p.: ill.; 28 cm. ISBN: 0819403237 Notes: Includes bibliographical references and index.

Subjects: Carbon dioxide lasers--Congresses. Carbon dioxide lasers--Industrial applications Congresses. Series: Proceedings of SPIE--the International Society for Optical Engineering; v. 1276. Variant Series: Proceedings / SPIE--the International Society for Optical Engineering; v. 1276 LC Classification: TA1695 .C62 1990 Dewey Class No.: 621.36/63 20

CO2 lasers and applications: 17-18 January 1989, Los Angeles, California / James D. Evans, Edward V. Locke, chairs/editors; sponsored by SPIE--the International Society for Optical Engineering; cooperating organizations, Applied Optics Laboratory/New Mexico State University ... [et. al.] Published/Created: Bellingham, Wash., USA: SPIE, c1989. Related Authors: Evans, James D. (James David), 1942- Locke, Edward V. Society of Photo-optical Instrumentation Engineers. Symposium on Lasers and Optics (1989: Los Angeles, Calif.) Description: vii, 139 p.: ill.; 28 cm. ISBN: 0819400777 Notes: Papers of one of a 19 part program held at the Symposium on Lasers and Optics. Includes bibliographical references. Subjects: Carbon dioxide lasers--Congresses. Carbon dioxide lasers--Industrial applications Congresses. Lasers--Military applications--Congresses. Series: Proceedings of SPIE--the International Society for Optical Engineering; v. 1042. Variant Series: Proceedings / SPIE--the International Society for Optical Engineering; v. 1042 LC Classification: TA1695 .C6 1989 Dewey Class No.: 621.36/63 20

Coherence and statistics of photons and atoms / edited by Jan Perina. Published/Created: New York: Wiley, c2001. Related Authors: Perina, Jan, 1936- Description: xviii, 520 p.: ill.; 25 cm. ISBN: 0471388610 (acid-free paper) Notes: Includes bibliographical references and index. Subjects: Quantum optics. Coherence (Optics) Series: Wiley series in lasers and applications LC Classification: QC446.2 .C628 2001 Dewey Class No.: 535/.2 21

Coherence phenomena in atoms and molecules in laser fields / edited by André D. Bandrauk and Stephen C. Wallace. Published/Created: New York: Plenum Press, c1992. Related Authors: Bandrauk, André D. Wallace, Stephen C. North Atlantic Treaty Organization. Scientific Affairs Division. NATO Advanced Research Workshop on Coherence Phenomena in Atoms and Molecules in Laser Fields (1991: Hamilton, Ont.) Description: ix, 406 p.: ill.; 26 cm. ISBN: 030644190X Notes: "Proceedings of a NATO Advanced Research Workshop on Coherence Phenomena in Atoms and Molecules in Laser Fields, held May 5-10, 1991, in Hamilton, Ontario, Canada"--T.p. verso. "Published in cooperation with NATO Scientific Affairs Division." Includes bibliographical references and indexes. Subjects: Lasers--Congresses. Coherence (Nuclear physics)--Congresses. Multiphoton processes--Congresses. Series: NATO ASI series. Series B, Physics; v. 287 LC Classification: QC685 .C625 1992 Dewey Class No.: 621.36/6 20

Coherence, amplification, and quantum effects in semiconductor lasers / edited by Yoshihisa Yamamoto. Published/Created: New York: Wiley, c1991. Related Authors: Yamamoto, Yoshihisa. Description: xi, 646 p.: ill.; 25 cm. ISBN: 0471512494 (alk. paper) Notes: "A Wiley-Interscience publication." Includes bibliographical references and index. Subjects: Semiconductor lasers. Series: Wiley series in pure and applied optics LC Classification: TA1700 .C64 1990 Dewey Class No.: 621.36/6 20

Coherent lightwave communications / edited by Paul S. Henry, Stewart D. Personick. Published/Created: New York: IEEE Press, c1990. Related Authors: Henry, Paul S., 1944- Personick, Stewart D. IEEE Communications Society. Description: ix, 501 p.: ill.; 29 cm. ISBN: 0879422629 Notes: Reprints of articles first published between Dec. 1961 and June 1989. "Published in cooperation with the IEEE Communications Society." Includes bibliographies and index. Subjects: Laser communication systems. Fiber optics. Series: Progress in lasers and electro-optics LC Classification: TK5103.6 .C629 1990 Dewey Class No.: 621.382/7 20

Coherent radiation generation and particle acceleration / A.M. Prokhorov, editor-in-chief; J.M. Buzzi, P. Sprangle & K. Wille, editors. Published/Created: New York: American Institute of Physics, c1992. Related Authors: Prokhorov, A. M. (Aleksandr Mikhailovich), 1916- Institute for Advanced Physics Studies. La Jolla International School of Physics. Description: xvii, 511 p.: ill.; 24 cm. ISBN: 0883189267 Notes: At head of Title - La Jolla International School of Physics, Institute for Advanced Physics Studies. "DOE CONF-910249"--T.p. verso. Includes bibliographical references and indexes. Subjects: Quantum electronics--Congresses. Free electron lasers--Congresses. Particle acceleration--Congresses. Series: Research trends in physics LC Classification: QC685 .C63 1992 Dewey Class No.: 537.5 20

Coldren, L. A. (Larry A.) Diode lasers and photonic integrated circuits / L.A. Coldren, S.W. Corzine. Published/Created: New York: Wiley, c1995. Related Authors: Corzine, S. W. (Scott W.) Description: xxiii, 594 p.: ill.; 25 cm. ISBN: 0471118753 (cloth: acid-free paper) Notes: "A Wiley-Interscience publication." Includes bibliographical references and index Subjects: Semiconductor lasers. Integrated circuits. Series: Wiley series in microwave and optical engineering LC Classification: TA1700 .C646 1995 Dewey Class No.: 621.36/6 20

Commercial and biomedical applications of ultrafast and free-electron lasers: 23-24 January 2002, San Jose, USA / Glenn S. Edwards ... [et al.], chairs/editors; sponsored ... by SPIE--the International Society for Optical Engineering. Published/Created: Bellingham, Wash., USA: SPIE, c2002. Related Authors: Edwards, Glenn S. Society of Photo-optical Instrumentation Engineers. Description: viii, 246 p.: ill.; 28 cm. ISBN: 0819443727 Notes: Includes bibliographical references and index. Subjects: Lasers in medicine--Congresses. Lasers in biology--Congresses. Lasers--Industrial applications--Congresses. Laser pulses, Ultrashort--Congresses. Free electron lasers--Congresses. Series: Proceedings of SPIE--the International Society for Optical Engineering; v. 4633. Variant Series: SPIE proceedings series, 0277-786X; v. 4633 LC Classification: R857.L37 C64 2002 Dewey Class No.: 610/.28 21

Commercial and biomedical applications of ultrafast lasers II: 24-25 January, 2000, San Jose, California / Joseph Neev, Murray K. Reed, chairs/editors; sponsored and published by SPIE--the International Society for Optical Engineering. Published/Created: Bellingham, Washington: SPIE, c2000. Related Authors: Neev, Joseph. Reed, Murray K. Society of Photo-optical Instrumentation Engineers. Description: v, 114 p.: ill.; 28 cm. ISBN: 0819435511 Notes: Includes bibliographical references and author index. Subjects: Lasers in medicine--Congresses. Lasers in biology--Congresses. Lasers--Industrial applications--Congresses. Laser pulses, Ultrashort--Congresses. Series: Proceedings of SPIE--the International Society for Optical Engineering; v. 3934. Variant Series: SPIE proceedings series; v. 3934 LC Classification: R857.L37 C65 2000 Dewey Class No.: 610/.28 21

Commercial and biomedical applications of ultrafast lasers: 28-29 January 1999, San Jose, California / Murray K. Reed, Joseph Neev, chairs/editors; sponsored ... by SPIE--the International Society for Optical Engineering. Published/Created: Bellingham, Wash., USA: SPIE, c1999. Related Authors: Reed, Murray K. Neev, Joseph. Society of Photo-optical Instrumentation Engineers. Description: x, 176 p.: ill.; 28 cm. ISBN: 0819430862 Notes: Includes bibliographical references and index. Subjects: Lasers--Industrial applications--Congresses. Laser pulses, Ultrashort--Congresses. Lasers in biology--

Congresses. Lasers in medicine--Congresses. Series: Proceedings of SPIE--the International Society for Optical Engineering; v. 3616. Variant Series: SPIE proceedings series; v. 3616 LC Classification: TA1673 .C64 1999 Dewey Class No.: 621.36/6 21

Commercial and biomedical applications of ultrashort pulse lasers; laser plasma generation and diagnostics: 23 January, 2001, San Jose, [California] USA / Richard F. Haglund, Jr., Joseph Neev, Richard F. Wood, chairs/editors; sponsored and published by SPIE--the International Society for Optical Engineering. Published/Created: Bellingham, Washington: SPIE, c2001. Related Authors: Haglund, R. F. (Richard F.), 1942- Neev, Joseph. Wood, Richard F. Description: v, 108 p.: ill.; 28 cm. ISBN: 0819439541 Notes: Includes bibliographic references and author index. Subjects: Laser pulses, Ultrashort--Lasers in ophthalmology--Laser ablation--Lasers in medicine--Lasers in surgery--Laser plasmas--Plasma generators--Lasers--Diagnostic use--Congresses. Series: Proceedings of SPIE--the International Society for Optical Engineering; v. 4276. Variant Series: SPIE proceedings series; v. 4276 LC Classification: R857.L37 C654 2001

Commercial applications of ultrafast lasers: 29-30 January 1998 / Murray K. Reed, chair/editor; sponsored ... by SPIE--the International Society for Optical Engineering. Published/Created: Bellingham, Wash., USA: SPIE, c1998. Related Authors: Reed, Murray K. Society of Photo-optical Instrumentation Engineers. Description: viii, 136 p.: ill. (some col.); 28 cm. ISBN: 081942708X Notes: Includes bibliographical references and index. Subjects: Lasers--Industrial applications--Congresses. Laser pulses, Ultrashort--Congresses. Picosecond pulses--Congresses. Lasers in medicine--Congresses. Series: Proceedings of SPIE--the International Society for Optical Engineering; v. 3269. Variant Series: SPIE proceedings series; v. 3269 LC Classification: TA1673 .C65 1998 Dewey Class No.: 621.36/6 21

Compact Blue-Green Lasers Topical Meeting (1992: Santa Fe, N.M.) Compact blue-green lasers: summaries of papers presented at the Compact Blue-Green Lasers Topical Meeting, February 20-21, 1992, Santa Fe, New Mexico / sponsored by Air Force Office of Scientific Research, National Science Foundation for Optical Society of America in cooperation with IEEE Lasers and Electro-optics Society. Edition Information: Postconference ed. Published/Created: Washington, DC: Optical Society of America, c1992. Related Authors: United States. Air Force. Office of Scientific Research. National Science Foundation (U.S.) Optical Society of America. Description: ix, 152 p.: ill.; 28 cm. ISBN: 155752226X Notes: Includes bibliographical references and indexes. Subjects: Semiconductor lasers--Congresses. Series: Technical digest series (Optical Society of America); 1992, v. 6. Variant Series: 1992 technical digest series; v. 6 LC Classification: TA1700 .C66 1992 Dewey Class No.: 621.36/6 20

Compact Blue-Green Lasers Topical Meeting (1993: New Orleans, La.) Compact blue-green lasers: summaries of papers presented at the Compact Blue-Green Lasers Topical Meeting, February 2-4, 1993, New Orleans, Louisiana / sponsored by Optical Society of America, in cooperation with IEEE/Lasers and Electro-optics Society. Edition Information: Postconference ed. Published/Created: Washington, DC: Optical Society of America, c1993. Related Authors: Optical Society of America. Lasers and Electro-optics Society (Institute of Electrical and Electronics Engineers) Description: ix, 176 p. ill.; 29 cm. ISBN: 1557522782 Notes: Includes bibliographical references and index. Subjects: Semiconductor lasers--Congresses. Series: Technical digest series (Optical Society of America); 1993, v. 2. Variant Series: Technical digest series; 1993, v. 2 LC Classification: TA1700 .C66 1993 Dewey Class No.: 621.36/6 20

Compact blue-green lasers: summaries of papers presented at the Compact Blue-Green Lasers Topical Meeting, February 10-11, 1994, Salt Lake City, Utah / sponsored by Optical Society of America in cooperation with IEEE/Lasers and Electro-Optics Society. Edition Information: Postconference ed. Published/Created: Washington, DC: Optical Society of America, c1994. Related Authors: Optical Society of America. Lasers and Electro-optics Society (Institute of Electrical and Electronics Engineers) Compact Blue-Green Lasers Topical Meeting (1994: Salt Lake City, Utah) Description: vii, 115 p. ill.; 29 cm. ISBN: 1557523258 Notes: Includes bibliographical references and index. Subjects: Semiconductor lasers--Congresses. Series: Technical digest series (Optical Society of America); 1994, v. 1. Variant Series: Technical digest series; 1994, v. 1 LC Classification: TA1700 .C648 1994 Dewey Class No.: 621.36/61 20

Compact sources of ultrashort pulses / edited by Irl N. Duling III. Published/Created: Cambridge; New York: Cambridge University Press, 1995. Related Authors: Duling, Irl N. Description: xviii, 430 p.: ill.; 24 cm. ISBN: 0521461928 Notes: Includes bibliographical references and index. Subjects: Laser pulses, Ultrashort. Lasers. Series: Cambridge studies in modern optics (Unnumbered) Variant Series: Cambridge studies in modern optics LC Classification: QC689.5.L37 C66 1995 Dewey Class No.: 621.36/6 20

Conference in Optics (4th: 1994: Bucharest, Romania) ROMOPTO '94, Fourth Conference in Optics: 5-8 September 1994, Bucharest, Romania / Valentin I. Vlad, chair/editor; sponsored by the Romanian Academy ... [et al.]. Published/Created: Bellingham, Wash.: SPIE--the International Society for Optical Engineering, c1995. Related Authors: Vlad, Valentin I. Academia Română. Society of Photo-optical Instrumentation Engineers. Description: xviii, 680 p.: ill.; 28 cm. ISBN: 0819418137 Notes: Includes bibliographical references and index. Subjects: Optics--Congresses. Lasers--Congresses. Series: Proceedings of SPIE--the International Society for Optical Engineering; v. 2461. Variant Series: Proceedings /SPIE--the International Society for Optical Engineering; v. 2461 LC Classification: TA1505 .C66 1994 Dewey Class No.: 621.36 20

Conference in Optics (5th: 1997: Bucharest, Romania) ROMOPTO '97, Fifth Conference on Optics, 9-12 September, 1997, Bucharest, Romania / Valentin I. Vlad, Dan C. Dumitras, chairs/editors; sponsored by the Romanian Ministry of Research and Technology ... [et al.]. Published/Created: Bellingham, Wash.: SPIE--the International Society for Optical Engineering, c1998. Related Authors: Vlad, Valentin I. Dumitras, Dan C. Description: 2 v. (xxiv, 1232 p.): ill.; 28 cm. ISBN: 0819428574 Notes: Includes bibliographical references and indexes. Subjects: Optics--Lasers--Optical detectors--Laser spectroscopy--Optoelectronics--Imaging systems in biology--Materials science--Congresses. Series: Proceedings of SPIE--the International Society for Optical Engineering; v. 3405. Variant Series: Proceedings of SPIE, 0277-786X; v. 3405 LC Classification: TA1505 .C66 1997 Dewey Class No.: 621.36 21

Conference in Optics (6th: 2000: Bucharest, Romania) ROMOPTO 2000: Sixth Conference on Optics: 4-7 September, 2000, Bucharest, Romania / Valentin I. Vlad, chair/editor; sponsored by National Agency for Science, Technology and Innovation (Romania) ... [et al.]; organized by Division of Optics and Quantum Electronics (Romania) ... [et al.]; published by SPIE--the International Society for Optical Engineering. Published/Created: Bellingham, Wash.: SPIE, c2001. Related Authors: Vlad, Valentin I. Description: xix, 918 p.: ill.; 28 cm. ISBN: 0819441414 Notes: Includes bibliographic references and author index. Subjects: Optics--Lasers--Optical detectors--Laser spectroscopy--Optoelectronics--Imaging systems in biology--Materials science--Congresses. Series: Proceedings of SPIE--the International Society for Optical Engineering; v. 4430. Variant Series: Proceedings of SPIE, 0277-786X; v. 4430 LC Classification: TA1505 .C66 2000 Dewey Class No.: 621.36 21

Conference on Lasers and Electro-optics (14th: 1994: Anaheim, Calif.) CLEO '94: summaries of papers presented at the Conference on Lasers and Electro-optics, May 8-13, 1994, Anaheim Convention Center, Anaheim, California / sponsored by Optical Society of America, IEEE/Lasers and Electro-optics Society in cooperation with Quantum Electronics Division of the European Physical Society, Japanese Quantum Electronics Joint Group. Edition Information: Postconference ed. Published/Created: Washington, DC: Optical Society of America, c1994. Description: xvi, 523 p.: ill.; 28 cm. ISBN: 155752341X (Pontconference ed.) 0780319710 (IEEE: casebound) 0780319729 (IEEE: microfiche) Notes: "[IEEE] catalog number 94CH3463-7"--T.p. verso. "Conference edition" on t.p. "Postconference edition" on cover and spine. Includes postdeadline papers. Includes bibliographical references and index. Subjects: Lasers--Electrooptics--Electrooptical devices--Congresses. Series: Technical digest series (Optical Society of America); 1994, v. 8. Variant Series: 1994 technical digest series; v. 8 LC Classification: TA1673 .C6663 1994 Dewey Class No.: 621.36/6 21

Conference on Lasers and Electro-optics (1993: Baltimore, Md.) Conference on lasers and electro-optics: summaries of papers presented at the Conference on Lasers and Electro-Optics, May 2-7, 1993, Baltimore, Maryland / sponsored by Optical Society of America ... [et al.]. Edition Information: Postconference ed. Published/Created: Washington, DC: The Society, c1993. Related Authors: Optical Society of America. Description: 742 p.: ill.; 28 cm. ISBN: 1557523002 (pbk.) Notes: Includes bibliographical references and indexes. Subjects: Lasers--Electrooptics--Electrooptical devices--Congresses. Series: Technical digest series (Optical Society of America); 1993, v. 11. Variant Series: 1993 technical digest series; v. 11 LC Classification: QC685 .C663 1993 Dewey Class No.: 621.36/6 20

Conference on Lasers and Electro-optics (1997: Baltimore, Md.) CLEO '97: summaries of papers presented at the Conference on Lasers and Electro-optics, May 18-23, 1997, Baltimore Convention Center, Baltimore, Maryland / sponsored by IEEE/Lasers and Electro-Optics Society, Optical Society of America in cooperation with Quantum Electronics Division of the European Physical Society, Japanese Quantum Electronics Joint Group. Edition Information: Conference ed. Published/Created: Washington, DC: Optical Society of America, c1997. Description: 548 p.: ill.; 27 cm. ISBN: 155752498X 0780341252 (IEEE: casebound) 0780341260 (IEEE: microfiche) Notes: "Catalog number 975CH361100"--T.p. verso. Includes bibliographical references and index. Subjects: Lasers--Electrooptics--Electrooptical devices--Congresses. Series: Technical digest series (Optical Society of America) (Conference ed.); 1997, v. 11. Variant Series: 1997 OSA technical digest series; v. 11 LC Classification: TA1673 .C6663 1997 Dewey Class No.: 621.36/6 21

Conference on Lasers and Electro-optics (1998: San Francisco, Calif.) CLEO '98--Conference on Lasers and Electro-Optics: the Moscone Center, San Francisco, California, May 3-8, 1998: technical digest, summaries of papers presented at the Conference on Lasers and Electro-Optics / CLEO '98 sponsored by IEEE/Lasers and Electro-Optics Society, Optical Society of America ... Published/Created: [Washington, DC]: Optical Society of America, c1998. Description: 559 p.: ill.; 28 cm. ISBN: 1557525390 (Conf. ed.) 1557525404 (Postconf. ed.) Notes: Includes bibliographical references and index.

Subjects: Lasers--Electrooptics--Electrooptical devices--Congresses. Series: Technical digest series (Optical Society of America) (Conference ed.) 1998, v. 6. Variant Series: Technical digest series; 1998, v. 6 LC Classification: TA1673 .C6663 1998 Dewey Class No.: 621.36/6 21

Conference on Lasers and Electro-Optics (CLEO 2000): May 7-12, 2000, the Moscone Convention Center, San Francisco, California / sponsored by IEEE/Lasers and Electro-Optics Society, Optical Society of America in cooperation with Quantum Electronics and Optics Division of the European Physical Society [and] Japanese Quantum Electronics Joint Group. Published/Created: Washington, DC: Optical Society of America, c2000. Description: 720 p.: ill.; 28 cm. ISBN: 1557526346 (Postconference ed.) Series: Trends in optics and photonics series; v. 39

Conference on lasers and electro-optics (Cleo '99) conference digest. Published/Created: Washington, DC: Optical Society of America, 1999. Description: p.; cm. ISBN: 1557525706 (conference: acid-free paper) Series: OSA technical digest series LC Classification: 9907 BOOK NOT YET IN LC

Conference on Lasers and Electro-optics Europe (1994: Amsterdam, Netherlands) 1994 Conference on Lasers and Electro-Optics Europe: RAI Congress Centre, Amsterdam, The Netherlands, 28 August-2 September, 1994 / sponsored by EPS-Quantum Electronics and Optics Division, IEEE/Lasers and Electro-Optics Society, Optical Society of America in cooperation with European Optical Society, the Institute of Physics, Institution of Electrical Engineers. Published/Created: [New York]: Institute of Electrical and Electronics Engineers, c1994. Related Authors: European Physical Society. Quantum Electronics and Optics Division. Lasers and Electro-optics Society (Institute of Electrical and Electronics Engineers) Optical Society of America. Description: ix, 436 p.: ill.; 30 cm. ISBN: 0780317890 (softbound) 0780317904 (microfiche) Notes: "Technical digest"--Cover. "IEEE catalog number 94TH0614-8." Includes bibliographical references and index. Subjects: Lasers-- Electrooptics--Congresses. Optoelectronic devices--Congresses. LC Classification: TA1673 .C667 1994 Dewey Class No.: 621.36/6 20

Conference on Lasers and Electro-optics Europe (1996: Hamburg, Germany) Medical and biological applications: featuring papers from CLEO/Europe '96, Conference on Lasers and Electro-Optics/Europe, September 8-13, 1996, Hamburg, Germany / edited by Rinaldo Cubeddu; sponsored by European Physical Society, Quantum Electronic and Optics Division, IEEE/Lasers and Electro-Optics Society, Optical Society of America in cooperation with European Optical Society. Published/Created: Washington, D.C.: Optical Society of America, c1996. Related Authors: Cubeddu, Rinaldo. European Physical Society. Quantum Electronics and Optics Division. Lasers and Electro-optics Society (Institute of Electrical and Electronics Engineers) Optical Society of America. European Optical Society. Description: viii, 105 p.: ill.; 28 cm. ISBN: 1557524645 Notes: Includes bibliographical references (p. 92-102) and indexes. Subjects: Lasers in medicine--Congresses. Lasers in biology--Congresses. Series: OSA trends in optics and photonics; v. 6. Variant Series: Trends in optics and photonics; v. 6 LC Classification: R857.L37 C66 1996 Dewey Class No.: 610/.28 21

Conference on Lasers and Electro-optics Europe (1998: Glasgow, Scotland) 1998 CLEO/Europe Conference on Lasers and Electro-Optics Europe: SECC-Scottish Exhibition and Conference Centre, Glasgow, Scotland, United Kingdom, 14-18 September, 1998: technical digest / sponsored by European Physical Society ... [et al.]. Published/Created: Piscataway, N.J.: IEEE, c1998. Related Authors: European Physical Society. Description: xv, 422 p.: ill.; 30 cm. ISBN: 078034233X (softbound) 0780342348 (microfiche)

Notes: "IEEE Catalog Number 98TH8362"--verso of T.p. Includes bibliographical references and author index. Subjects: Lasers--Electrooptics--Congresses. Optoelectronic devices--Congresses. LC Classification: TA1673 .C667 1998 Dewey Class No.: 621.36/6 21

Conference on Lasers and Electro-optics Europe (2000: Nice, France) 2000 Conference on Lasers and Electro-Optics Europe: conference digest: Nice Acropolis, Nice, France, 10-15 September 2000 / sponsored by European Physical Society ... [et al.]. Published/Created: Piscataway, N.J.: IEEE, c2000. Related Authors: European Physical Society. Description: xii, 394 p.: ill.; 30 cm. ISBN: 0780363191 Notes: "IEEE Catalog Number 00TH8505."--T.p. verso. Includes bibliographical references and author index. Subjects: Lasers--Congresses. Electrooptics--Congresses. Optoelectronic devices--Congresses. LC Classification: TA1673 .C667 2000 Dewey Class No.: 621.36/6 21

Conference on Lasers and Electro-optics Europe (2nd: 1996: Hamburg, Germany) 1996 CLEO/Europe: Congress Centrum Hamburg (CCH), Hamburg, Germany, 8-13 September 1996 / sponsored by European Physical Society ... [et al.]; in cooperation with the European Optical Society. Published/Created: [New York]: Institute of Electrical and Electronics Engineers; Piscataway, N.J.: Additional copies from IEEE Service Center, c1996. Related Authors: European Physical Society. European Optical Society. Description: viii, 366 p.: ill.; 21 x 30 cm. ISBN: 0780331710 (softbound ed.) 0780331702 (microfiche ed.) Notes: "Technical digest"--Cover. Includes bibliographical references and index. Subjects: Lasers--Research--Europe--Congresses. Lasers--Industrial applications--Congresses. Quantum optics--Electrooptics--Congresses. LC Classification: QC685 .C6633 1996 Dewey Class No.: 621.36/6 21

Conference on lasers and electro-optics vol.73. Published/Created: Washington, DC: Optical Society of America, 2002. Projected Pub. Date: 0206 Description: p. cm. ISBN: 1557527067 Series: OSA trends in optics and photonics series; 73

Conference on lasers and electro-optics. Edition Information: conference ed. Published/Created: Washington, DC: Optical Society of America, 2001. Projected Pub. Date: 0105 Description: p.; cm. ISBN: 1557526761 (conference edition) Series: Osa technical digest series

Conference on lasers and electro-optics. Published/Created: Washington, DC: Optical Society of America, 2002. Projected Pub. Date: 0205 Description: p. cm. ISBN: 1557527059

Conference on Lasers and Electro-optics. Summaries of papers presented at the Conference on Lasers and Electro-optics. Edition Information: Postconference ed. Published/Created: Washington, D.C.: Optical Society of America, c1988-c1999. Description: 12 v.: ill.; 28 cm. 25-29 Apr. 1988-May 23-28, 1999. Current Frequency: Annual Continues: Conference on Lasers and Electro-optics Digest of technical papers (Postconference ed.) 1054-0377 (DLC) 90657288 (OCoLC)22717351 Continued by: Conference on Lasers and Electro-optics. Technical digest (DLC) 00242381 (OCoLC)45353348 ISSN: 1054-0393 Notes: Sponsored by the Lasers and Electro-optics Society and Optical Society of America in cooperation with the Quantum Electronics Division of the European Physical Society and Japanese Quantum Electronic Joint Group. SERBIB/SERLOC merged record Subjects: Lasers--Electrooptics--Optoelectronic devices--Congresses. Series: Technical digest series (Optical Society of America) Variant Series: Technical digest series LC Classification: TA1673 .C664b Dewey Class No.: 621.36/6 20

Conference on Lasers and Electro-optics. Technical digest / Conference on Lasers and Electro-optics (CLEO). Edition Information: Postconference ed. Published/Created: Washington, DC: Optical Society of America, c2000- Description: v.: ill.; 28 cm. May 7-12, 2000- Current Frequency: Annual Continues: Conference on Lasers and Electro-optics. Summaries of papers presented at the Conference on Lasers and Electro-optics (Postconference ed.) 1054-0393 (DLC) 90657372 (OCoLC)22717284 Notes: Sponsored by the IEEE/Lasers and Electro-optics Society and Optical Society of America in cooperation with the Quantum Electronics and Optics Division of the European Physical Society and Japanese Quantum Electronic Joint Group. Additional Form Avail.: Available also online via the World Wide Web by subscription, in PDF format. Subjects: Lasers--Congresses. Electrooptics--Congresses. Optoelectronic devices--Congresses. Series: OSA trends in optics and photonics. Variant Series: Trends in optics and photonics, 1094-5695

Conference on Lasers and Electro-optics/Pacific Rim (1995: Chiba-shi, Japan) CLEO/Pacific Rim '95: the Pacific Rim Conference on Lasers and Electro-optics, Makuhari Messe Convention Center, July 10-14, 1995; co-located with InterOpto '95: technical digest / sponsoring organizations, Japan Society of Applied Physics ... [et al.]; cosponsoring and cooperating organizations, the Institute of Electrical Engineers of Japan ... [et al.]. Published/Created: [Piscataway, N.J.]: Institute of Electrical and Electronics Engineers, c1995. Description: xi, 313 p.: ill.; 30 cm. ISBN: 0780324005 (softbound ed.) Notes: Includes bibliographical references and index. Subjects: Lasers--Congresses. Electrooptics--Congresses. Optoelectronic devices--Congresses. LC Classification: TA1673 .C6675 1995

Conference on Lasers and Electro-optics/Pacific Rim (1997: Chiba-shi, Japan) CLEO/Pacific Rim '97: the Pacific Rim Conference on Lasers and Electro-optics, Nippon Convention Center, Makuhari Messe, Chiba, Japan, 14-18 July 1997; co-located with InterOpto '97: technical digest / sponsored by the Japan Society of Applied Physics ... [et al.]. Published/Created: New York: Institute of Electrical and Electronics Engineers; Piscataway, NJ: IEEE Service Center, c1997. Related Authors: . InterOpto '97 (1997: Chiba-shi, Japan) Description: xi, 320 p.: ill.; 30 cm. ISBN: 0780338898 (softbound) 0780338901 (microfiche) Notes: "IEEE Catalog Number: 97TH8275"--T.p. verso. Includes bibliographical references and index. Subjects: Lasers--Electrooptics--Optoelectronic devices--Congresses. LC Classification: TA1673 .C6675 1997 Dewey Class No.: 621.36/6 21

Conference on Optical Fiber Communication (11th: 1988: New Orleans, La.) Optical Fiber Communication Conference: summaries of papers presented at the Optical Fiber Communication Conference, 25-28 Jan. 1988, New Orleans, Louisiana / sponsored by the Optical Society of America, Lasers and Electro-optics Society of the Institute of Electrical and Electronics Engineers. Edition Information: Conference ed. Published/Created: Washington, D.C.: Optical Society of America, c1988. Related Authors: Optical Society of America. Lasers and Electro-optics Society (Institute of Electrical and Electronics Engineers) Description: 208 p.: ill.; 28 cm. Notes: Includes bibliographical references and index. Subjects: Fiber optics--Optical communications--Integrated optics--Congresses. Series: Technical digest series (Optical Society of America) (Conference ed.); 1988, v. 1. Variant Series: Technical digest series; 1988, v. 1 LC Classification: TA1800 .C65 1988 Dewey Class No.: 621.38/0414 19

Conference on Optical Fiber Communication (12th: 1989: Houston, Tex.) Optical Fiber Communication Conference: summaries of papers presented at the Optical Fiber Communication Conference, 6-9 February 1989, Houston, Texas / cosponsored by the Optical Society of America, and Lasers and Electro-optics Society of the Institute of Electrical and Electronics Engineers. Edition Information: Conference ed. Published/Created: Washington, D.C.: Optical Society of America, c1989. Related Authors: Optical Society of America. Lasers and Electro-optics Society (Institute of Electrical and Electronics Engineers) Description: 192 p.: ill.; 28 cm. ISBN: 1557520720 Notes: Includes bibliographical references. Subjects: Fiber optics--Congresses. Optical communications--Congresses. Integrated optics--Congresses. Series: Technical digest series (Optical Society of America) (Conference ed.); 1989, v. 5. Variant Series: Technical digest series; 1989, v. 5 LC Classification: TA1800 .C65 1989 Dewey Class No.: 621.382/75 20

Conference on Optical Fiber Communication (13th: 1990: San Francisco, Calif.) Optical Fiber Communication Conference: summaries of papers presented at the Optical Fiber Communication Conference, 22-26 January 1990, San Francisco, California / cosponsored by the Optical Society of America and Lasers and Electro-optics Society of the Institute of Electrical and Electronics Engineers. Edition Information: Postconference ed. Published/Created: Washington, DC: OSA, c1990. Related Authors: Optical Society of America. Lasers and Electro-optics Society (Institute of Electrical and Electronics Engineers) Description: 382 p.: ill.; 29 cm. ISBN: 1557521131 Notes: Cover Title - Optical fiber communication. Includes bibliographical references and index. Subjects: Fiber optics--Optical communications--Integrated optics--Congresses. Series: Technical digest series (Optical Society of America); 1990, v. 1. Variant Series: 1990 technical digest series; v. 1 LC Classification: TA1800 .C65 1990 Dewey Class No.: 621.382/75 20

Conference on Optical Fiber Communication (13th: 1990: San Francisco, Calif.) Optical Fiber Communication Conference: summaries of papers presented at the Optical Fiber Communication Conference, 22-26 January, 1990,San Francisco, California / sponsored by the Optical Society of America, Lasers and Electro-Optics Society of the Institute of Electrical and Electronics Engineers. Edition Information: Conference ed. Published/Created: Washington, DC: Optical Society of America, c1990. Related Authors: Optical Society of America. Lasers and Electro-optics Society (Institute of Electrical and Electronics Engineers) Description: 232 p.: ill.; 28 cm. ISBN: 1557521123 (softcover) Notes: Cover Title - OFC '90. Spine Title - Optical fiber communication, 22-26 January 1990. "IEEE catalog number 90CH2821-7"--T.p. verso. Includes bibliographical references and index. Subjects: Fiber optics--Congresses. Optical communications--Congresses. Integrated optics--Congresses. Series: Technical digest series (Optical Society of America) (Conference ed.); 1990, v. 1. Variant Series: Technical digest series; 1990, v. 1 LC Classification: TA1800 .C65 1980a Dewey Class No.: 621.382/75 20

Conference on Optical Fiber Communication (15th: 1992: San Jose, Calif.) Optical Fiber Communication Conference: summaries of papers presented at the Optical Fiber Communication Conference, 2-7 February 1992, San Jose, California / sponsored by the Optical Society of America, Lasers and Electro-Optics Society of the Institute of Electrical and Electronics Engineers, Communications Society of the Institute of Electrical and Electronics Engineers. Edition Information: Postconference ed. Published/Created: Washington, DC: Optical Society of America, c1992. Related Authors: Optical Society of America. Lasers and Electro-Optics Society (Institute of Electrical and Electronics Engineers) IEEE Communications Society Description: xiv, 410 p.: ill.; 28 cm. ISBN: 1557522227 (pbk.): Notes: Spine Title - Optical fiber communication. "IEEE catalog number 92CH3101-3"--T.p. verso. Includes bibliographical references. Subjects: Optical communications--Congresses. Fiber optics--Congresses. Series: Technical digest series (Optical Society of America; 1992, v. 5. Variant Series: 1992 technical digest series; v. 5 LC Classification: TK5103.59 .C65 1992 Dewey Class No.: 621.382/7 20

Conference on Optical Fiber Communication (15th: 1992: San Jose, Calif.) Optical Fiber Communication Conference: summaries of papers presented at the Optical Fiber Communication Conference, February 2-7, 1992, San Jose, California / sponsored by the Optical Society of America, Lasers and Electro-Optics Society of the Institute of Electrical and Electronics Engineers, Communications Society of the Institute of Electrical and Electronics Engineers. Edition Information: Conference ed. Published/Created: Washington, DC: Optical Society of America, c1992. Related Authors: Optical Society of America. Lasers and Electro-optics Society (Institute of Electrical and Electronics Engineers) IEEE Communications Society. Description: xiv, 306 p.: ill.; 28 cm. ISBN: 1557522219 (pbk.) 0780305418 (lib. bdg.) 0780305426 (microfiche) Notes: Spine Title - Optical fiber communication. Includes bibliographical references and index. Subjects: Optical communications--Congresses. Fiber optics--Congresses. Series: Technical digest series (Optical Society of America) (Conference ed.); 1992, v. 5. Variant Series: Technical digest series; 1992, v. 5 LC Classification: TK5103.59 .C65 1992a Dewey Class No.: 621.382/75 20

Conference on Optical Fiber Communication (1991: San Diego, Calif.) Technical digest, OFC '91: San Diego, California, February 18-22, 1991 / Optical Fiber Communication Conference; cosponsored by IEEE/Communications Society, IEEE/Lasers and Electro-Optics Society, Optical Society of America. Edition Information: Conference ed. Published/Created: Washington, DC: Director of Publications, Optical Society of America, c1991. Description: xix, 226 p.: ill.; 29 cm. ISBN: 078030571X (lib. bdg.) 1557521662 (pbk.) 0780305728 (microfiche) 1557521921 (1991 series) Notes: Cover Title - 1991 Optical Fiber Communication Conference. "91CH2958-7"--Spine. Includes bibliographical references and index. Subjects: Optical communications--Congresses. Fiber optics--Congresses. LC Classification: TK5103.59 .C65 1991a Dewey Class No.: 621.382/75 20

Conference on Optical Fiber Communication (1991: San Diego, Calif.) Technical digest, OFC '91: San Diego, California, February 18-22, 1991 / Optical Fiber Communication Conference; cosponsored by IEEE/Communications Society, IEEE/Lasers and Electro-optics Society, Optical Society of America. Edition Information: Postconference ed. Published/Created: Washington, DC: Optical Society of America, c1991. Related Authors: IEEE Communications Society. Lasers and Electro-optics Society (Institute of Electrical and Electronics Engineers) Optical Society of America. Description: xix, 326 p.: ill.; 29 cm. ISBN: 1557521670 (hardcover) Notes: Cover Title - Optical fiber communication. "IEEE catalog number 91CH2958-7"--Verso t.p. Includes bibliographical references and index. Subjects: Optical communications--Congresses. Fiber optics--Congresses. Series: 1991 technical digest series; v. 4 Technical digest series (Optical Society of America); 1991, v. 4. LC Classification: TK5103.59 .C65 1991 Dewey Class No.: 621.382/7 20

Conference on Optical Fiber Communication (1993: San Jose, Calif.) OFC/IOOC '93, Conference on Optical Fiber Communication/International Conference on Integrated Optics and Optical Fiber Communication: summaries of papers presented at the Conference on Optical Fiber Communication/International Conference on Integrated Optics and Optical Fiber Communication, February 21-26, 1993, San Jose, California / sponsors, Optical Society of America, Lasers and Electro-optics Society of the Institute of Electrical and Electronics Engineers, Communications Society of the Institute of Electrical and Electronics

Engineers. Edition Information: Postconference ed. Published/Created: Washington, DC: Optical Society of America, c1993. Related Authors: Optical Society of America. Lasers and Electro-optics Society (Institute of Electrical and Electronics Engineers) IEEE Communications Society. International Conference on Integrated Optics and Optical Fiber Communication (1993: San Jose, Calif.) Description: xv, 399 p.: ill.; 28 cm. ISBN: 1557522820 Notes: "IEEE catalog number: 93CH3275-5"--T.p. verso. Includes bibliographical references and index. Subjects: Optical communications--Congresses. Fiber optics--Congresses. Series: Technical digest series (Optical Society of America); 1993, v. 4. Variant Series: Technical digest series; 1993, v. 4 LC Classification: TK5103.59 .C65 1993 Dewey Class No.: 621.382/7 20

Conference on Optical Fiber Communication (1994: San Jose, Calif.) OFC '94, optical fiber communication: summaries of papers presented at the Conference on Optical Fiber Communication, February 20-25, 1994, San Jose Convention Center, San Jose, California / sponsored by Optical Society of America, Lasers and Electro-Optics Society of the Institute of Electrical and Electronics Engineers, Communications Society of the Institute of Electrical and Electronics Engineers. Edition Information: Postconference ed. Published/Created: Washington, DC: Optical Society of America, 1994. Related Authors: Optical Society of America. Lasers and Electro-optics Society (Institute of Electrical and Electronics Engineers) IEEE Communications Society. Description: 456 p.: ill.; 28 cm. ISBN: 1557523312 Notes: Includes bibliographical references and index. Subjects: Optical communications--Congresses. Fiber optics--Congresses. Optoelectronics--Congresses. Integrated optics--Congresses. Series: Technical digest series; 1994, v. 4 Technical digest series (Optical Society of America); 1994, v. 4. LC Classification: TK5103.59 .C65 1994 Dewey Class No.: 621.382/7 20

Conference on Optical Fiber Communication (1996: San Jose, Calif.) OFC '96, optical fiber communication: February 25-March 1, 1996, San Jose Convention Center, San Jose, California / sponsored by Optical Society of America, IEEE/Lasers and Electro-Optics Society, IEEE/Communications Society. Edition Information: Postconference ed. Published/Created: Washington, DC: Optical Society of America, c1996. Related Authors: Optical Society of America. Lasers and Electro-optics Society (Institute of Electrical and Electronics Engineers) IEEE Communications Society. Description: ix, 476 p.: ill.; 28 cm. ISBN: 1557524238 Notes: Includes bibliographical references and index. Subjects: Optical communications--Fiber optics--Optoelectronics--Integrated optics--Congresses. Series: Technical digest series; 1996, v. 2. Variant Series: 1996 technical digest series; v. 2 LC Classification: TK5103.59 .C65 1996 Dewey Class No.: 621.382/75 21

Conference on Optical Fiber Communication (1997: Dallas, Tex.) Conference on Optical Fiber Communications: technical digest, February 16-21, 1997, Dallas Conference Center, Dallas, Texas / sponsored by IEEE/Lasers and Electro-Optics Society, IEEE Communications Society, Optical Society of America. Edition Information: Postconference ed. Published/Created: Washington, DC: Optical Society of America, c1997. Related Authors: Lasers and Electro-optics Society (Institute of Electrical and Electronics Engineers) IEEE Communications Society. Optical Society of America. Description: ix, 488 p.: ill.; 28 cm. ISBN: 1557524815 (postconference ed.) Notes: Includes bibliographical references and index. Subjects: Optical communications--Fiber optics--Broadband communication systems--Multiplexing--Congresses. Series: Technical digest series (Optical Society of America); 1997, v. 6. Variant Series: 1997 OSA technical digest series; v. 6 LC Classification: TK5103.59 .C65 1997b Dewey Class No.: 621.382/75 21

Conference on Optical Fiber Communication (1997: Dallas, Texas) Conference on Optical Fiber Communications: technical digest, February 16-21, 1997, Dallas Convention Center, Dallas, Texas / sponsored by IEEE/Lasers and Electro-Optics Society, IEEE Communications Society, Optical Society of America. Edition Information: Conference ed. Published/Created: Washington, D.C.: Optical Society of America, c1997. Related Authors: Lasers and Electro-optics Society (Institute of Electrical and Electronics Engineers) IEEE Communications Society. Optical Society of America. Description: ix, 365 p.: ill.; 28 cm. ISBN: 1557524807 (Optical Society of America) 078033860X (IEEE casebound) 0780338618 (IEEE microfiche) Notes: "Catalog number 97CH36049"--T.p. verso. Includes bibliographical references. Subjects: Optical communications--Congresses. Fiber optics--Congresses. Broadband communication systems--Congresses. Multiplexing--Congresses. Series: Technical digest series (Optical Society of America) (Conference ed.); 1997, v. 6. Variant Series: OSA technical digest series; 1997, v. 6 LC Classification: TK5103.59 .C65 1997 Dewey Class No.: 621.382/7 21

Conference on Optical Fiber Communication (1998: San Jose, Calif.) OFC '98, Optical Fiber Communication Conference and Exhibit: technical digest, February 22-27, 1998, San Jose Convention Center, San Jose, California / sponsored by IEEE/Lasers and Electro-Optics Society, IEEE Communications Society, Optical Society of America. Edition Information: Conference ed. Published/Created: Washington, DC: Optical Society of America, c1998. Related Authors: Lasers and Electro-optics Society (Institute of Electrical and Electronics Engineers) IEEE Communications Society. Optical Society of America. Description: vii, 421 p.: ill.; 28 cm. ISBN: 1557525285 Notes: "Catalog number 98CH36177"--T.p. verso. Includes bibliographical references and index. Subjects: Optical communications--Optical fibers--Multiplexing--Broadband amplifiers--Congresses. Series: Technical digest series (Optical Society of America) (Conference ed.); 1998, v. 2. Variant Series: 1998 OSA technical digest series; v. 2 LC Classification: TK5103.59 .C65 1998 Dewey Class No.: 621.382/7 21

Conference on Optical Fiber Communication (1998: San Jose, Calif.) OFC'98: Optical Fiber Communication Conference and Exhibit: technical digest: February 22-27, 1998, San Jose, California / sponsored by IEEE/Lasers and Electro-Optics Society, IEEE Communications Society, Optical Society of America. Edition Information: Postconference ed. Published/Created: Washington, DC: Optical Society of America, c1998. Related Authors: Lasers and Electro-optics Society (Institute of Electrical and Electronics Engineers) IEEE Communications Society. Optical Society of America. Description: vii, 541 p.: ill.; 28 cm. ISBN: 1557525293 (pbk.) Notes: Includes bibliographical references. Subjects: Optical communications--Optical fibers--Multiplexing--Broadband amplifiers--Congresses. Series: Technical digest series (Optical Society of America); 1998, v. 2. Variant Series: 1998 OSA technical digest series; v. 2 LC Classification: TK5103.59 .C65 1998a Dewey Class No.: 621.382/7 21

Conference on Optical Fiber Communication (2001: Anaheim, Calif.) OFC 2001, Optical Fiber Communication Conference and Exhibit: March 17-22, 2001, Anaheim Convention Center, Anaheim, California / sponsored by IEEE/Communications Society, IEEE/Lasers and Electro-Optics Society, Optical Society of America. Edition Information: Postconference ed. Published/Created: Washington, DC: Optical Society of America, c2001. Related Authors: IEEE Communications Society. Lasers and Electro-optics Society (Institute of Electrical and Electronics Engineers) Optical Society of America. Description: 4 v.: ill.; 28 cm. ISBN: 1557526559 Contents: [1] Presentations from Monday, March 19, 2001 -- [2] Presentations from Tuesday, March 20, 2001 -- [3] Presentations from Wednesday,

March 21, 2001 -- [4] Presentations from Thursday, March 22, 2001 plus OFC postdeadline papers. Subjects: Optical communications--Fiber optics--Integrated optics--Congresses. Series: Technical digest series (Optical Society of America) OSA trends in optics and photonics; v. 54. Variant Series: OSA trends in optics and photonics series; v. 54 Technical digest LC Classification: TK5103.59 .C65 2001 Dewey Class No.: 621.382/7 21

Congress on Modern Optics (5th: 1998: Budapest, Hungary) OPTIKA '98: 5th Congress on Modern Optics: 14-17 September, 1998, Budapest, Hungary / György Ákos, Gábor Lupkovics, András Podmaniczky, chairs/editors; organized by Scientific Society for Optics, Acoustics, Motion Picture and Theater Technology (OPAKFI) in association with HUNGOPTIKA--SPIE Hungary Chapter; sponsored by ICO--The International Commission for Optics ... [et al.]; published by SPIE--the International Society for Optical Engineering. Published/Created: Bellingham, Washington: SPIE, c1998. Related Authors: Ákos, Gy. Lupkovics, G. (Gábor) Podmaniczky, A. (András) Scientific Society for Optics, Motion Picture and Theater Technology (Hungary) Society of Photo-optical Instrumentation Engineers. Society of Photo-optical Instrumentation Engineers. Hungarian Chapter. Description: xvii, 628 p.: ill.; 28 cm. ISBN: 0819430382 Notes: Includes bibliographical references and author index. Subjects: Optics--Congresses. Lasers--Congresses. Series: Proceedings of SPIE--the International Society for Optical Engineering; v. 3573. Variant Series: SPIE proceedings series; v. 3573 LC Classification: TA1505 .C67 1998 Dewey Class No.: 621.36 21

Congresso nazionale Elettronica quantistica e plasmi (6th: 1990: Rome, Italy) Quantum Electronics and Plasma Physics: 6th Italian Conference: Roma, 5-7 November 1990 / edited by G.C. Righini. Published/Created: Bologna, Italy: Italian Physical Society, c1991. Related Authors: Righini, Giancarlo C. Description: xxii, 504 p.: ill.; 25 cm. ISBN: 8877940395: Notes: Title on added t.p.: 6° Congresso nazionale di elettronica quantistica e plasmi. Includes bibliographical references. Subjects: Quantum electronics--Plasma (Ionized gases)--Lasers--Nonlinear optics--Congresses. Series: Conference proceedings (Società italiana di fisica); v. 29. Variant Series: Conference proceedings; v. 29 LC Classification: QC685 .C665 1990 Dewey Class No.: 537.5 20

Cook, William R., M.D. Manual of tumescent liposculpture and laser cosmetic surgery: including The weekend alternative to the facelift / William R. Cook, Jr., Kim K. Cook. Published/Created: Philadelphia: Lippincott Williams & Wilkins, c1999. Related Authors: Cook, Kim K. Description: xv, 217 p.: col. ill.; 26 cm. ISBN: 0781719879 (hardcover) Notes: Includes bibliographical references and index. Subjects: Liposculpture--Liposuction--Surgery, Plastic--Lasers in surgery--Handbooks, manuals, etc. Lipectomy--methods. Skin--surgery. Laser Surgery--Surgery, Plastic--methods. LC Classification: RD119.5.L55 C66 1999 Dewey Class No.: 617.9/5 21

Cosmetic laser surgery / [edited by] Richard E. Fitzpatrick, Mitchel P. Goldman. Published/Created: St. Louis, Mo.: Mosby, 2000. Related Authors: Fitzpatrick, Richard E. Goldman, Mitchel P. Description: xi, 239 p.: col. ill.; 28 cm. ISBN: 0815186746 Notes: Includes bibliographical references and index. Subjects: Surgery, Plastic. Lasers in surgery. Cosmetic Techniques. Laser Surgery. LC Classification: RD119 .C653 2000 Dewey Class No.: 617.9/5 21

Cosmetic laser surgery / edited by Tina S. Alster, David B. Apfelberg. Published/Created: New York: Wiley-Liss: Wiley, c1996. Related Authors: Alster, Tina S. Apfelberg, David B. Description: xvii, 152 p.: col. ill.; 29 cm. ISBN: 0471122424 (acid-free paper) Notes: Includes bibliographical references and index. Subjects: Surgery, Plastic. Lasers in surgery. Surgery, Plastic. Laser Surgery. LC Classification: RD119 .C65 1996 Dewey Class No.: 617.9/5 20

Cosmetic laser surgery: a practitioner's guide / edited by Tina S. Alster, David B. Apfelberg. Edition Information: 2nd ed. Published/Created: New York: Wiley-Liss, c1999. Related Authors: Alster, Tina S. Apfelberg, David B. Description: xx, 393 p.: ill. (some col.); 29 cm. ISBN: 0471252700 (cloth: alk. paper) Notes: Includes bibliographical references and index. Subjects: Surgery, Plastic. Lasers in surgery. Reconstructive Surgical Procedures. Laser Surgery. Cosmetic Techniques. LC Classification: RD119 .C65 1999 Dewey Class No.: 617.9/5 21

Croydon, Michael. 1991 fourth international exhibition of holography: catalogue of holograms / introduction by Tung H. Jeong; catalogue compiled and edited by Michael Croydon and Ed Wesly. Published/Created: Lake Forest, Ill.: Lake Forest College, c1991. Related Authors: Wesly, Ed. Durand Art Institute. Description: 1 v. (unpaged): ill.; 22 cm. ISBN: 0910535094 Notes: Title on added t.p.: 4th international exhibition of holography: July 20-August 18, 1991, Durand Art Institute, Lake Forest College. Exhibition held with the Fourth International Symposium on Display Holography. Subjects: Lasers in art--Holography in art--Exhibitions. Art, Modern--20th century--Exhibitions. LC Classification: N6494.L3 C76 1991 Dewey Class No.: 709/.04/907477321 20

Current developments in optical design and optical engineering / sponsored and published by SPIE--The International Society for Optical Engineering. Published/Created: Bellingham, WA: The Society, c1991- Related Authors: Society of Photo-optical Instrumentation Engineers. Description: v.: ill.; 28 cm. Vols. for 1992-<1995 numbered: 2-<5. [1] (12-13 July 1990)- Current Frequency: Annual Continues: Current developments in optical engineering (DLC) 96644619 (OCoLC)33473090 Notes: SERBIB/SERLOC merged record Subjects: Optical instruments--Design and construction--Congresses. Lasers--Design and construction--Congresses. Series: Proceedings of SPIE-the International Society of Optical Engineers. Variant Series: Proceedings / SPIE--the International Society for Optical Engineering LC Classification: TS510 .C718 Dewey Class No.: 621.36 20

Current developments in optical design and optical engineering VIII: 19-21 July 1999, Denver, Colorado / Robert E. Fischer, Warren J. Smith, chairs/editors; sponsored ... by SPIE--The International Society for Optical Engineering. Published/Created: Bellingham, Wash., USA: SPIE, c1999. Related Authors: Fischer, Robert Edward, 1943- Smith, Warren J. Society of Photo-optical Instrumentation Engineers. Description: ix, 448 p.: ill.; 28 cm. ISBN: 0819432652 Notes: Includes bibliographical references and index. Subjects: Optical instruments--Design and construction--Congresses. Lasers--Design and construction--Congresses. Series: Proceedings of SPIE--the International Society for Optical Engineering; v. 3779. Variant Series: SPIE proceedings series; v. 3779 LC Classification: TS510 .C734 1999 Dewey Class No.: 621.36 21

Current trends in optics / edited by J.C. Dainty. Published/Created: London; San Diego: Academic Press, c1994. Related Authors: Dainty, J. C. Description: xiii, 310 p.: ill. (some col.); 25 cm. ISBN: 0122007204 Notes: Includes bibliographical references and index. Subjects: Optics. Series: Lasers and optical engineering LC Classification: QC355.2 .C87 0994 Dewey Class No.: 535 20

Current trends in vertical cavity surface emitting lasers / editor, T.P. Lee. Published/Created: Singapore; River Edge, NJ: World Scientific, c1995. Related Authors: Lee, T. P. (Tien-Pei) Description: viii, 764 p.: ill.; 26 cm. ISBN: 9810222882 Notes: "This book is a reprint of a special issue of the International journal of high speed electronics and systems (IJHSES)"--Foreword. Includes bibliographical references. Subjects: Semiconductor lasers. Series: Selected topics in electronics and systems; vol. 3 LC Classification: TA1700 .C87 1995 Dewey Class No.: 621.36/6 21

Das, Pankaj K., 1937- Lasers and optical engineering / P. Das. Published/Created: New York: Springer-Verlag, c1991. Description: xxii, 470 p.: ill.; 24 cm. ISBN: 0387971084 (Springer-Verlag New York: alk. paper) 3540971084 (Springer-Verlag Berlin: alk. paper) Notes: Includes bibliographical references (p. [459]-462) and index. Subjects: Lasers. Optics. LC Classification: TA1677 .D37 1991 Dewey Class No.: 621.36/6 20

Dattoli, G. Lectures on the free electron laser theory and related topics / G. Dattoli, A. Renieri, & A. Torre. Published/Created: Singapore; River Edge, NJ: World Scientific, c1993. Related Authors: Renieri, A. Torre, A. Description: xxi, 637 p.: ill.; 23 cm. ISBN: 9810205651 Notes: Includes bibliographical references and index. Subjects: Free electron lasers. LC Classification: TA1693 .D38 1993 Dewey Class No.: 621.36/6 20

Davis, Christopher C., 1944- Lasers and electro-optics: fundamentals and engineering / Christopher C. Davis. Published/Created: Cambridge [England]; New York, NY, USA: Cambridge University Press, 1996. Description: xxi, 720 p.: ill.; 26 cm. ISBN: 0521308313 (hardback) 0521484030 (pbk.) Notes: Includes bibliographical references and index. Subjects: Lasers. Electrooptics. LC Classification: TA1675 .D38 1996 Dewey Class No.: 621.36 20

Design, fabrication, and characterization of photonic devices II: 27-30 November, 2001, Singapore / Marek Osi′nski, Soo Jin Chua, Akira Ishibashi, chairs/editors; sponsored by SPIE--the International Society for Optical Engineering [and] Nanyang Technological University (Singapore); published by SPIE--the International Society for Optical Engineering. Published/Created: Bellingham, Washington: SPIE, c2001. Related Authors: Osi′nski, Marek. Chua, Soo-Jin. Ishibashi, Akira. Society of Photo-optical Instrumentation Engineers. Nanyang Technological University. Description: xiii, 500 p.: ill.; 28 cm. ISBN: 0819443247 Notes: Includes bibliographic references and author index. Subjects: Optoelectronic devices--Design and constructions Congresses. Optoelectronic devices--Materials--Congresses. Semiconductor lasers--Design and construction--Congresses. Polymers--Optical properties--Congresses. Photonics--Congresses. Series: Proceedings of SPIE--the International Society for Optical Engineering; v. 4594. Variant Series: SPIE proceedings series; v. 4594

Design, fabrication, and characterization of photonic devices: 30 November-3 December 1999, Singapore / Marek Osi′nski, Soo Jin Chua, Shigefusa F. Chichibu, chairs/editors; sponsored by SPIE--the International Society for Optical Engineering [and] Nanyang Technological University, Singapore; cosponsored by SPIE Singapore Chapter ... [et al.]; cooperating organizations, National University of Singapore ... [et al.]. Published/Created: Bellingham, Wash., USA: SPIE, c1999. Related Authors: Osi′nski, Marek. Chua, Soo-Jin. Chichibu, Shigefusa F., 1963-. Description: xiv, 772 p.: ill.; 28 cm. ISBN: 0819434981 Notes: Includes bibliographical references and index. Subjects: Optoelectronic devices--Design and constructions Congresses. Optoelectronic devices--Materials--Congresses. Semiconductor lasers--Design and construction--Congresses. Polymers--Optical properties--Congresses. Photonics--Congresses. Series: Proceedings of SPIE--the International Society for Optical Engineering; v. 3896. Variant Series: SPIE proceedings series; v. 3896 LC Classification: TK8300 .D47 1999 Dewey Class No.: 621.36 21

Detectors for crystallography and diffraction studies at synchrotron sources: 19 July

1999, Denver, Colorado / George W. Fraser, Edwin M. Westbrook, Gareth E. Derbyshire, chairs/editors; sponsored ... by SPIE--the International Society for Optical Engineering. Published/Created: Bellingham, Wash.: SPIE, c1999. Related Authors: Fraser, G. W. Westbrook, Edwin M. Derbyshire, Gareth E. Description: v, 130 p.: ill.; 28 cm. ISBN: 0819432601 Notes: Includes bibliographical references and index. Subjects: Crystal optics--Congresses. X-ray crystallography--Congresses. Crystals--Effect of radiation on--Congresses. Synchrotron radiation--Congresses. Solid-state lasers--Congresses. Series: Proceedings of SPIE--the International Society for Optical Engineering; v. 3774. Variant Series: SPIE proceedings series, 0277-786X; v. 3774 LC Classification: QD941 .D48 1999 Dewey Class No.: 548/.83 21

Developments in laser techniques and applications to fluid mechanics: proceedings of the 7th international symposium, Lisbon, Portugal, 11-14 July, 1994 / (eds.), R.J. Adrian ... [et al.]. Published/Created: Berlin; New York: Springer, c1996. Related Authors: Adrian, R. J. (Ronald J.) International Symposium on Applications of Laser Techniques to Fluid Mechanics (7th: 1994: Lisbon, Portugal) Description: 477 p.: ill.; 25 cm. ISBN: 3540602364 (hardcover: alk. paper) Notes: Proceedings of the 7th International Symposium on Applications of Laser Techniques to Fluid Mechanics. Includes bibliographical references and index. Subjects: Fluid dynamic measurements--Congresses. Lasers--Congresses. LC Classification: TA357.5.M43 D46 1996 Dewey Class No.: 681.2 20

Digital optical computing II: 17-19 January 1990, Los Angeles, California / Raymond Arrathoon, chair/editor; sponsored by SPIE--the International Society for Optical Engineering. Published/Created: Bellingham, Wash., U.S.A.: SPIE, c1990. Related Authors: Arrathoon, Raymond. Description: x, 560 p.: ill.; 28 cm. ISBN: 0819402567 Notes: Papers presented at a technical conference held at the Symposium on High-Power Lasers and Optical Computing, held 14-19-January 1990, in Los Angeles, Calif. Includes bibliographical references and index. Subjects: Optical data processing--Computers, Optical--Computer architecture--Congresses. Series: Proceedings of SPIE--the International Society for Optical Engineering; v. 1215. Variant Series: Proceedings / SPIE--the International Society for Optical Engineering; v. 1215 LC Classification: TA1630 .D5 1990 Dewey Class No.: 621.36/7 20

Diode laser arrays / edited by Dan Botez and Don R. Scifres. Published/Created: Cambridge; New York: Cambridge University Press, 1994. Related Authors: Botez, Dan. Scifres, Don R. Description: xv, 448 p.: ill.; 24 cm. ISBN: 0521419751 (hardback) Notes: Includes bibliographical references and index. Subjects: Semiconductor lasers. Series: Cambridge studies in modern optics; 14 LC Classification: TA1700 .D56 1994 Dewey Class No.: 621.36/6 20

Diode pumping of average-power solid state lasers: 21-22 January 1993, Los Angeles, California / Georg F. Albrecht, Raymond J. Beach, Stephan P. Velsko, chairs/editors; sponsored and published by SPIE--the International Society for Optical Engineering. Published/Created: Bellingham, Wash., USA: SPIE, c1993. Related Authors: Albrecht, Georg F. Beach, Raymond J. Velsko, Stephan Paul, 1955- Description: vii, 176 p.: ill.; 28 cm. ISBN: 0819410926 (pbk.) Notes: Includes bibliographical references and author index. Subjects: Solid-state lasers--Optical pumping--Congresses. Series: Proceedings of SPIE--the International Society for Optical Engineering; v. 1865. Variant Series: Proceedings / SPIE--the International Society for Optical Engineering; v. 1865 LC Classification: TA1705 .D57 1993 Dewey Class No.: 621.36/61 20

Doped fiber devices II: 2-3 November, 1998, Boston, Massachusetts / Michel J.F.

Digonnet, François Ouellette, chairs/editors; sponsored and published by SPIE--the International Society for Optical Engineering. Published/Created: Bellingham, Washington: SPIE, c1998. Related Authors: Digonnet, Michel J. F. Ouellette, François, 1958- Society of Photo-optical Instrumentation Engineers. Description: v, 126 p.: ill.; 28 cm. ISBN: 081943003X Notes: Includes bibliographic references and author index. Subjects: Lasers--Materials--Congresses. Optical fibers--Materials--Congresses. Optical amplifiers--Congresses. Diffraction gratings--Congresses. Series: Proceedings of SPIE--the International Society for Optical Engineering; v. 3542. Variant Series: Proceedings / SPIE--the International Society for Optical Engineering; v. 3542 LC Classification: TA1673 .D673 1998 Dewey Class No.: 621.36 21

Doped fiber devices: 8-9 August 1996, Denver, Colorado / Michel J.F. Digonnet, François Ouellette, chairs/editors; sponsored by SPIE--the International Society for Optical Engineering. Published/Created: Bellingham, Wash.: SPIE, c1996. Related Authors: Digonnet, Michel J. F. Ouellette, François, 1958- Description: vii, 268 p.: ill.; 28 cm. ISBN: 0819422290 Notes: Includes bibliographical references and index. Subjects: Lasers--Optical fibers--Materials--Congresses. Optical amplifiers--Diffraction gratings--Congresses. Series: Proceedings of SPIE--the International Society for Optical Engineering; v. 2841. Variant Series: Proceedings / SPIE--the International Society for Optical Engineering; v. 2841 LC Classification: TA1673 .D67 1996 Dewey Class No.: 621.36 21

Dosimetry of laser radiation in medicine and biology: 30 November-3 December 1988, Berlin, Federal Republic of Germany / Gerhard J. Müller, David H. Sliney, editors; Roy F. Potter, general editor; Lewis Larmore, Emery L. Moore, Brian J. Thompson, advisory committee; sponsored by SPIE--the International Society for Optical Engineering, Laser-Medizin-Zentrum GmbH (FRG). Published/Created: Bellingham, Wash.: SPIE Optical Engineering Press, c1989. Related Authors: Müller, Gerhard J. Sliney, David H. Potter, Roy F. Description: viii, 253 p.: ill.; 28 cm. ISBN: 081940070X Notes: Papers from the Institute on Dosimetry of Laser Radiation in Medicine and Biology, 1988. "A publication of SPIE--the International Society for Optical Engineering." Includes bibliographical references. Subjects: Lasers in medicine--Lasers in biology--Radiation dosimetry--Laser beams--Safety measures--Lasers--therapeutic use--Radiometry--Congresses. Series: SPIE Institutes for Advanced Optical Technologies; v. IS 5 LC Classification: R857.L37 D67 1989 Dewey Class No.: 612/.01448 20

Dye laser principles, with applications / edited by F. J. Duarte, Lloyd W. Hillman. Published/Created: Boston: Academic Press, c1990. Related Authors: Duarte, F.J. (Frank J.) Hillman, Lloyd William, 1955- Description: xi, 456 p.: ill.; 24 cm. ISBN: 012222700X (alk. paper) Notes: Includes bibliographical references. Subjects: Dye lasers. Quantum electronics. Series: Quantum electronics--principles and applications LC Classification: QC688 .D94 1990 Dewey Class No.: 621.36/64 20

Dye lasers / edited by F.P. Schäfer; with contributions by K.H. Drexhage ... [et al.]. Edition Information: 3rd enl. and rev. ed. Published/Created: Berlin; New York: Springer-Verlag, c1990. Related Authors: Schäfer, F. P. (Fritz Peter) Drexhage, K. H. Description: ix, 244 p.: ill.; 24 cm. ISBN: 0387515585 (New York) Notes: Includes index. Includes bibliographical references (p. 221-234) Subjects: Dye lasers. Series: Topics in applied physics; v. 1 LC Classification: TA1690 .D84 1990 Dewey Class No.: 621.36/64 20

Dye lasers: 25 years / edited by Michael Stuke. Published/Created: Berlin; New York: Springer-Verlag, c1992. Related Authors: Stuke, M. (Michael) Description: xvi, 247 p.: ill.; 25 cm. ISBN: 3540549536 (Berlin: acid-free paper) 0387549536 (New York:

acid-free paper) Notes: Includes bibliographical references and index. Subjects: Dye lasers. Series: Topics in applied physics; v. 70 LC Classification: TA1690 .D85 1992 Dewey Class No.: 621.36/64 20

Effects of low-power light on biological systems V: 7 July 2000, Amsterdam, Netherlands / Tiina I. Karu, Rachel Lubart, chairs/editors; sponsored by EOS--the European Optical Society, SPIE--the International Society for Optical Engineering, [and] ELA--the European Laser Association; cooperating organizations, NMLA--Netherlands Medical Laser Association ... [et al.]. Published/Created: Bellingham, Wash., USA: SPIE, c2000. Related Authors: Karu, T. I. (Tiina I.) Lubart, Rachel. Description: v, 82 p.: ill.; 28 cm. ISBN: 0819438154 Notes: Includes bibliographical references and index. Subjects: Lasers--Physiological effect--Lasers in cytology--Congresses. Series: Progress in biomedical optics and imaging; vol. 1, no. 30 Proceedings EurOpt series. Proceedings of SPIE--the International Society for Optical Engineering; v. 4159. Variant Series: EurOpto Proceedings of SPIE; v. 4159 LC Classification: QP82.2.L3 E37

Elementary processes in clusters, lasers, and plasmas: proceedings of the Pentagonale Workshop in Kühtai (Innsbruck), Austria, April 8-12, 1991 / editors, T.D. Märk, R.W. Schrittwieser. Published/Created: [S.l.: s.n., 1991](Innsbruck: Studia Studienförderungs-Ges.) Description: x, 407 p.; 24 cm. LC Classification: IN PROCESS

Encyclopedia of chemical technology / executive editor, Jacqueline I. Kroschwitz; editor, Mary Howe-Grant. Edition Information: 4th ed. Published/Created: New York: Wiley, c1991- Related Authors: Kirk, Raymond E. (Raymond Eller), 1890-1957. Othmer, Donald F. (Donald Frederick), 1904- Kroschwitz, Jacqueline I. Howe-Grant, Mary, 1943- Description: v. <1-25: ill.; 26 cm. ISBN: 047152669X (v. 1: acid-free) Incomplete Contents: v. 1. A to alkaloids -- v. 2. Alkanolamines to antibiotics (glycopeptides) -- v. 3. Antibiotics to batteries -- v. 4. Bearing materials to carbon -- v. 5. Carbon and graphite fibers to chlorocarbons and chlorohydrocarbons-Ci -- v. 6. Chlorocarbons and chlorohydrocarbons-C2 to combustion technology -- v. 7. Composite materials to detergency -- v. 8. Deuterium and tritium to elastomers, polyethers -- v. 9. Elastomers, polyisoprene to expert systems -- v. 10. Explosives and propellants to flame retardants for textiles -- v. 11. Flavor characterization to fuel cells -- v. 12. Fuel resources to heat stabilizers -- v. 13. Helium group to hypnotics -- v. 14. Imaging technology to lanthanides -- v. 15. Lasers to mass spectrometry -- v. 16. Mass transfer to neuroregulators -- v. 17. Nickel and nickel alloys to paint -- v. 18. Paper to pigment dispersions -- v. 19. Pigments to powders, handling -- v. 20. Power generation to recycling, glass -- v. 21. Recycling, oil to silicon -- v. 22. Silicon compounds to succinic acid and succinic anhydride -- v. 23. Sugar to thin films -- v. 24. Thioglycolic acid to vinyl polymers -- v. 25. Vitamins to zone refining Notes: At head of Title - Kirk-Othmer. "A Wiley-Interscience publication." Includes supplement volume issued in 1998 and separately published index volumes for v. <1-4, 5-8, 9-12, 13-16, 17-20; 21-24; in 6 . Includes bibliographical references. Subjects: Chemistry, Technical--Encyclopedias. LC Classification: TP9 .E685 1992 Dewey Class No.: 660/.03 20

Encyclopedia of lasers and optical technology / Robert A. Meyers, editor. Published/Created: San Diego: Academic Press, c1991. Related Authors: Meyers, Robert A. (Robert Allen), 1936- Description: xii, 764 p.: ill.; 27 cm. ISBN: 0122266935 (alk. paper) Notes: Includes bibliographical references and index. Subjects: Optics--Encyclopedias. Lasers--Encyclopedias. LC Classification: TA1509 .E53 1991 Dewey Class No.: 621.36/03 20

Engineering and the advancement of human welfare: 10 outstanding achievements,

1964-1989 / selected by the National Academy of Engineering on the occasion of its 25th anniversary, December 5, 1989. Published/Created: Washington, D.C.: Office of Public Awareness, The Academy, c1989. escription: 48 p.: col. ill.; 28 cm. ISBN: 0309041856 Notes: "NAE 25." Bibliography: p. 46-47. Subjects: Space flight to the moon. Scientific satellites. Microprocessors. CAD/CAM systems. Diagnostic imaging. Composite materials. Jet transports. Lasers. Optical communications. Genetic engineering. LC Classification: T20 .E54 1989

Engineering optics: an Institute of Physics journal. Published/Created: Bristol, UK: IOP Pub., Related Authors: Institute of Physics (Great Britain) American Institute of Physics. Description: v.: ill.; 30 cm. Began in 1988. Current Frequency: Quarterly ISSN: 0952-8911 Cancel/Invalid LCCN: sn 89007372 CODEN: ENOPEI Notes: Description based on: Vol. 1, no. 4 (Nov. 1988); title from cover. Published in association with the American Institute of Physics. SERBIB/SERLOC merged record Subjects: Optical detectors--Lasers--Integrated optics--Optical instruments--Fiber optics--Optical data processing--Periodicals. LC Classification: TA1501 .E54 Dewey Class No.: 621.36 20

European centres of expertise, lasers / [compiled by Martech Publications; prepared by Charles McGinley and Alain-Michel Antchandie]. Edition Information: 1st. ed. Published/Created: London: Metra Martech, 1991. Related Authors: McGinley, Charles, 1940- Antchandie, Alain-Michel. Metra Publications. Metra Martech Limited. Description: 1 v. (unpaged); 30 cm. Cancelled ISBN: 090223715 Notes: Includes index. Subjects: Lasers--Europe--Directories. Lasers--Europe--Handbooks, manuals, etc. Research, Industrial--Europe--Laboratories--Directories. Research, Industrial--Europe--Laboratories--Handbooks, manuals, etc. LC Classification: QC688 .E87 1991 Dewey Class No.: 621.36/6/0254 20

European electro-optics. Published/Created: Westford, MA: Advanced Technology Group, PennWell Publ. Co., c1991- Description: v.: ill. (some col.); 28 cm. Spring 1991- Current Frequency: Quarterly Continues: Laser focus world. European supplement (OCoLC)23748491 (DLC) 91650334 ISSN: 1057-4956 CODEN: EEOPEN Notes: Title from cover. SERBIB/SERLOC merged record Indx'd selectively by: Computer & control abstracts 0036-8113 1991- Electrical & electronics abstracts 0036-8105 1991- Physics abstracts 0036-8091 1991- Supplement to: Laser focus world 1043-8092 (OCoLC)19045940 (DLC) 89642029 Subjects: Lasers--Europe--Electrooptical devices--Optoelectronic devices--Periodicals. LC Classification: TA1501 .L375 Dewey Class No.: 621.36/6 20

European ophthalmology equipment and markets. Published/Created: Mountain View, Calif.: Frost & Sullivan, c1994-c1995. Related Authors: Frost & Sullivan. Description: 4 v.: ill.; 29 cm. ISBN: 0788900013 (v. 1) Contents: v. 1. Contact lenses and lens care products -- v. 2. Ophthalmic lasers -- v. 3. Ophthalmic diagnostics -- v. 4. Intra-ocular lenses. Notes: Vol. 4 has European ophthalmology equipment and device markets. "1764-54"--V. 1, cover. "1747-54"--V. 2, cover. "1748-54"--V. 3, cover. "#1749-54"--V. 4, cover. Subjects: Ophthalmic equipment industry--Europe. Contact lens industry--Europe. Intraocular contact lens industry--Europe. Optical trade--Europe. Market surveys--Europe. LC Classification: HD9995.O673 E8514 1994

European Quantum Elesctronics Conference (3rd: 1998: Glasgow, Scotland) Technical digest, 1998 EQEC, European Quantum Electronics Conference: SECC--Scottish Exhibition and Conference Centre, Glasgow, Scotland, United Kingdom: 14-18 September 1998 / sponsored by European Physical Society ... [et al.]; in cooperation with the European Optical Society. Published/Created: Piscataway, N.J.: Institute of Electrical and Electronics Engineers, c1998. Description: xvi, 277 p.:

ill.; 30 cm. ISBN: 0780342313 (softbound) Notes: Includes bibliographical references and index. Subjects: Quantum electronics--Research--Europe--Lasers--Industrial applications--Electrooptics--Congresses. LC Classification: QC685 .E97 1998 Dewey Class No.: 537.5 21

Excimer beam applications: 6 September 1988, Boston, Massachusetts / Anthony N. Pirri, Bernhard P. Piwczyk, chairs/editors; sponsored by SPIE--the International Society for Optical Engineering; cooperating organizations, Applied Optics Laboratory, New Mexico State University ... [et al.]. Published/Created: Bellingham, Wash., USA: SPIE, c1988. Related Authors: Pirri, Anthony N. Piwczyk, Bernhard P. Description: vi, 128 p.: ill.; 28 cm. ISBN: 0819400335 Notes: Includes bibliographical references. Subjects: Excimer lasers--Congresses. Series: Proceedings of SPIE--the International Society for Optical Engineering; v. 998. Variant Series: Proceedings / SPIE--the International Society for Optical Engineering; v. 998 LC Classification: TA1695 .E92 1988

Excimer laser materials processing and beam delivery systems: 8-9 November 1990, Boston, Massachusetts / Bernhard P. Piwczyk, chair/editor; sponsored and published by SPIE--the International Society for Optical Engineering. Published/Created: Bellingham, Wash., USA: SPIE, c1991. Related Authors: Piwczyk, Bernhard P. Society of Photo-optical Instrumentation Engineers. Description: vii, 135 p.: ill.; 28 cm. ISBN: 0819404446 Notes: Includes bibliographical references and index. Subjects: Excimer lasers--Congresses. Series: Proceedings of SPIE--the International Society for Optical Engineering; v. 1377. Variant Series: Proceedings / SPIE--the International Society for Optical Engineering; v. 1377 LC Classification: TA1695 .E9345 1991 Dewey Class No.: 621.36/63 20

Excimer laser refractive surgery: practice and principles / [edited by] Jeffery J. Machat. Published/Created: Thorofare, NJ: Slack, c1996. Related Authors: Machat, Jeffery J., 1961- Description: xx, 456 p.: ill. (some col.); 29 cm. ISBN: 1556422741 (alk. paper) Notes: Includes bibliographical references (p. [447]-452) and index. Subjects: Eye--Laser surgery. Excimer lasers. Myopia--surgery. Astigmatism--surgery. Keratectomy, Photorefractive, Excimer Laser--methods. LC Classification: RE86 .E97 1996 Dewey Class No.: 617.7/55 20

Excimer lasers / edited by Lucien D. Laude. Published/Created: Dordrecht; Boston: Kluwer Academic Publishers, c1994. Related Authors: Laude, Lucien D. North Atlantic Treaty Organization. Scientific Affairs Division. NATO Advanced Study Institute on Excimer Lasers: the Tools, Fundamental Processes, and Applications (1993: Eloúnda, Greece) Description: xi, 495 p.: ill.; 25 cm. ISBN: 0792328191 Notes: "Proceedings of the NATO Advanced Study Institute on Eximer Lasers: the Tools, Fundamental Processes, and Applications, Elounda, Crete, Greece, September 6-17, 1993"--T.p. verso. "Published in cooperation with NATO Scientific Affairs Division." Includes bibliographical references and index. Subjects: Excimer lasers--Congresses. Series: NATO ASI series. Series E, Applied sciences; no. 265. Variant Series: NATO ASI series. Series E, Applied sciences; vol. 265 LC Classification: TA1695 .N38 1994 Dewey Class No.: 621.36/63 20

Excimer lasers and applications II: proceedings: ECO3, the Congress of EPS--the European Physical Society, EUROPTICA--the European Federation for Applied Optics, SPIE--the International Society for Optical Engineering; 15 March 1990, the Hague, the Netherlands / T. Letardi, chair/editor; cooperating organizations, ANRT--Association nationale de la recherche technique ... [et al.]. Published/Created: Bellingham, Wash., USA: SPIE, c1990. Related Authors: Letardi, T. (Tommaso) European Physical Society. European Federation for Applied Optics. Society of

Photo-optical Instrumentation Engineers. Association nationale de la recherche technique. European Congress on Optics (3rd: 1990: Hague, Netherlands) Description: vii, 147 p.: ill.; 28 cm. ISBN: 0819403253 Notes: Includes bibliographical references and index. Subjects: Excimer lasers--Congresses. Series: Proceedings of SPIE--the International Society for Optical Engineering; v. 1278. Variant Series: Proceedings / SPIE--the International Society for Optical Engineering; v. 1278 LC Classification: TA1695 .E9338 1990 Dewey Class No.: 621.36/63 20

Excimer lasers and applications III: proceedings: ECO4: 13-15 March 1991, the Hague, the Netherlands / Tommaso Letardi, Lucien D. Laude, chairs/editors; sponsored by the congress of EPS--the European Physical Society, Europtica--the European Ferderation for Applied Optics, SPIE--the International Society for Optical Engineering; cooperating organizations, ANRT--Association nationale de la recherche technique ... [et al.]. Published/Created: Bellingham, Wash.: SPIE, c1991. Related Authors: Letardi, T. (Tommaso) Laude, Lucien D. European Physical Society. European Federation for Applied Optics. Society of Photo-optical Instrumentation Engineers. Association nationale de la recherche technique. European Congress on Optics (4th: 1991: Hague, Netherlands) Description: xi, 511 p.: ill.; 28 cm. ISBN: 0819406120 Notes: Includes bibliographical references and index. Subjects: Excimer lasers--Congresses. Series: Proceedings of SPIE--the International Society for Optical Engineering; v. 1503. Variant Series: SPIE proceedings series; v. 1503 LC Classification: TA1695 .E93382 1991 Dewey Class No.: 621.36/63 20

Excimer lasers in ophthalmology: principles and practice / Charles N.J. McGhee. ... [et al.]. Published/Created: Boston: Butterworth-Heinemann, 1997. Related Authors: McGhee, Charles N. J. Description: xii, 453 p.: ill. (some col.); 29 cm. ISBN: 0750697857 Notes: Includes bibliographical references and index. Subjects: Cornea--Eye--Refractive errors--Laser surgery. Excimer lasers. Lasers in ophthalmology. Keratectomy, Photorefractive, Excimer Laser. LC Classification: RE336 .E963 1997 Dewey Class No.: 617.7/19059 21

Excimer lasers, optics, and applications: 12-13 February 1997, San Jose, California / Harry Shields, Peter E. Dyer, chairs/editors; sponsored and published by SPIE--the International Society for Optical Engineering, Published/Created: Bellingham, Wash.: SPIE, c1997. Related Authors: Shields, Harry. Dyer, Peter E. Description: vii, 160 p.: ill.; 28 cm. ISBN: 081942403X Notes: Includes bibliographical references and index. Subjects: Excimer lasers--Industrial applications--Congresses. Series: Proceedings of SPIE--the International Society for Optical Engineering; v. 2092. Variant Series: Proceedings / SPIE--the International Society for Optical Engineering, 0277-786X; v. 2992 LC Classification: TA1695 .E9348 1997 Dewey Class No.: 621.36/6 21

Excimer lasers: applications, beam delivery systems, and laser design: 18-19 November 1992, Boston, Massachusetts / James A. Greer, chair/editor; sponsored and published by SPIE--the International Society for Optical Engineering. Published/Created: Bellingham, Wash., USA: SPIE, c1993. Related Authors: Greer, James A. Description: vii, 222 p.: ill.; 28 cm. ISBN: 0819410365 (pbk.) Notes: Includes bibliographical references and index. Subjects: Excimer lasers--Congresses. Series: Proceedings of SPIE--the International Society for Optical Engineering; v. 1835. Variant Series: Proceedings / SPIE--the International Society for Optical Engineering; v. 1835 LC Classification: TA1695 .E93385 1993 Dewey Class No.: 621.36/63 20

Extreme ultraviolet lithography: from the topical meeting, May 1-3, 1996, Boston, Massachusetts / edited by Glenn D. Kubiak and Don R. Kania; sponsored by Optical

Society of America. Published/Created: Washington, DC: The Society, c1996. Related Authors: Kubiak, Glenn D. Kania, Don R. Optical Society of America. Description: ix, 235 p.: ill.; 28 cm. ISBN: 1557524351 Cancel/Invalid LCCN: 95072755 Notes: Includes bibliographical references (p. 222-232) and indexes. Subjects: Optical coatings--Congresses. Photolithography--Congresses. Ultraviolet radiation--Industrial applications Congresses. Interferometry--Congresses. Lasers--Industrial applications--Congresses. Series: OSA trends in optics and photonics; v. 4 LC Classification: TS517.2 .E98 1996 Dewey Class No.: 621.3815/31 21

Extreme ultraviolet lithography: summaries of papers presented at the topical meeting, Extreme Ultraviolet Lithography, September 19-21, 1994, Monterey, California / sponsored by Optical Society of America. Edition Information: Conference ed. Published/Created: Washington, DC: The Society, c1994. Related Authors: Optical Society of America. Description: ix, 146 p.; 28 cm. ISBN: 1557523622 Notes: Includes bibliographical references and index. Subjects: Optical coatings--Photolithography--Ultraviolet radiation--Industrial applications Congresses. Interferometry--Lasers--Industrial applications--Congresses. Series: Technical digest series (Optical Society of America) Variant Series: Technical digest LC Classification: TS517.2 .E99 1994 Dewey Class No.: 621.36 21

Eyesafe lasers: components, systems, and applications: 21 January 1991, Los Angeles, California / Anthony M. Johnson, chair/editor; sponsored and published by SPIE--the International Society for Optical Engineering. Published/Created: Bellingham, Wash., USA: SPIE, c1991. Related Authors: Johnson, Anthony M. Society of Photo-optical Instrumentation Engineers. Description: vii, 170 p.: ill.; 28 cm. ISBN: 0819405094 Notes: "Part of a five-conference program ... held at SPIE's Symposium on High-Power Lasers, a part of OE/LASE '91, 20-25 January 1991"--P. v. Includes bibliographical references and index. Subjects: Eye--Protection--Congresses. Lasers--Sasfety measures--Congresses. Lasers--Health aspects--Congresses. Series: Proceedings of SPIE--the International Society for Optical Engineering; v. 1419. Variant Series: Proceedings / SPIE--the International Society for Optical Engineering; v. 1419 LC Classification: RE840 .E94 1991 Dewey Class No.: 621.36/6/0289 20

Fabrication, testing, and reliability of semiconductor lasers II: 13-14 February, 1997, San Jose, California / Mahmoud Fallahi, S.C. Wang, chairs/editors; sponsored and published by SPIE--the International Society for Optical Engineering; cooperating organization DARPA--Defense Advanced Research Projects Agency. Published/Created: Bellingham, Washington: SPIE, c1997. Related Authors: Fallahi, Mahmoud. Wang, S. C. (Sing Chung), 1934- Description: v, 176 p.: ill.; 28 cm. ISBN: 0819424153 Notes: Includes bibliographic references and author index. Subjects: Semiconductor lasers--Design and construction--Congresses. Series: Proceedings of SPIE--the International Society for Optical Engineering; v. 3004. Variant Series: Proceedings / SPIE--the International Society for Optical Engineering; v. 3004 LC Classification: TA1700 .F332 1997 Dewey Class No.: 621.36/6 21

Fabrication, testing, and reliability of semiconductor lasers: 31 January-1 February, 1996, San Jose, California / Mahmoud Fallahi, S.C. Wang, chairs/editors; sponsored and published by SPIE--the International Society for Optical Engineering; cooperating organization ARPA--Advanced Research Projects Agency. Published/Created: Bellingham, Wash.: SPIE, c1996. Related Authors: Fallahi, Mahmoud. Wang, S. C. (Sing Chung), 1934- Description: vii, 162 p.: ill.; 28 cm. ISBN: 0819420573 Notes: Includes bibliographical references and index. Subjects: Semiconductor lasers--Design and construction--Congresses. Series: Proceedings of SPIE--the International Society for Optical Engineering; v. 2683. Variant Series: Proceedings / SPIE--the International Society for Optical Engineering; v. 2683 LC Classification: TA1700 .F33 1996

Facial rejuvenation / edited by Paul Carniol. Published/Created: New York: Wiley-Liss, c2000. Related Authors: Carniol, Paul J. Description: xiii, 446 p.: ill. (chiefly col.); 26 cm. ISBN: 0471318469 (alk. paper) Notes: Includes bibliographical references and index. Subjects: Surgery, Plastic. Face--Surgery. Lasers in surgery. Rhytidoplasty--methods. Facial Bones--surgery. Laser Surgery--methods. Reconstructive Surgical Procedures. Rejuvenation. Surgical Procedures, Endoscopic. LC Classification: RD119.5.F33 F328 2000 Dewey Class No.: 617.5/20592 21

Fedorov, M. V., 1940- Atomic and free electrons in a strong light field / Mikhail V. Fedorov. Published/Created: Singapore; River Edge, NJ: World Scientific, c1997. Description: xiii, 452 p.: ill.; 23 cm. ISBN: 981022902X (acid-free paper) Notes: Includes bibliographical references (p. 443-452). Subjects: Laser manipulation (Nuclear physics) Multiphoton processes. Free electron lasers. LC Classification: QC689.5.L35 F43 1997 Dewey Class No.: 537.5 21

Fedorov, M. V., 1940- Interaction of intense laser light with free electrons / M.V. Fedorov. Published/Created: Chur, Switzerland; New York: Harwood Academic Publishers, c1991. Description: vii, 77 p.: ill.; 23 cm. ISBN: 3718651262 Notes: Includes bibliographical references (p. 70-75) and index. Subjects: Laser beams--Scattering. Free electron lasers. Multiphoton processes. Series: Laser science and technology, 0899-2711; v. 13 LC Classification: QC688 .F44 1991 Dewey Class No.: 621.36/6 20

Femtosecond and nanosecond high-intensity lasers and applications: 17-18 January 1990, Los Angeles, California / E.M. Campbell, chair/editor; sponsored by SPIE--the International Society for Optical Engineering. Published/Created: Bellingham, Wash., USA: SPIE, c1990. Related Authors: Campbell, E. M. (Edward M.) Description: vii, 224 p.: ill.; 28 cm. ISBN: 0819402702 Notes: Papers presented at a technical conference at the Symposium on High-Power Lasers and Optical Computing, held 14-19 Jan. 1990, in Los Angeles, Calif. Includes bibliographical references and index. Subjects: High power lasers--Congresses. Series: Proceedings of SPIE--the International Society for Optical Engineering; v. 1229. Variant Series: Proceedings / SPIE--the International Society for Optical Engineering; v. 1229 LC Classification: TA1673 .F46 1990 Dewey Class No.: 621.36/6 20

Femtosecond technology: from basic research to future applications / T. Kamiya ... [et al.]. Published/Created: Berlin; New York: Springer, c1999. Related Authors: Kamiya, T. (Takeshi), 1939- Description: xxiii, 426 p.: ill.; 24 cm. ISBN: 354065996X (hardcover: alk. paper) Notes: Includes bibliographical references. Subjects: Optoelectronic devices. Optical detectors--Industrial applications. High power lasers. Laser pulses, Ultrashort. Optical communications. Series: Springer series in photonics, 1437-0379; v. 2 LC Classification: TA1750 .F46 1999 Dewey Class No.: 621.36 21

Fiber laser sources and amplifiers. Published/Created: Bellingham, Wash.: SPIE, c1990- Related Authors: Society of Photo-optical Instrumentation Engineers. Description: v.: ill.; 28 cm. 6-8 Sept. 1989- Current Frequency: Annual Notes: SERBIB/SERLOC merged record Subjects: Lasers--Congresses. Fiber optics--Congresses. Series: Proceedings of SPIE--the International Society for Optical Engineering. Variant Series: Proceedings / SPIE--the International Society for Optical Engineering LC Classification: TA1673 .F5 Dewey Class No.: 621.36/6/05 20

Filtering resonators / S.K. Dixit (editor). Published/Created: Huntington, N.Y.: Nova Science Publishers, 2001. Projected Pub. Date: 0108 Related Authors: Dixit, S. K. Description: p. cm. ISBN: 159033003X Notes: Includes bibliographical references and index. Subjects: Lasers--Resonators. Optical resonance. Laser beams. LC Classification: TA1677 .F55 2001 Dewey Class No.: 621.36/6 21

First of its kind / [production company unknown]. Published/Created: United States: Embassy of Israel, [1988?] Related Authors: Israel. Shagrirut (U.S.) Embassy of Israel Collection (Library of Congress) Description: 1 videocassette of 1 (VHS) (ca. 27 min.): sd., [col.]; 1/2 in. viewing copy. Summary: To a great extent, Israel relies on high technology for its economic development. Focusing on laser technology, this documentary depicts several advances in various high-tech areas by Israeli entrepreneurs and documents the challenges facing Israelis in breaking into competitive international markets. Notes: Copyright: reg. unknown. Title taken from videocassette label and Embassy of Israel home page, films catalog, 9/17/97. Possible release date taken from Embassy of Israel home page, films catalog, 9/17/97; may have been released in U.S. before this date. Summary taken from Embassy of Israel home page, films catalog, 9/17/97. Embassy of Israel films catalog no. S-2. Sources used: Embassy of Israel home page, films catalog, 9/17/97; videocassette label. Source of Acquisition: Received: 8/28/97; viewing copy; exchange; Embassy of Israel Collection. Subjects: Lasers--Laser industry--High technology--High technology industries--Business enterprises--Export marketing--Exports--Israel. Genre/Form: Documentary--Short. LC Classification: VAF 3501

Flatow, Ira. They all laughed--: from light bulbs to lasers, the fascinating stories behind the great inventions that have changed our lives / Ira Flatow. Edition Information: 1st ed. Published/Created: New York: HarperCollins, c1992. Description: xv, 238 p., [16] p. of plates: ill.; 22 cm. ISBN: 006016445X (cloth): Notes: Includes bibliographical references (p. 227-229) and index. Subjects: Inventions--History. LC Classification: T212 .F53 1992 Dewey Class No.: 609 20

Fox, Mary Virginia. Lasers / Mary Virginia Fox. Published/Created: Tarrytown, N.Y.: Benchmark Books, c1996. Description: 63 p.: ill. (some col.); 26 cm. ISBN: 0761400672 Summary: Describes the discovery, principles, and types of lasers, the light they produce, their contributions to industry, medicine, war, crime detection, communication, and other fields--and future uses of their amazing powers. Notes: Includes bibliographical references (p. 61) and index. Subjects: Lasers--Juvenile literature. Lasers. Series: Inventors & inventions LC Classification: TA1682 .F68 1996 Dewey Class No.: 621.36/6 20

Free-Electron Laser Applications in the Ultraviolet Topical Meeting (1988: Cloudcroft, N.M.) Free-electron laser applications in the ultraviolet: summaries of papers presented at the Free-Electron Laser Applications in the Ultraviolet Topical Meeting, March 2-5, 1988, Cloudcroft, New Mexico / cosponsored by the Optical Society of America, Air Force Office of Scientific Research, Department of Energy. Edition Information: Postconference ed. Published/Created: Washington, D.C.: The Society, c1988. Description: xi, 233 p.: ill.; 28 cm. ISBN: 1557520283 Notes: Includes bibliographical references. Subjects: Free electron lasers--Ultraviolet radiation--Congresses. Series: Technical digest series (Optical Society of America); 1988, v. 4. Variant Series: Technical digest series; 1988, v. 4 LC Classification: TA1673 .F72 1988 Dewey Class No.: 621.36/6 20

Free-electron laser challenges II: 26-27 January 1999, San Jose, California / Harold E. Bennett, David H. Dowell, chairs/editors; sponsored ... by SPIE--the International Society for Optical Engineering. Published/Created: Bellingham, Wash., USA: SPIE, c1999. Related Authors: Bennett, Harold Earl, 1929- Dowell, David

Harry, 1950- Description: vii, 194 p.: ill.; 28 cm. ISBN: 0819430846 Notes: Includes bibliographical references and index. Subjects: Free-electron lasers--Congresses. Series: Proceedings of SPIE--the International Society for Optical Engineering; v. 3614. Variant Series: SPIE proceedings series; v. 3614 LC Classification: TA1693 .F715 1999 Dewey Class No.: 621.36/6 21

Free-electron laser challenges: 13-14 February, 1997, San Jose, California / Patrick G. O'Shea, Harold E. Bennett, chairs/editors; sponsored and published by SPIE--the International Society for Optical Engineering. Published/Created: Bellingham, Washington: SPIE, c1997. Related Authors: O'Shea, Patrick G. Bennett, Harold Earl, 1929- Description: vii, 294 p.: ill.; 28 cm. ISBN: 0819423998 Notes: Includes bibliographic references and author index. Subjects: Free-electron lasers--Congresses. Series: Proceedings of SPIE--the International Society for Optical Engineering; v. 2988. Variant Series: Proceedings / SPIE--the International Society for Optical Engineering; v. 2988 LC Classification: TA1693 .F717 1997 Dewey Class No.: 621.36/6 21

Free-electron laser spectroscopy in biology, medicine, and materials science: 22 January 1993, Los Angeles, California / H. Alan Schwettman, chair/editor; sponsored and published by SPIE--the International Society for Optical Engineering. Published/Created: Bellingham, Wash., USA: SPIE, c1993. Related Authors: Schwettman, H. Alan. Description: vii, 176 p.: ill.; 28 cm. ISBN: 0819410802 Notes: Includes bibliographical references and author index. Subjects: Free-electron lasers--Laser spectroscopy--Lasers in biology--Lasers in medicine--Congresses. Series: Proceedings of SPIE--the International Society for Optical Engineering; v. 1854. Variant Series: Proceedings / SPIE--the International Society for Optical Engineering; v. 1854 LC Classification: TA1693 .F72 1993 Dewey Class No.: 621.36/6 20

Free-electron lasers and applications: 18-19 January 1990, Los Angeles, California / Donald Prosnitz, chair/editor; sponsored by SPIE--the International Society for Optical Engineering. Published/Created: Bellingham, Wash., USA: SPIE, c1990. Related Authors: Prosnitz, Donald. Description: vii, 205 p.: ill.; 28 cm. ISBN: 0819402680 Notes: Papers presented at a technical conference of the Symposium on High-Power Lasers and Optical Computing, held 14-19 Jan. 1990, in Los ANgeles, Calif. Includes bibliographical references and index. Subjects: Free electron lasers--Congresses. Series: Proceedings of SPIE--the International Society for Optical Engineering; v. 1227. Variant Series: Proceedings / SPIE--the International Society for Optical Engineering; v 1227 LC Classification: TA1693 .F73 1990 Dewey Class No.: 621.36/6 20

Free-electron lasers: 15-16 January, 1987, Los Angeles, California / sponsored by SPIE--the International Society for Optical Engineering, in cooperation with Center for Applied Optics/University of Alabama in Huntsville ... [et al.]; Brian E. Newnam, editor. Published/Created: Bellingham, Wash., USA: SPIE, c1988. Related Authors: Newnam, Brian E. Description: vi, 177 p.: ill.; 28 cm. ISBN: 0892527730 Notes: Conference proceedings. Includes bibliographies and index. Subjects: Free electron lasers--Congresses. Series: Critical reviews of optical science and technology Proceedings of SPIE--the International Society for Optical Engineering; v. 738. Variant Series: SPIE; v. 738 LC Classification: TA1673 .F74 1988 Dewey Class No.: 621.36/6 19

French-Israeli Workshop on Solid State Lasers (1988: Jerusalem) French-Israeli Workshop on Solid State Lasers: proceedings, 12-14 December 1988, Jerusalem, Israel / George Boulon, Christian K. Jørgensen, Renata Reisfeld, chairs/editors; organized by the Ministry of Science and Technology (Israel), le Ministère des affaires étrangères (France); sponsoring organization, SPIE--the

International Society for Optical Engineering. Published/Created: Bellingham, Wash., USA: SPIE, c1989. Related Authors: Boulon, George. Jørgensen, Christina Klixbüll. Reisfeld, Renata. Description: vii, 240 p.: ill.; 28 cm. ISBN: 0819402184 (pbk.) Notes: "89-11 NCRD"--Cover. Includes bibliographical references and index. Subjects: Solid-state lasers--Congresses. Series: Proceedings of SPIE--the International Society for Optical Engineering; v. 1182. Variant Series: SPIE proceedings series; v. 1182 LC Classification: TA1705 .F74 1988 Dewey Class No.: 621.36/61 20

French-Israeli Workshop on Solid State Lasers (1988: Jerusalem) French-Israeli Workshop on Solid State Lasers: scientific programme and abstracts: Jerusalem, December 12-14, 1988 / Ministère des affaires étrangères, France [and] the National Council for Research and Development (NCRD), Israel. Published/Created: Jerusalem: The Council, [1988] Description: 1 v. (unpaged); 29 cm. Notes: "88-11 N.C.R.D."--Cover. Includes bibliographical references. Subjects: Solid-state lasers--Congresses. LC Classification: TA1705 .F74 1988a Dewey Class No.: 621.36/61 20

Frequency control of semiconductor lasers / edited by Motoichi Ohtsu. Published/Created: New York: Wiley, c1996. Related Authors: Ohtsu, Motoichi. Description: xiii, 240 p.: ill.; 25 cm. ISBN: 0471013412 (alk. paper) Notes: Includes bibliographical references and index. Subjects: Semiconductor lasers. Frequency stability. Series: Wiley series in microwave and optical engineering LC Classification: TA1700 .F74 1996 Dewey Class No.: 621.36/6 20

Freund, H. P. (Henry P.) Principles of free-electron lasers / H.P. Freund and T.M. Antonsen, Jr. Edition Information: 1st ed. Published/Created: London; New York: Chapman & Hall, 1992. Related Authors: Antonsen, T. M. (Thomas M.) Description: xix, 460 p.: ill.; 24 cm. ISBN: 0442316348 (alk. paper) Notes: Includes bibliographical references and indexes. Subjects: Free electron lasers. LC Classification: QC688 .F74 1992 Dewey Class No.: 621.36/6 20

Freund, H. P. Principles of free-electron lasers / H.P. Freund. Edition Information: 2nd ed. Published/Created: New York: Chapman & Hall, 1995. Description: p. cm. ISBN: 0412725401 LC Classification: 9512

Freund, Henry P. Principles of free electron lasers / Henry P. Freund and T.M. Antonsen Jr. Published/Created: London: Chapman and Hall, 1992. Description: 448 p. ISBN: 0412457903

Fukuda, Mitsuo. Reliability and degradation of semiconductor lasers and LEDs / Mitsuo Fukuda. Published/Created: Boston: Artech House, c1991. Description: x, 343 p.: ill.; 24 cm. ISBN: 0890064652 Notes: Includes bibliographical references and index. Subjects: Semiconductor lasers--Reliability. Light emitting diodes--Reliability. LC Classification: TA1700 .F85 1991 Dewey Class No.: 621.36/6 20

Fuller, Terry A. Thermal surgical lasers: a technical monograph / by Terry A. Fuller. Published/Created: Oaks, PA: T.A. Fuller: Surgical Laser Technologies, c1993. Description: viii, 55 p.: ill.; 22 cm. ISBN: 1883765005 Subjects: Lasers in surgery--Handbooks, manuals, etc. LC Classification: RD73.L3 F85 1993 Dewey Class No.: 617/.05 20

Functional photonic integrated circuits: 9-10 February 1995, San Jose, California / Mario N. Armenise, Ka-Kha Wong, chairs/editors; sponsored and published by SPIE--the International Society for Optical Engineering. Bellingham, Wash., USA: SPIE, c1995. Related Authors: Armenise, Mario N. Wong, Ka-Kha. Description: ix, 228 p.: ill.; 28 cm. ISBN: 0819417483 (pbk.) Notes: Includes bibliographical references and author index. Subjects: Integrated optics--Semiconductor lasers--Optical wave guides--Congresses. Series: Proceedings of SPIE--the International Society for Optical Engineering; v. 2401.

Variant Series: Proceedings / SPIE--the International Society for Optical Engineering; v. 2401 LC Classification: TA1660 .F86 1995

Fundamental issues of nonlinear laser dynamics: concepts, mathematics, physics, and applications, international spring school: Texel, The Netherlands, 16-19 April 2000 / editors, Bernd Krauskopf, Daan Lenstra. Melville, N.Y.: American Institute of Physics, 2000. Related Authors: Krauskopf, Bernd. Lenstra, Daan, 1947- Description: v, 303 p.: ill.; 25 cm. ISBN: 1563969777 Notes: Includes bibliographical references and index. Subjects: Lasers--Nonlinear optics--Congresses. Series: AIP conference proceedings; no. 548. Variant Series: AIP conference proceedings, 0094-243X; v. 548 LC Classification: QC685 .F86 2000 Dewey Class No.: 621.36/6 21

Future trends in biomedical applications of lasers: 24-25 May 1991, Berlin, Germany / Lars O. Svaasand, chair; sponsored by Laser-Medizin-Zentrum GmbH, SPIE--the International Society for Optical Engineering. Published/Created: Bellingham, Wash.: SPIE, c1991. Related Authors: Svaasand, Lars O. Laser-Medizin-Zentrum. Description: ix, 421 p.: ill.; 28 cm. ISBN: 0819406538 Notes: Papers from the SPIE/MedTech '91 Conference. Includes bibliographical references and index. Subjects: Lasers in medicine--Congresses. Series: Proceedings of SPIE--the International Society for Optical Engineering; v. 1525. Variant Series: Proceedings / SPIE--the International Society for Optical Engineering; v. 1525 LC Classification: R857.L37 F87 1991 Dewey Class No.: 610/.28 20

Gallium nitride and related materials II: symposium held April 1-4, 1997, San Francisco, California, U.S.A. / editors, C.R. Abernathy, H. Amano, J.C. Zolper. Published/Created: Pittsburgh, Pa.: Materials Research Society, c1997. Related Authors: Abernathy, C. R. Amano, H. Zolper, J. C. Description: xv, 506 p.: ill.; 24 cm. ISBN: 155899372X Notes: Includes bibliographical references and indexes. Subjects: Gallium nitride--Semiconductors--Materials--Electroluminescent devices--Materials--Lasers--Materials--Epitaxy--Congresses. Series: Materials Research Society symposia proceedings; v. 468. Variant Series: Materials Research Society symposium proceedings, 0272-9172; v. 468 LC Classification: TK7871.15.G33 G35 1997 Dewey Class No.: 621.3815/2 21

GaN and related alloys, 1999: symposium held November 28-December 3, 1999, Boston, Massachusetts, U.S.A. / editors, Thomas H. Myers ... [et al.]. Published/Created: Warrendale, Pa.: Materials Research Society, c2000. Related Authors: Myers, Thomas H. Description: 1 v. (various pagings): ill.; 24 cm. ISBN: 155899503X Notes: Includes bibliographical references and index. Subjects: Gallium nitride--Gallium alloys--Semiconductors--lectroluminescent devices--Lasers--Materials--Epitaxy--Congresses. Series: Materials Research Society symposia proceedings; v. 595. Variant Series: Materials Research Society symposium proceedings; v. 595 LC Classification: TK7871.15.G33 G37 2000 Dewey Class No.: 621.384/134 21

GaN and related alloys: symposium held November 30-December 4, 1998, Boston, Massachusetts, U.S.A. / editors Stephen J. Pearton ... [et al.]. Published/Created: Warrendale, Pa.: Materials Research Society, c1999. Related Authors: Pearton, S. J. Description: 1 v (unpaged): ill.; 24 cm. ISBN: 1558994432 Notes: Includes bibliographical references and index. Subjects: Gallium nitride--Semiconductors--Electroluminescent devices--Lasers--Materials--Epitaxy--Congresses. Series: Materials Research Society symposia proceedings; v. 537. Variant Series: Materials Research Society symposium proceedings; v. 537 LC Classification: TK7871.15.G3 G357 1999 Dewey Class No.: 621.3815/2 21

Gao, Chunqing, 1967- Characterization and transformation of astigmatic laser beams / Chunqing Gao. Edition Information: 1. Aufl. Published/Created: Berlin: Wissenschaft und Technik Verlag, c1999. Description: x, 127 p.: ill.; 21 cm. ISBN: 3896853082 Notes: Includes bibliographical references (p. [119]-125). Subjects: Laser beams. Semiconductor lasers. Diodes, Semiconductor. LC Classification: QC689.55 .S45 G36 1999

Gas and chemical lasers and applications II: 10 February, 1997, San Jose, California / Robert C. Sze, Ernest A. Dorko, chairs/editors; sponsored and published by SPIE--the International Society for Optical Engineering. Published/Created: Bellingham, Wash., USA: SPIE, c1997. Related Authors: Sze, Robert C. Dorko, Ernest A., 1936- Society of Photo-optical Instrumentation Engineers. Description: ix, 228 p.: ill.; 28 cm. ISBN: 081942398X Notes: Includes bibliographic references and author index. Subjects: Gas lasers--Congresses. Chemical lasers--Congresses. Series: Proceedings of SPIE--the International Society for Optical Engineering; v. 2987. Variant Series: Proceedings / SPIE--the International Society for Optical Engineering; v. 2987 LC Classification: TA1695 .G293 1997 Dewey Class No.: 621.36/63 21

Gas and chemical lasers and intense beam applications II: 25-26 January 1999, San Jose, California / Ernest A. Dorko, chair/editor; sponsored ... by SPIE--the International Society for Optical Engineering. Published/Created: Bellingham, Wash., USA: SPIE, c1999. Related Authors: Dorko, Ernest A., 1936- Description: ix, 184 p.: ill.; 28 cm. ISBN: 081943082X Notes: Includes bibliographical references and index. Subjects: Gas lasers--Congresses. Chemical lasers--Congresses. Series: Proceedings of SPIE--the International Society for Optical Engineering; v. 3612. Variant Series: SPIE proceedings series; v. 3612 LC Classification: TA1695 .G294 1999 Dewey Class No.: 621.36/63 21

Gas and chemical lasers: 31 January-1 February, 1996, San Jose, California / Robert C. Sze, chair/editor; sponsored and published by SPIE--the International Society for Optical Engineering. Published/Created: Bellingham, Wash., USA: SPIE, c1996. Related Authors: Sze, Robert C. Description: ix, 458 p.: ill.; 28 cm. ISBN: 081942076X Notes: Includes bibliographic references and author index. Subjects: Gas lasers--Congresses. Chemical lasers--Congresses. Optical radar--Congresses. Series: Proceedings of SPIE--the International Society for Optical Engineering; v. 2702. Variant Series: Proceedings / SPIE--the International Society for Optical Engineering; v. 2702 LC Classification: TA1695 .G29 1996 Dewey Class No.: 621.36/63 21

Gas and metal vapor lasers and applications: 22-23 January 1991, Los Angeles, California / Jin J. Kim, Frank K. Tittel, chairs/editors; sponsored and published by SPIE--the International Society for Optical Engineering. Published/Created: Bellingham, Wash., USA: SPIE, c1991. Related Authors: Kim, Jin J. Tittel, Frank K. Society of Photo-optical Instrumentation Engineers. Symposium on High-Power Lasers (1991: Los Angeles, Calif.) Description: ix, 278 p.: ill.; 28 cm. ISBN: 0819405027 Notes: "Part of a four-conference program on High-Power Lasers, held at SPIE's Symposium on High-Power Lasers, a part of OE/LASE '91, 20-25 January 1991, in Los Angeles, California"--P. vii. Includes bibliographical references and index. Subjects: Gas lasers--Congresses. Metal vapor lasers--Congresses. Series: Proceedings of SPIE--the International Society for Optical Engineering; v. 1412. Variant Series: Proceedings / SPIE--the International Society for Optical Engineering; v. 1412. LC Classification: TA1695 .G32 1991 Dewey Class No.: 621.36/63 20

Gas laser technology / Roland A. Sauerbrey, James H. Tillotson, Peter P. Chenausky, chairs/editors; sponsored by SPIE--the International Society for Optical Engineering; cooperating organizations,

American Academy of Otolaryngology--Head and Neck Surgery ... [et al.]. Published/Created: Bellingham, Wash., USA: SPIE, c1988. Related Authors: Sauerbrey, Roland A. Tillotson, James H. Chenausky, Peter P. Description: vi, 139 p.: ill.; 28 cm. ISBN: 0892529296 Notes: "11-12 January, 1988, Los Angeles, California." Includes bibliographies and index. Subjects: Gas lasers--Congresses. Series: Proceedings of SPIE--the International Society for Optical Engineering; v. 894 LC Classification: TA1695 .G338 1988 Dewey Class No.: 621.36/63 20

Gas lasers--recent developments and future prospects / edited by W.J. Witteman and V.N. Ochkin. Published/Created: Dordrecht; Boston: Kluwer Academic Publishers, c1996. Related Authors: Witteman, W. J. Ochkin, V. N. (Vladimir Nikolaevich) Description: x, 365 p.: ill.; 25 cm. ISBN: 0792339886 (hb: acid-free paper) Notes: "Published in cooperation with NATO Scientific Affairs Division." "Proceedings of the NATO Advanced Research Workshop on Gas Laser--Recent Developments and Future Prospects, Moscow, Russia, July 2-5, 1995"--T.p. verso. Subjects: Gas lasers--Congresses. Series: NATO ASI series. Partnership sub-series 3, High technology; vol. 10 LC Classification: TA1673 .N37 1996 Dewey Class No.: 621.36/63 20

Gas, chemical, and electrical lasers and intense beam control and applications: 24-25 January, 2000, San Jose, California / Santanu Basu, Steven J. Davis, Ernest A. Dorko, chairs/editors; sponsored and published by SPIE--the International Society for Optical Engineering. Published/Created: Bellingham, Washington: SPIE, c2000. Related Authors: Basu, S. (Sanatanu) Davis, Steven J., Dr. Dorko, Ernest A., 1936- Description: vii, 334 p.: ill.; 28 cm. ISBN: 0819435481 Cancel/Invalid LCCN: 00711274 Notes: Includes bibliographic references and author index. Subjects: Lasers--Congresses. Laser beams--Congresses. Series: Proceedings of SPIE--the International Society for Optical Engineering; v. 3931. Variant Series: SPIE proceedings series; v. 3931 LC Classification: TA1673 .G37 2000 Dewey Class No.: 621.36/6 21

Gas, metal vapor, and free-electron lasers and applications: 25-26 January 1994, Los Angeles, California / Vern N. Smiley, Frank K. Tittel, chairs/editors; sponsored and published by SPIE--the International Society for Optical Engineering. Published/Created: Bellingham, Wash., USA: SPIE, c1994. Related Authors: Smiley, Vern N. Tittel, Frank K. Description: ix, 280 p.: ill.; 28 cm. ISBN: 0819414115 Notes: Includes bibliographical references and author index. Subjects: Gas lasers--Metal vapor lasers--Free electron lasers--Congresses. Series: Proceedings of SPIE--the International Society for Optical Engineering; v. 2118. Variant Series: Proceedings / SPIE--the International Society for Optical Engineering; v. 2118 LC Classification: TA1695 .G35 1994 Dewey Class No.: 621.36/63 20

Ghafouri-Shiraz, H. Distributed feedback laser diodes: principles and physical modeling / H. Ghafouri-Shiraz, B.S.K. Lo. Published/Created: New York: Wiley, 1996. Related Authors: Lo, B. S. K. Description: xxii, 220 p.: ill.; 25 cm. ISBN: 0471960055 Notes: Includes bibliographical references and index. Subjects: Optical communications. Optical fibers. Semiconductor lasers. Diodes, Semiconductor. LC Classification: TK5103.59 .G45 1996 Dewey Class No.: 621.36/61 20

Ghafouri-Shiraz, H. Fundamentals of laser diode amplifiers / H. Ghafouri-Shiraz Published/Created: Chichester; New York: J. Wiley, c1996. Description: xiii, 240 p.: ill.; 25 cm. ISBN: 0471958727 Notes: Includes bibliographical references and index. Subjects: Semiconductor lasers. Optical amplifiers. LC Classification: TA1700 .G53 1996 Dewey Class No.: 621.36/6 20

Gibilisco, Stan. Understanding lasers / Stan Gibilisco. Edition Information: 1st ed. Published/Created: Blue Ridge Summit, PA: Tab Books, c1989. Description: vi, 169 p.: ill.; 24 cm. ISBN: 0830692754: 0830631755 (pbk.): Notes: Includes index. Bibliography: p. 164. Subjects: Lasers. LC Classification: TA1675 .G53 1989 Dewey Class No.: 621.36/6 20

Glosari teknologi laser dan gentian optik: bahasa Inggeris-huraian-bahasa Melayu, bahasa Melayu-bahasa Inggeris. Edition Information: Cet. 1. Published/Created: Kuala Lumpur: Dewan Bahasa dan Pustaka, Kementerian Pendidikan, Malaysia, 1996-<2000 Related Authors: Dewan Bahasa dan Pustaka. Description: v. <1-2; 14 x 22 cm. ISBN: 9836247513 (v. 1) 9836266992 (v. 2) Summary: English-Malay, Malay-English dictionary of lasers and optical fibres terms. Notes: Includes bibliographical references (v. 1, p. 105; v. 2, p. 95). English and Malay. Subjects: Lasers--Dictionaries. Optical fibers--Dictionaries. Lasers--Optical fibers--English language--Dictionaries--Malay. Malay language--Dictionaries--English. LC Classification: TA1675 .G58 1996 Dewey Class No.: 621.36/6/03 21

Goldman, Mitchel P. Cutaneous laser surgery: the art and science of selective photothermolysis / Mitchel P. Goldman, Richard E. Fitzpatrick. Edition Information: 2nd ed. Published/Created: St. Louis: Mosby Year Book, c1999. Related Authors: Fitzpatrick, Richard E. Description: xxiii, 531 p.: ill. (chiefly col.); 28 cm. ISBN: 0815136102 Notes: Includes bibliographical references and index. Subjects: Skin--Laser surgery. Laser Surgery--methods. Skin--surgery. Skin--radiation effects. Lasers--therapeutic use. LC Classification: RL120.L37 G65 1999 Dewey Class No.: 617.4/77059 21

Gordiets, B. F. Kinetic processes in gases and molecular lasers / by Boris F. Gordiets, A.I. Osipov, and L.A. Shelepin; translated from the Russian. Published/Created: New York: Gordon and Breach Science Publishers, c1988. Related Authors: Osipov, Aleksei Iosifovich. Shelepin, L. A. Description: xvi, 688 p.: ill.; 24 cm. ISBN: 2881246680 Notes: Translation of: Kineticheskie protsessy v gazakh i molekuliarnye lazery. Includes index. Bibliography: p. 603-679. Subjects: Chemical lasers. Molecular gas lasers. Kinetic theory of gases. Relaxation phenomena. LC Classification: QC688 .G6713 1988 Dewey Class No.: 621.36/64 19

Gorton, E. K. CO2 laser frequency doubling using AgGaSe2 / authors, E.K. Gorton & P.D. Mason. Published/Created: [London: Controller, HMSO, c1991] Related Authors: Mason, P. D. Royal Signals and Radar Establishment (Great Britain) Description: 12 p.: ill.; 30 cm. Notes: Cover title. At head of Title - Royal Signals & Radar Establishment. "Procurement Executive, Ministry of Defence, RSRE Malvern, Worcs." Includes bibliographical references (p. 11-12). Subjects: Carbon dioxide lasers. Series: RSRE memorandum; no. 4528 LC Classification: TA1695 .G67 1991

Gradient-Index Optical Systems Topical Meeting (1991: Monterey, Calif.) Gradient-index optical systems: summaries of papers / presented at the Gradient-Index Optical Systems Topical Meeting; sponsored by Optical Society of America; in cooperation with IEEE/Lasers and Electro-optics Society, Japan Society of Applied Physics. Edition Information: Postconference ed. Published/Created: Washington, DC: Optical Society of America, c1991. Description: x, 187 p.: ill.; 29 cm. ISBN: 1557521832 (hardcover) 1557521824 (conference ed.: softcover) Notes: Includes bibliographical references and index. Subjects: Lenses--Design and construction--Congresses. Geometrical optics--Congresses. Series: Technical digest series (Optical Society of America); 1991, v. 9. Variant Series: 1991 technical digest series; v. 9 LC Classification: QC385.2.D47 G72 1991 Dewey Class No.: 681/.423 20

Graham, Ian, 1953- Lasers and holograms / Ian Graham. Published/Created: New York: Gloucester Press, 1991. Description: 32 p.: ill. (some col.); 30 cm. ISBN: 0531172643 (lib. bdg.) Summary: Shows how lasers are used to create holograms, which are perfect three-dimensional images of objects that aren't actually there. Notes: Includes index. Subjects: Lasers--Holography--Juvenile literature. Series: How it works (Gloucester Presss) Variant Series: How it works LC Classification: TA1682 .G73 1991 Dewey Class No.: 621.36/6 20

GR-I International Conference on New Laser Technologies and Applications (2nd: 1997: Olympia, Greece) Second GR-I International Conference on New Laser Technologies and Applications: 1-4 June 1997, Olympia, Greece / Alexis Carabelas ... [et al.], chairs/editors; organized by The General Secretariat of Research and Technology (Greece), ENEA, INN-FIS Division, Frascati (Italy), University of Patras; cosponsors, OTE--the Hellenic Telecommunication Organization (Greece) ... [et al.]. Published/Created: Bellingham, Wash.: SPIE--the International Society for Optical Engineering, c1998. Related Authors: Carabelas, Alexis. Description: xvii, 466 p.: ill.; 28 cm. ISBN: 0819428787 Notes: Includes bibliographical references and index. Subjects: Lasers--Industrial applications--Laser materials--Lasers in medicine--Congresses. Series: Proceedings of SPIE--the International Society for Optical Engineering; v. 3423. Variant Series: Proceedings of SPIE, 0277-786X; v. 3423 LC Classification: TA1673 .G75 1997 Dewey Class No.: 621.36/6 21

Grigor′iants, A. G. (Aleksandr Grigor′evich) Basics of laser material processing / Alexander G. Grigoryants; translated from the Russian by P.S. Ivanov. Published/Created: Moscow: Mir Publishers; Boca Raton: CRC Press, c1994. Description: 312 p.: ill.; 25 cm. ISBN: 0849375347 (alk. paper) Notes: Includes bibliographical references (p. [299]-306) and index. Subjects: Lasers--Industrial applications. Manufacturing processes. Series: Advances in science and technology in the USSR. Variant Series: Advances in science and technology LC Classification: TA1677 .G75 1994 Dewey Class No.: 621.36/6 20

Growth, characterization, and applications of laser host and nonlinear crystals II: 17-18 January 1993, Los Angeles, California / Bruce H.T. Chai, chair/editor; sponsored and published by SPIE--the International Society for Optical Engineering. Published/Created: Bellingham, Wash., USA: SPIE, c1993. Related Authors: Chai, Bruce Huai-Tzu. Description: x, 206 p.: ill.; 28 cm. ISBN: 081941090X (pbk.) Notes: Includes bibliographies and author index. Subjects: Solid state lasers--Nonlinear optics--Crystal optics--Congresses. Series: Proceedings of SPIE--the International Society for Optical Engineering; v. 1863 LC Classification: TA1673 .G76 1993 Dewey Class No.: 621.36/61 20

Guide to laser materials processing / Sidney S. Charschan, editor. Published/Created: Orlando, Fla.: Laser Institute of America, c1993. Related Authors: Charschan, Sidney S. Laser Institute of America. Description: 224 p.: ill.; 23 cm. ISBN: 0912035110 Notes: Includes bibliographical references. Subjects: Lasers--Industrial applications. LC Classification: TA1675 .G85 1993

Guided-wave optoelectronics / Theodor Tamir (ed.); with contributions by R.C. Alferness ... [et al.]. Edition Information: 2nd ed. Published/Created: Berlin; New York: Springer-Verlag, c1990. Related Authors: Tamir, Theodor, 1927- Alferness, R. C. Description: xv, 419 p.: ill.; 24 cm. ISBN: 038752780X (New York: alk. paper) Notes: Includes bibliographical references and index. Subjects: Optoelectronic devices. Integrated optics. Optical wave guides. Semiconductor lasers. Series: Springer series in electronics and photonics; v. 26 LC Classification: TA1750 .G85 1990 Dewey Class No.: 621.381/045 20

Guided-wave optoelectronics / Theodor Tamir, (ed.); with contributions by R.C. Alferness ... [et. al.]. Published/Created: Berlin; New York: Springer-Verlag, c1988. Related Authors: Tamir, Theodor, 1927- Alferness, R. C. Description: xiii, 401 p.: ill.; 24 cm. ISBN: 0387187952 (U.S.) Notes: Includes bibliographies and index. Subjects: Optoelectronic devices. Integrated optics. Optical wave guides. Semiconductor lasers. Series: Springer series in electronics and photonics; v. 26 LC Classification: TA1750 .G85 1988 Dewey Class No.: 621.381 19

Guided-wave optoelectronics: device characterization, analysis, and design / edited by Theodor Tamir, Giora Griffel, and Henry L. Bertoni. Published/Created: New York: Plenum Press, c1995. Related Authors: Tamir, Theodor, 1927- Griffel, Giora. Bertoni, Henry L. Description: xi, 501 p.: ill.; 26 cm. ISBN: 0306451077 Notes: "Proceedings of the Fourth Weber Research Institute (WRI) International Symposium on Guided-Wave Optoelectronics: Device Characterization, Analysis, and Design, held October 26-28, 1994 in Brooklyn, N.Y."--t.p. verso. Includes bibliographical references and index. Subjects: Optical wave guides--Lasers--Design and construction--Quantum electronics--Light modulators--Congresses. LC Classification: TA1750 .G86 1995 Dewey Class No.: 621.381/045 20

Handbook of optical biomedical diagnostics / Valery V. Tuchin, editor. Published/Created: Bellingham, Wash., USA: SPIE Press, 2002. Projected Pub. Date: 0201 Related Authors: Tuchin, V. V. (Valerii Viktorovich) Description: p. cm. ISBN: 0819439150 Subjects: Imaging systems in medicine--Handbooks, manuals, etc. Lasers in medicine--Handbooks, manuals, etc. Spectroscopic imaging--Handbooks, manuals, etc. Series: SPIE Press monograph; PM107 LC Classification: R857.O6 .H36 2002 Dewey Class No.: 616.07/54 21

Handbook of solid-state lasers / edited by Peter K. Cheo. Published/Created: New York: M. Dekker, 1988, c1989. Projected Pub. Date: 1111 Related Authors: Cheo, Peter K., 1930- Description: p. cm. ISBN: 082477857X Notes: Includes bibliographies and index. Subjects: Solid-state lasers--Handbooks, manuals, etc. Series: Optical engineering (Marcel Dekker, Inc.); v. 18. Variant Series: Optical engineering; v. 18 LC Classification: TA1705 .H36 1989 Dewey Class No.: 621.36/61 19

High energy beam manufacturing technologies: presented at the Winter Annual Meeting of the American Society of Mechanical Engineers, San Francisco, California, December 10-15, 1989 / sponsored by the Product Engineering Division, ASME; edited by E.S. Geskin, M.C. Leu. Published/Created: New York, N.Y.: ASME, c1989. Related Authors: Geskin, E. S. Leu, M. C. American Society of Mechanical Engineers. Production Engineering Division. American Society of Mechanical Engineers. Winter Meeting (1989: San Francisco, Calif.) Description: v, 85 p.: ill.; 28 cm. ISBN: 0791804399 Notes: "H00573"--P. [4] of cover. Includes bibliographical references. Subjects: Lasers--Industrial applications--Manufacturing processes--Congresses. Series: PED (Series); vol. 41. Variant Series: PED; vol. 41 LC Classification: TA1673 .H52 1989 Dewey Class No.: 621.36/6 20

High field interactions and short wavelength generation: summaries of papers presented at the topical meeting ... August 22-25, 1994, St. Malo, France / cosponsored by Optical Society of America in cooperation with European Physical Society/Quantum Electronics and Optics Division, Société française d'optique. Edition Information: Postconference ed. Published/Created: Washington, DC: Optical Society of America, c1994. Related Authors: Optical Society of America. Lasers and Electro-optics Society (Institute of Electrical and Electronics Engineers). European Physical Society. Quantum Electronics and Optics Division. Société française d'optique. Description: xiii, 297 p.: ill.; 28 cm. ISBN:

1557523614 (Postconference ed.) Notes: Includes bibliographical references and index. Subjects: X-ray lasers--Lasers--Congresses. Series: Technical digest series (Optical Society of America); 1994, v. 16. Variant Series: 1994 technical digest series; v. 16 LC Classification: TA1673 .H525 1994 Dewey Class No.: 621.36/6 20

High power and solid state lasers II: 19-20 January 1989, Los Angeles, California / George Dubé, chair/editor; sponsored by SPIE-the International Society for Optical Engineering; cooperating organizations, Applied Optics Laboratory/New Mexico State University ... [et al.]. Published/Created: Bellingham, Wash., USA: The Society, c1989. Related Authors: Dubé, George. Society of Photo-optical Instrumentation Engineers. New Mexico State University. Applied Optics Laboratory. Description: viii, 201 p.: ill.; 28 cm. ISBN: 0819400750 Notes: Includes bibliographical references and index. Subjects: Solid-state lasers--Congresses. High power lasers--Congresses. Series: Proceedings of SPIE--the International Society for Optical Engineering; v. 1040. Variant Series: SPIE proceedings series; v. 1040 LC Classification: TA1705 .H54 1989 Dewey Class No.: 621.36/61 20

High speed diode lasers / editor, Sergei A. Gurevich. Published/Created: Singapore; New Jersey: World Scientific, c1998. Related Authors: Gurevich, Sergei, 1949- Description: xi, 198 p.: ill.; 26 cm. ISBN: 9810232373 Notes: Includes bibliographical references. Subjects: Semiconductor lasers. Diodes, Semiconductor. Modulation (Electronics) Laser pulses, Ultrashort. Series: Selected topics in electronics and systems; vol. 11 LC Classification: TA1700 .H546 1998 Dewey Class No.: 621.36/6 21

High-power diode lasers: fundamentals, technology, applications, with contributions by numerous experts / Roland Diehl, (Ed.). Published/Created: Berlin; New York: Springer, c2000. Related Authors: Diehl, R. D. (Renee D.) Description: xiv, 416 p.: ill.; 25 cm. ISBN: 3540666931 (alk. paper) Notes: Includes bibliographical references and index. Subjects: Semiconductor lasers. Diodes, Semiconductor. Series: Topics in applied physics, 0303-4216; v. 78 LC Classification: TA1700 .H52 2000 Dewey Class No.: 621.36/6 21

High-power dye lasers / Francisco J. Duarte, ed. Published/Created: Berlin; New York: Springer-Verlag, c1991. Related Authors: Duarte, Francisco J. Description: xii, 252 p.: ill.; 24 cm. ISBN: 3540540660 (Springer-Verlag Berlin Heidelberg New York: acid-free paper) 0387540660 (Springer-Verlag New York Berlin Heidelberg: acid-free paper) Notes: Includes bibliographical references and index. Subjects: Dye lasers. Series: Springer series in optical sciences; v. 65 LC Classification: TA1690 .H54 1991 Dewey Class No.: 621.36/64 20

High-power gas and solid state lasers: 5-8 April 1994, Vienna, Austria / Markus Bohrer ... [et al.], chairs/editors; sponsored by the Commission of the European Communities, Directorate General for Science, Research, and Development ... [et al.] Published/Created: Bellingham, Wash., USA: SPIE--the International Society for Optical Engineering, c1994. Related Authors: Bohrer, Markus. Commission of the European Communities. Directorate-General for Science, Research, and Development. Description: xi, 602 sssp.: ill.; 28 cm. ISBN: 0819415073 (pbk.) Notes: Includes bibliographical references and author index. Subjects: High power lasers--Congresses. Gas lasers--Congresses. Solid-state lasers--Congresses. Series: Proceedings EurOpt series. Proceedings of SPIE--the International Society for Optical Engineering; v. 2206.

High-speed electronic and optoelectronics: 26 March 1992, Somerset, New Jersey / John E. Bowers, Umesh K. Mishra, editors; sponsored by SPIE--the International Society for Optical Engineering. Published/Created: Bellingham, WA: SPIE (The Society of Photo-Optical Instrumentation Engineers), 1992. Related

Authors: Bowers, John E. Mishra, Umesh Kumar, 1958- Society of Photo-optical Instrumentation Engineers. Description: vii, 177 p.: ill.; 28 cm. ISBN: 0819408417 (pbk.) Notes: Includes bibliographical references and index. Subjects: Integrated circuits--Congresses. Lasers--Congresses. Optoelectronic devices--Congresses. Series: Proceedings of the SPIE--the International Society for Optical Engneering; v. 1680. Variant Series: Proceedings SPIE - The International Society for Optical Engineering; vol. 1680 LC Classification: TK7874 .H5245 1992 Dewey Class No.: 621.3815 20

High-speed semiconductor laser sources: 1-2 February 1996, San Jose, California / Paul A. Morton, Deborah L. Crawford, chairs/editors; sponsored and published by SPIE--the International Society for Optical Engineering; cooperating organization ARPA--Advanced Research Projects Agency. Published/Created: Bellingham, Wash., USA: SPIE, c1996. Related Authors: Morton, Paul A. Crawford, Deborah L. Society of Photo-optical Instrumentation Engineers. United States. Advanced Research Projects Agency. Description: vii, 208 p.: ill.; 28 cm. ISBN: 0819420581 Notes: Includes bibliographical references and index. Subjects: Semiconductor lasers--Congresses. Laser communication systems--Congresses. Series: Proceedings of SPIE--the International Society for Optical Engineering; v. 2684. Variant Series: Proceedings / SPIE--the International Society for Optical Engineering; v. 2684 LC Classification: TA1700 .H55 1996 Dewey Class No.: 621.36/61 21

High-speed semiconductor lasers for communication: 10-11 February, 1997, San Jose, California / Norman S. Kwong, Radhakrishnan Nagarajan, chairs/editors; sponsored and published by SPIE--the International Society for Optical Engineering; cooperating organization DARPA--Defense Advanced Research Projects Agency. Published/Created: Bellingham, Washington: SPIE, c1997 Related Authors: Kwong, Norman S. Nagarajan, Radhakrishnan. Society of Photo-optical Instrumentation Engineers. United States. Defense Advanced Research Projects Agency. Description: vii, 212 p.: ill.; 28 cm. ISBN: 0819424498 Notes: Includes bibliographic references and author index. Subjects: Semiconductor lasers--Congresses. Laser communication systems--Congresses. Series: Proceedings of SPIE--the International Society for Optical Engineering; v. 3038. Variant Series: Proceedings / SPIE--the International Society for Optical Engineering; v. 3038 LC Classification: TA1700 .H548 1997 Dewey Class No.: 621.382/7 21

Holart report: the journal of international holographic art sales. Published/Created: San Francisco, CA: Holart Consultants, c1992- Description: v.: ill.; 28 cm. Vol. 1, no. 1 (May 1992)- Current Frequency: Four times a year ISSN: 1062-6360 Cancel/Invalid LCCN: sn 92002788 Notes: Title from caption. SERBIB/SERLOC merged record Subjects: Lasers in art. Holography in art. Art, Modern--20th century. LC Classification: N6494.L3 H62 Dewey Class No.: 774 20

ICALEO '90, laser materials processing: proceedings / chairs, Stanley L. Ream, Friedrich Dausinger, Tomoo Fujioka. Published/Created: Orlando, Fla.: Laser Institute of America; Bellingham, Wash.: SPIE--the International Society for Optical Engineering, c1991. Related Authors: Ream, Stanley L. Dausinger, Friedrich. Fujioka, Tomoo, 1935- Description: 547 p.: ill.; 28 cm. ISBN: 0912035420 Notes: "4-9 November 1990, Hynes Convention Center, Boston, Massachusetts"--Cover. Includes bibliographical references and indexes. Subjects: Lasers--Industrial applications--Congresses. Series: Proceedings of SPIE--the International Society for Optical Engineering; v. 1601. Variant Series: SPIE proceedings series; v. 1601 LC Classification: IN PROCESS

ICALEO '90: optical methods in flow and particle diagnostics: proceedings / chairs,

Robert W. Dibble, Dominique Fourguette, Wolfgang Ketterle; [sponsored by Laser Institute of America]. Published/Created: Orlando, Fla.: The Institute; Bellingham, Wash.: SPIE--the International Society for Optical Engineering, c1991. Related Authors: Dibble, Robert W. Fourguette, Dominique. Ketterle, Wolfgang. Laser Institute of America. Society of Photo-optical Instrumentation Engineers. International Congress on Applications of Lasers and Electro-optics (9th: 1990: Boston, Mass.) Description: 140 p.: ill.; 28 cm. ISBN: 0912035439 Notes: Papers from the Optical Methods in Flow & Particle Diagnostics Symposium. "4-9 November, 1980, Hynes Convention Center, Boston, Massachusetts"--Cover. Includes bibliographical references and indexes. Subjects: Laser Doppler velocimeter--Particles--Measurement--Flow visualization--Congresses. Series: Proceedings of SPIE--the International Society for Optical Engineering; v. 1602. Variant Series: SPIE proceedings series; v. 1602 LC Classification: TA357 .I29 1991 Dewey Class No.: 681/.2 20

ICS lectures on industrial applications of lasers / N.U. Wetter and W. de Rossi. Published/Created: Vienna: United Nations Industrial Development Organization, 2000. Description: 93 p. ISBN: 9211064082

IEEE International Semiconductor Laser Conference (11th: 1988: Boston, Mass.) Conference digest / 11th IEEE International Semiconductor Laser Conference, August 19-September 1, 1988, Westin Hotel, Boston, Massachusetts; sponsored by the IEEE Lasers and Electro Optics Society. Published/Created: [United States]: The Society; Piscataway, NJ: Order from IEEE Service Center, c1988. Description: xvi, 220 p.: ill.; 28 cm. Notes: Spine Title - 1988 conference digest of the 11th IEEE International Semiconductor Laser Conference. Includes bibliographical references and index. Subjects: Semiconductor lasers--Congresses. LC Classification: TA1700 .I33 1988 Dewey Class No.: 621.36/6 20

IEEE International Semiconductor Laser Conference (13th: 1992: Takamatsu-shi, Japan) Conference digest / 13th IEEE International Semiconductor Laser Conference, September 21-25, 1992, Takamatsu Kokusai Hotel, Takamatsu, Kagawa, Japan; cosponsored by the Institute of Electronics, Information and Communication Engineers, the Japan Society of Applied Physics, Optoelectronic Industry and Technology Development Association in cooperation with the IEEE Lasers and Electro-optics Society. Published/Created: [New York]: IEEE Lasers and Electro-optics Society; Tokyo, Japan: Order from Business Center for Academic Societies, [1993?] Related Authors: Denshi J¯oh¯o Ts¯ushin Gakkai (Japan) ¯Oy¯o Butsuri Gakkai. Optoelectronic Industry and Technology Development Association (Japan) Description: xx, 276 p.: ill.; 30 cm. + Post-deadline papers (ii, 32 p.: ill.; 28 cm.) ISBN: 4930813514 Notes: Includes bibliographical references and index. Subjects: Semiconductor lasers--Congresses. LC Classification: TA1770 .I35 1992 Dewey Class No.: 621.36/6 21

IEEE International Semiconductor Laser Conference (15th: 1996: Haifa, Israel) 15th IEEE International Semiconductor Laser Conference: 13-18 October 1996, Dan Carmel Hotel, Haifa, Israel. Published/Created: [New York]: Institute of Electrical and Electronics Engineers, c1996. Related Authors: Lasers and Electro-optics Society (Institute of Electrical and Electronics Engineers) Description: xii, 193 p.: ill.; 28 cm. ISBN: 078033163X (pbk.) 0780331648 (case) 0780331656 (microfiche) Notes: IEEE catalog number: 96CH35896. Sponsored by the IEEE Lasers and Electro-Optics Society. Includes bibliographical references and index. Subjects: Semiconductor lasers--Congresses. LC Classification: TA1700 .I33 1996 Dewey Class No.: 621.36/6 21

IEEE International Semiconductor Laser Conference (16th: 1998: Nara, Japan) Conference digest: ISLC 1998 NARA: 1998 IEEE 16th International Semiconductor Laser Conference: (4-8 October, 1998), Nara, Japan / sponsored by the IEEE Lasers and Electro-Optics Society ... [et al.]. Published/Created: Piscataway, NJ: IEEE, 1998. Description: xviii, 275 p.: ill.; 28 cm. ISBN: 0780342232 (softbound edition) 0780342240 (casebound edition) 0780342259 (microfiche edition) Notes: Cover title. "IEEE Catalog Number: 98CH36130"--T.p. verso. Includes bibliographical references. Subjects: Semiconductor lasers--Congresses. LC Classification: TA1700 .I33 1998 Dewey Class No.: 621.36/6 21

IEEE journal of selected topics in quantum electronics: a publication of the IEEE Lasers and Electro-optics Society. Published/Created: New York, NY: IEEE, c1995- Description: v.: ill.; 28 cm. Vol. 1, no. 1 (Apr. 1995)- Current Frequency: Bimonthly, Former Frequency: Four no. a year ISSN: 1077-260X Cancel/Invalid LCCN: sn 94002673 CODEN: IJSQEN Notes: Title from cover. SERBIB/SERLOC merged record Additional Form Avail.: Also available by subscription, in PDF format, via the World Wide Web. Subjects: Quantum electronics--Periodicals. LC Classification: QC685 .I44 Dewey Class No.: 537.5/344 20

IEEE LCS: the magazine of lightwave communications systems. Published/Created: New York, NY: IEEE Communications Society in cooperation with the IEEE Lasers and Electro-Optics Society, 1990-1991. Description: 2 v.: ill.; 28 cm. Vol. 1, no. 1 (Feb. 1990)-v. 2, no. 1 (Feb. 1991). Current Frequency: Quarterly Continued by: IEEE LTS 1055-6877 (DLC) 91642343 (OCoLC)23269746 ISSN: 1045-9235 Cancel/Invalid LCCN: sn 89003772 CODEN: IELCED Notes: Title from cover. SERBIB/SERLOC merged record Additional Form Avail.: Also available by subscription via the World Wide Web. Subjects: Fiber optics--Periodicals. Optical communications--Periodicals. LC Classification: TA1800 .I33 Dewey Class No.: 621.382/75 20

IEEE LTS: the magazine of lightwave telecommunications systems. Published/Created: New York, NY: IEEE Communications Society, 1991- Description: v.: ill.; 28 cm. Vol. 2, no. 2 (May 1991)- Ceased with v. 3, no. 4, published in 1992. Current Frequency: Quarterly Continues: IEEE LCS 1045-9235 (DLC) 91642342 (OCoLC)20287891 ISSN: 1055-6877 Cancel/Invalid LCCN: sn 91000570 CODEN: IELTEU Notes: Title from cover. Published in cooperation with the IEEE Lasers and Electro-Optics Society. SERBIB/SERLOC merged record Indx'd selectively by: Computer & control abstracts 0036-8113 May 1991- Electrical & electronics abstracts 0036-8105 May 1991- Physics abstracts 0036-8091 May 1991- Additional Form Avail.: Beginning 1991-1992 also available by subscription, in PDF format, via the World Wide Web. Subjects: Fiber optics--Periodicals. Optical communications--Periodicals. LC Classification: TA1800 .I33 Dewey Class No.: 621.382/75 20

IEEE photonics technology letters: a publication of the IEEE Laser and Electro-optics Society. Published/Created: [New York, NY: Institute of Electrical and Electronics Engineers, c1989- Description: v.: ill.; 28 cm. Vol. 1, no. 1 (Jan. 1989)- Current Frequency: Monthly ISSN: 1041-1135 Cancel/Invalid LCCN: sf 93094192 sn 88008224 Notes: Title from cover. SERBIB/SERLOC merged record Additional Form Avail.: Also available by subscription via the World Wide Web. Subjects: Photonics--Lasers--Quantum electronics--Periodicals. LC Classification: TA1501 .I34 Dewey Class No.: 621.36/05 21

IEEE transactions on advanced packaging: a publication of the IEEE Components, Packaging, and Manufacturing Technology Society and the Lasers and Electro Optics Society. Published/Created: Piscataway,

NJ: Institute of Electrical and Electronics Engineers, c1999- Description: v.: ill.; 28 cm. Vol. 22, no. 1 (Feb. 1999)- Current Frequency: Quarterly Continues: IEEE transactions on components, packaging, and manufacturing technology. Part B, Advanced packaging 1070-9894 (DLC) 94649785 (OCoLC)28525078 ISSN: 1521-3323 Cancel/Invalid LCCN: sn 98001781 CODEN: ITAPFZ Notes: Title from cover. SERBIB/SERLOC merged record Indexed by: Chemical Abstracts 0009-2258 Additional Form Avail.: Also available by subscription via the World Wide Web. Subjects: Electronic packaging--Electronic industries--Periodicals. LC Classification: TK7869 .I184 Dewey Class No.: 621.381/046/05 20

IEEE transactions on components, packaging, and manufacturing technology. Part B, Advanced packaging: a publication of the IEEE Components, Packaging, and Manufacturing Technology Society and the IEEE Lasers and Electro-Optics Society. Published/Created: New York, NY: Institute of Electrical and Electronics Engineers, c1994-c1998.Description: 5 v.: ill.; 28 cm. Vol. 17, no. 1 (Feb. 1994)-v. 21, no. 4 (Nov. 1998). Current Frequency: Quarterly Continues in part: IEEE transactions on components, hybrids, and manufacturing technology 0148-6411 (DLC) 78645660 (OCoLC)3523341 Continued by: IEEE transactions on advanced packaging 1521-3323 (DLC) 99111625 (OCoLC)39742480 ISSN: 1070-9894 Cancel/Invalid LCCN: sn 93002843 CODEN: IMTBE4 Notes: Title from cover. SERBIB/SERLOC merged record Indx'd selectively by: Chemical abstracts 0009-2258 Additional Form Avail.: Also available by subscription via the World Wide Web. Subjects: Electronic packaging--Electronic industries--Periodicals. LC Classification: TK7869 .I184 Dewey Class No.: 621.381/046/05 20

Iffländer, Reinhard. Solid-state lasers for materials processing: fundamental relations and technical realizations / Reinhard Iffländer; translated by Stefan Weber. Published/Created: Berlin; New York: Springer, c2001. Description: xvi, 350 p.: ill.; 24 cm. ISBN: 3540669809 (alk. paper) Notes: Includes bibliographical references and index. Subjects: Solid-state lasers. Series: Springer series in optical sciences; v. 77 LC Classification: TA1705 .I3313 2001 Dewey Class No.: 621.36/61 21

Iga, Ken'ichi, 1940- Fundamentals of laser optics / Kenichi Iga; technical editor, Richard B. Miles. Published/Created: New York: Plenum Press, c1994. Related Authors: Miles, Richard B. (Richard Bryant), 1948- Description: xv, 285 p.: ill.; 24 cm. ISBN: 0306446049 Notes: Includes bibliographical references and index. Subjects: Lasers. Electrooptics. Series: Lasers, photonics, and electro-optics LC Classification: TA1675 .I33 1994 Dewey Class No.: 621.36/6 20

Iga, Ken'ichi, 1940- Process technology for semiconductor lasers: crystal growth and microprocesses / Kenichi Iga, Susumu Kinoshita. Published/Created: Berlin; New York: Springer, c1996. Related Authors: Kinoshita, Susumu, 1959- Description: x, 169 p.: ill.; 24 cm. ISBN: 3540589724 (hard: alk. paper) Notes: Includes bibliographical references (p. 155-166) and index. Subjects: Semiconductor lasers--Design and construction. Laser materials. Crystal growth. Epitaxy. Series: Springer series in materials science; 30 LC Classification: TA1700 .I49 1996 Dewey Class No.: 621.36/6 20

IGD Scientific Workshop (2nd: 1988: Novara, Italy) High energy density technologies in materials science: proceedings of the 2nd IGD Scientific Workshop, Novara, May 3-4, 1988 / edited by F. Garbassi and E. Occhiello. Published/Created: Dordrecht; Boston: Kluwer Academic, c1990. Related Authors: Garbassi, F. Occhiello, E. Description: x, 170 p.: ill.; 25 cm. ISBN: 0792305639 (alk. paper) Notes: Includes bibliographical references. Subjects: Lasers--Industrial applications--Materials--Effect of radiation on--Congresses. LC Classification: TA1673 .I37 1988 Dewey Class No.: 621.36/6 20

II-VI blue/green laser diodes: 2 November 1994, Boston, Massachusetts / Robert L. Gunshor, Arto V. Nurmikko, chairs/editors; sponsored and published by SPIE--the International Society for Optical Engineering. Published/Created: Bellingham, Wash., USA: SPIE, c1994. Related Authors: Gunshor, Robert L. Nurmikko, Arto V. Description: ix, 200 p.: ill.; 28 cm. ISBN: 0819416797 Notes: Includes bibliographical references and index. Subjects: Semiconductor lasers--Diodes, Semiconductor--Heterostructures--Epitaxy--Congresses. Blue light. Series: Proceedings of SPIE--the International Society for Optical Engineering; v. 2346. Variant Series: Proceedings / SPIE--the International Society of Optical Engineering; v. 2346 LC Classification: TA1700 .A15 1994 Dewey Class No.: 621.36/6 20

Ikegami, T. (Tetsuhiko) Frequency stabilization of semiconductor laser diodes / Tetsuhiko Ikegami, Shoichi Sudo, Yoshihisa Sakai. Published/Created: Boston: Artech House, c1995. Related Authors: Sudo, S. (Shoichi) Sakai, Yoshihisa. Description: x, 356 p.: ill.; 24 cm. ISBN: 0890066485 (hard: alk paper) Notes: Includes bibliographical references and index. Subjects: Semiconductor lasers. Frequency stability. Series: Artech House optoelectronics library LC Classification: TA1700 .I54 1995 Dewey Class No.: 621.6/6 20

In situ process diagnostics and intelligent materials processing: symposium held December 2-5, 1997, Boston, Massachusetts, U.S.A. / editors, Peter A. Rosenthal, Walter M. Duncan, John A. Woollam. Published/Created: Warrendale, Pa.: Materials Research Society, c1998. Related Authors: Rosenthal, Peter A. Duncan, Walter Marvin. Woollam, John A. Description: ix, 290 p.: ill.; 24 cm. ISBN: 1558994076 Notes: Includes bibliographical references and indexes. Subjects: Electronics--Materials--Manufacturing processes--Semiconductors--Thin films--Lasers--Industrial applications--Congresses. Series: Materials Research Society symposia proceedings; v. 502. Variant Series: Materials Research Society symposium proceedings; v. 502 LC Classification: TK7871 .I55 1998 Dewey Class No.: 621.381 21

In situ process diagnostics and modelling: symposium held April 6-7, 1999, San Francisco, California, U.S.A. / editors, Orlando Auciello ... [et al.]. Published/Created: Warrendale, PA: Materials Research Society, 1999. Related Authors: Auciello, Orlando, 1945- Description: xi, 199 p.: ill.; 24 cm. ISBN: 1558994769 Notes: Includes bibliographical references and indexes. Subjects: Thin film devices--Design and construction--Plasma diagnostics--Lasers--Industrial applications--Congresses. Series: Materials Research Society symposia proceedings; v. 569. Variant Series: Materials Research Society symposium proceedings, 02729172; v. 569 LC Classification: TK7872.T55 I53 1999 Dewey Class No.: 621.3815/2 21

Indo-USSR Workshop on Growth and Characterisation of Laser and Non-linear Crystals (1988: Bhabha Atomic Research Centre) Proceedings of the Indo-USSR Workshop on Growth and Characterisation of Laser and Non-linear Crystals, Bhabha Atomic Research Centre, Bombay ... February 23-27, 1988 [microform] / compiled by G.P. Kothiyal and B. Ghosh; sponsored by Government of India, Department of Science and Technology, and Indian Physics Association. Published/Created: Bombay, India: The Centre, [1988] Related Authors: Kothiyal, G. P. (Govind P.) Ghosh, B. Description: i, 419 p.: ill.; 24 cm Notes: Includes index. Includes bibliographical references. Microfiche. New Delhi: Library of Congress Office; Washington, D.C.: Library of Congress Photoduplication Service, 1990. 5 microfiches; 11 x 15 cm. Subjects: Solid-state lasers. LC Classification: Microfiche 90/60534

Industrial and scientific uses of high power lasers: 13-15 March 1991, the Hague, the Netherlands: proceedings, ECO4 / Jean P.

Billon, Edouard Fabre, chairs/editors; sponsored by the congress of EPS--European Physical Society, Europtica--the European Federation for Applied Optics, SPIE--the International Society for Optical Engineering; cooperating organizations, ANRT--Association nationale de la recherche technique ... [et al.]. Published/Created: Bellingham, Wash.: SPIE, c1991. Related Authors: Billon, Jean P. Fabre, Edouard. European Physical Society. European Federation for Applied Optics. Society of Photo-optical Instrumentation Engineers. European Congress on Optics (4th: 1991: Hague, Netherlands) Description: ix, 344 p.: ill.; 28 cm. ISBN: 0819406112 Notes: Includes bibliographical references and index. Subjects: High power lasers--Industrial applications--Congresses. Series: Proceedings of SPIE--the International Society for Optical Engineering; v. 1502. Variant Series: SPIE proceedings series; v. 1502 LC Classification: TA1673 .I54 1991 Dewey Class No.: 621.36/6 20

Industrial laser interferometry II: 27-28 June 1988, Dearborn, Michigan / Michael Y.Y. Hung, Ryszard Pryputniewicz, chairs/editors; sponsored by SPIE--the International Society for Optical Engineering and ESD--the Engineering Society; cooperating organizations, Applied Optics Laboratory/New Mexico State University ... [et al.]. Published/Created: Bellingham, Wash., USA: SPIE, c1988. Related Authors: Hung, Michael Y. Y. Pryputniewicz, Ryszard J. Description: vi, 163; 28 cm. ISBN: 0892529903 Notes: Includes bibliographical references. Subjects: Lasers--Industrial applications--Congresses. Laser interferometers--Industrial applications Congresses. Series: Proceedings of SPIE--the International Society for Optical Engineering; v. 955 LC Classification: TA1673 .I555 1988 Dewey Class No.: 621.36/6 20

Industrial laser materials processing: the best of 1986/1987 Industrial laser annual handbook / David Belforte, Morris Levitt, editors. Published/Created: Tulsa, Okla.: PennWell Books, 1988. Related Authors: Belforte, David. Levitt, Morris R. Description: viii, 223 p.: ill.; 29 cm. ISBN: 087814336X: Notes: "Laser Focus." Includes bibliographies and index. Subjects: Lasers--Industrial applications. Manufacturing processes. LC Classification: TA1677 .I54 1988 Dewey Class No.: 621.36/6 19

Industrial lasers and laser material processing: Russia national conference, 14-16 April 1993, Shatura, Moscow Region, Russia / Vladislav Ya. Panchenko, Vladimir S. Golubev, chairs/editors; organized by Scientific Resea[r]ch Center for Technological Lasers ... [et al.]; cosponsored by Russia Academy of Sciences ... [et al.]; cooperating organizations, Institute of General Physics, Russia Academy of Sciences ... [et al.]. Published/Created: Bellingham, Wash.: SPIE--the International Society for Optical Engineering, c1994. Related Authors: Panchenko, Vladislav IAkovlevich. Golubev, V. S. (Vladimir Stepanovich) Description: xi, 236 p.: ill.; 28 cm. ISBN: 0819415715 Notes: "Russia National Conference on Industrial Lasers and Laser Applications '93 (ILLA '93) ... held in the Scientific Research Center for Technological Lasers, Shatura, Moscow Region, Russia, 14-16 April 1993"--P. ix. Includes bibliographical references and index. Subjects: Lasers--Industrial applications--Congresses. Series: Proceedings of SPIE--the International Society for Optical Engineering; v. 2257. Variant Series: Proceedings / SPIE--the International Society for Optical Engineering; v. 2257 LC Classification: TA1677 .I55 1994 Dewey Class No.: 621.36/6 20

Inertial confinement fusion: ICF quarterly report / Lawrence Livermore National Laboratory. Published/Created: Livermore, CA: The Laboratory; Springfield, Va.: Available from National Technical Information Service, [1990?-] Description: v.: ill.; 28 cm. Vol. 1, no. 1 (Oct.-Dec. 1990)- Current Frequency: Four no. a year Continues in part: Laser program annual report 0882-0473 (OCoLC)7105001 (DLC) 85646874 Notes: Title from cover. SERBIB/SERLOC merged record Also issued annually in a compendium of the articles from the quarterly. Inertial confinement fusion (Livermore, Calif.: annual) (DLC)sn 95043545 (OCoLC)27021910 Additional Form Avail.: Also available on microfiche. Subjects: Lasers--Laser-plasma interactions--Plasma confinement--Periodicals. LC Classification: TA1671 .I54 Dewey Class No.: 621.48/4/05 20

Infrared absorbing dyes / edited by Masaru Matsuoka. Published/Created: New York: Plenum Press, c1990. Related Authors: Matsuoka, Masaru, 1942- Description: xiv, 220 p.: ill.; 24 cm. ISBN: 0306434784 Notes: Includes bibliographical references and index. Subjects: Dye lasers--Materials. Series: Topics in applied chemistry LC Classification: TA1690 .I53 1990 Dewey Class No.: 621.36/2 20

Infrared applications of semiconductors II: symposium held December 1-4, 1997, Boston, Massachusetts, U.S.A. / editors, Donald L. McDaniel, Jr. ... [et al.]. Published/Created: Pittsburgh, PA: Materials Research Society, 1998. Related Authors: McDaniel, Donald L. Description: xvii, 692 p.: ill.; 24 cm. ISBN: 1558993894 Notes: Includes bibliographical references and index. Subjects: Infrared technology--Materials--Semiconductors--Semiconductor lasers--Superlattices as materials--Quantum wells--Congresses. Series: Materials Research Society symposia proceedings; v. 484. Variant Series: Materials Research Society symposium proceedings; v. 484 LC Classification: TA1570 .I5239 1998 Dewey Class No.: 621.36/2 21

Infrared fiber optics II: 18-19 January 1990, Los Angeles, California / James A. Harrington, Abraham Katzir, chairs/editors; sponsored by SPIE--the International Society for Optical Engineering. Published/Created: Bellingham, Wash., USA: The Society, c1990. Related Authors: Harrington, James A., 1942- Katzir, Abraham. Description: viii, 271 p.: ill.; 28 cm. ISBN: 0819402699 (pbk.) Notes: Papers from the Symposium on High-Power Lasers and Optical Computing. Includes bibliographical references and index. Subjects: Fiber optics--Congresses. Infrared technology--Congresses. Series: Proceedings of SPIE--the International Society for Optical Engineering; v. 1228. Variant Series: SPIE proceedings series; v. 1228 LC Classification: TA1800 .I525 1990 Dewey Class No.: 621.36/92 20

Innovative Science and Technology Symposium (1988: Los Angeles, Calif.) Short and ultrashort wavelength lasers / C. Randol Jones, chair/editor; sponsored by SPIE-the International Society for Optical Engineering. Published/Created: Bellingham, Wash.: The Society , c1988. Related Authors: Jones, C. Randol. Society of Photo-optical Instrumentation Engineers. Description: viii, 185 p.: ill.; 28 cm. ISBN: 0892529105 (pbk.) Notes: "Part of the 1988 Innovative Science and Technology Symposium ... 14-15 January 1988, Los Angeles, California." Includes bibliographies and index. Subjects: Gamma ray lasers--X-ray lasers--Chemical lasers--Congresses. Series: Proceedings of SPIE--the International Society for Optical Engineering; v. 875 LC Classification: TA1673 .I557 1988 Dewey Class No.: 621.36/6 19

Inorganic optical materials: proceedings of a conference held 6-7 August 1996, Denver, Colorado / Paul Klocek, editor; sponsored by SPIE--the International Society for Optical Engineering. Published/Created: Bellingham, Wash.: SPIE Optical Engineering Press, c1996. Related Authors: Klocek, Paul. Description: vii, 354 p.: ill.; 26 cm. ISBN: 0819422568 (softcover) Notes: Includes bibliographical references. Subjects: Lasers--Materials--Optical materials--Inorganic compounds--Congresses. Series: Critical reviews of optical science and technology; v. CR64 LC Classification: TA1673 .I55713 1996 Dewey Class No.: 621.36 20

In-plane semiconductor lasers III: 27-29 January 1999, San Jose, California / Hong K. Choi, Peter S. Zory, chairs/editors; sponsored by SPIE--the International Society for Optical Engineering; cooperating organization, DARPA--Defense Advanced Research Projects Agency. Published/Created: Bellingham, Wash., USA: SPIE, c1999. Related Authors: Choi, Hong Kyun. Zory, Peter S., 1936- Society of Photo-optical Instrumentation Engineers. United States. Defense Advanced Research Projects Agency. Description: x, 284 p.: ill.; 28 cm. ISBN: 0819430986 Notes: Includes bibliographical references and index. Subjects: Semiconductor lasers--High power lasers--Congresses. Series: Proceedings of SPIE--the International Society for Optical Engineering; v. 3628. Variant Series: SPIE proceedings series; v. 3628 LC Classification: TA1700 .I559 1999 Dewey Class No.: 621.36/6 21

In-plane semiconductor lasers IV: 24-25 January, 2000, San Jose, California / Luke J. Mawst, Ramon U. Martinelli, chairs/editors; sponsored and published by SPIE--the International Society for Optical Engineering. Published/Created: Bellingham, Washington: SPIE, c2000. Related Authors: Mawst, Luke J. Martinelli, Ramon U. Society of Photo-optical Instrumentation Engineers. Description: xi, 228 p.: ill.; 28 cm. ISBN: 0819435643 Notes: Includes bibliographic references and author index. Subjects: Semiconductor lasers--Congresses. High power lasers--Congresses. Series: Proceedings of SPIE--the International Society for Optical Engineering; v. 3947. Variant Series: SPIE proceedings series; v. 3947 LC Classification: TA1700 .I5592 2000

In-plane semiconductor lasers V: 22-23 January 2001, San Jose, USA / Luke J. Mawst, Ramon U. Martinelli, chairs/editors; sponsored and published by SPIE--the International Society for Optical Engineering. Published/Created: Bellingham, Wash., USA: SPIE, c2001. Related Authors: Mawst, Luke J. Martinelli, Ramon U. Society of Photo-optical Instrumentation Engineers. Description: xxxii, 204 p.: ill.; 28 cm. ISBN: 0819439657 Notes: Includes bibliographic references and index. Subjects: Semiconductor lasers--Congresses. High power lasers--Congresses. Series: Proceedings of SPIE--the International Society for Optical Engineering; v. 4287. Variant Series: SPIE proceedings series; v. 4287 LC Classification: TA1700 .I5593 2001 Dewey Class No.: 621.36/6 21

In-plane semiconductor lasers: from ultraviolet to mid-infrared II: 26-28 January 1998, San Jose, California / Hong K. Choi, Peter S. Zory, chairs/editors; sponsored ... by SPIE--the International Society for Optical Engineering. Published/Created: Bellingham, Wash., USA: SPIE, c1998. Related Authors: Choi, Hong Kyun. Zory, Peter S., 1936- Society of Photo-optical Instrumentation Engineers. Description: x, 334 p.: ill.; 28 cm. ISBN: 0819427233 Notes: Includes bibliographical references and index. Subjects: Semiconductor lasers--Congresses. High power lasers--Congresses. Series: Proceedings of SPIE--the International Society for Optical Engineering; v. 3284. Variant Series: SPIE proceedings series; v. 3284 LC Classification: TA1700 .I562 1998 Dewey Class No.: 621.36/6 21

In-plane semiconductor lasers: from ultraviolet to midinfrared: 10-13 February 1997, San Jose, California / Hong K. Choi, Peter S. Zory, chairs/editors; sponsored ... by SPIE--the International Society for Optical Engineering; cooperating organization, DARPA--Defense Advanced Research Projects Agency. Published/Created: Bellingham, Wash., USA: SPIE, c1997. Related Authors: Choi, Hong Kyun. Zory, Peter S., 1936- Society of Photo-optical Instrumentation Engineers. United States. Defense Advanced Research Projects Agency. Description: x, 422 p.: ill.; 28 cm. ISBN: 0819424129 Notes: Includes bibliographical references and index. Subjects: Semiconductor lasers--Congresses. High power lasers--

Congresses. Series: Proceedings of SPIE--the International Society for Optical Engineering; v. 3001. Variant Series: SPIE proceedings series; v. 3001 LC Classification: TA1700 .I56 1997 Dewey Class No.: 621.36/6 21

In-situ patterning: selective area deposition and etching: symposium held November 29-December 1, 1989, Boston, Massachusetts, U.S.A. / editors, Anthony F. Bernhardt, Jerry G. Black, Robert Rosenberg. Published/Created: Pittsburgh, Pa.: Materials Research Society, c1990. Related Authors: Bernhardt, Anthony. Black, Jerry G. Rosenberg, R. Description: xi, 496 p.: ill.; 24 cm. ISBN: 1558990461 Notes: Includes bibliographical references and indexes. Subjects: Semiconductors--Etching--Congresses. Semiconductor doping--Congresses. Lasers--Industrial applications--Congresses. Plasma etching--Congresses. Series: Materials Research Society symposia proceedings; v. 158. Variant Series: Materials Research Society symposium proceedings; v. 158 LC Classification: TK7871.85 .I49 1990 Dewey Class No.: 621.381/52 20

Integrated optics devices: potential for commercialization: 12-14 February, 1997, San Jose, California / S. Iraj Najafi, Mario Nicolo Armenise, chairs/editors; sponsored and published by SPIE--The International Society for Optical Engineering; cooperating organization, DARPA--Defense Advanced Research Project Agency. Published/Created: Bellingham, Wash., USA: SPIE, c1997. Related Authors: Najafi, S. Iraj. Armenise, Mario N. Description: vii, 362 p.: ill.; 28 cm. ISBN: 0819424080 Notes: Includes bibliographic references and author index. Subjects: Integrated optics--Congresses. Lasers--Congresses. Nanotechnology--Congresses. Series: Proceedings of SPIE--the International Society for Optical Engineering; v. 2997. Variant Series: Proceedings / SPIE--the International Society for Optical Engineering; v. 2997 LC Classification: TA1660 .I5528 1997

Integrated optics: devices and applications / edited by Joseph T. Boyd. Published/Created: New York: IEEE Press, c1991. Related Authors: Boyd, J. T. Description: viii, 457 p.: ill.; 29 cm. ISBN: 0879422688 Notes: A collection of reprints of articles orginally published from 1974 to 1988. "IEEE order number: PC0259-2"--T.p. verso. Includes bibliographical references and indexes. Subjects: Integrated optics. Series: Progress in lasers and electro-optics LC Classification: TA1660 .I5527 1991 Dewey Class No.: 621.36/93 20

Integrated photonics research: July 19-21, 1999, Fess Parker's Doubletree Resort, Santa Barbara, California / partial support provided by Office of Naval Research; technically cosponsored by IEEE/Lasers and Electro-Optics Society; sponsored by Optical Society of America. Edition Information: Postconference ed. Published/Created: Washington, DC: Optical Society of America, 1999. Description: 382 p.; 28 cm. ISBN: 1557525862 (postconference ed.) 1557525846 (1999 Technical Digest Series) Series: 1999 technical digest series

Intense beams and applications: lasers, ions, and microwaves: 27-28 January 1994, Los Angeles, California / William E. McDermott, chair/editor; sponsored and published by SPIE--the International Society for Optical Engineering. Published/Created: Bellingham, Wash., USA: SPIE, c1994. Related Authors: McDermott, William E. Description: v, 230 p.: ill.; 28 cm. ISBN: 0819414123 Notes: Includes bibliographical references and author index. Subjects: High power lasers--Chemical lasers--Ion bombardment--Congresses. Microwaves--Congresses. Series: Proceedings of SPIE--the International Society for Optical Engineering; v. 2119. Variant Series: Proceedings / SPIE--the International Society for Optical Engineering; v. 2119 LC Classification: TA1673 .I5572 1994 Dewey Class No.: 621.36/6 20

Intense laser beams / Richard C. Wade, Peter B. Ulrich, chairs/editors; sponsored by SPIE--the International Society for Optical Engineering. Published/Created: Bellingham, Wash.: SPIE, 1992. Related Authors: Wade, Richard C. Ulrich, Peter B. Society of Photo-Optical Instrumentation Engineers. Description: x, 342 p.: ill.; 28 cm. ISBN: 0819407747 (pbk.) Notes: Includes bibliographical references and index. Subjects: High power lasers--Congresses. Laser beams--Congresses. Series: Proceedings of SPIE--the International Society for Optical Engineering; v. 1628. Variant Series: SPIE proceedings series; v. 1628 LC Classification: TA1673 .I5575 1992 Dewey Class No.: 621.36/6 20

Intense laser beams and applications: 20-22 January 1993, Los Angeles, California / William E. McDermott, chair/editor; sponsored and published by SPIE--the International Society for Optical Engineering. Published/Created: Bellingham, Wash., USA: SPIE, c1993. Related Authors: McDermott, William E. Society of Photo-Optical Instrumentation Engineers. Description: ix, 422 p.: ill.; 28 cm. ISBN: 0819410985 Notes: Includes bibliographical references and index. Subjects: High power lasers--Congresses. Laser beams--Congresses. Series: Proceedings of SPIE--the International Society for Optical Engineering; v. 1871. Variant Series: Proceedings / SPIE--the International Society for Optical Engineering; v. 1871 LC Classification: TA1673 .I5576 1993 Dewey Class No.: 621.36/6 20

Intense microwave and particle beams II: 21-24 January 1991, Los Angeles, California / Howard E. Brandt, chair/editor; sponsored and published by SPIE--the International Society for Optical Engineering. Published/Created: Bellingham, Wash., USA: SPIE, c1991. Related Authors: Brandt, Howard E. Society of Photo-optical Instrumentation Engineers. Description: xiv, 655 p.: ill.; 28 cm. ISBN: 0819404977 Notes: "Part of a three-conference program on Nonlinear Optics and Directed Energy Propagation, held at SPIE's Symposium on High-Power Lasers, a part of OE/LASE '91, 20-25 January 1991, in Los Angeles, California"--P. ix. Includes bibliographical references and index. Subjects: Microwave devices--Congresses. Particle beams--Congresses. Series: Proceedings of SPIE--the International Society for Optical Engineering; v. 1407. Variant Series: Proceedings / SPIE--the International Society for Optical Engineering; v. 1407 LC Classification: TK7876 .I53 1991 Dewey Class No.: 621.381/3 20

International Conference on Advanced Laser Dentistry (1994: Saint Petersburg, Russia) International Conference on Advanced Laser Dentistry: 20-23 June 1994, St. Petersburg, Russia / Grigori B. Altshuler, Richard J. Blankenau, Harvey A. Wigdor; organized by Laser Center, Institute of Fine Mechanics and Optics, St. Petersburg, Russia, LMS Laser Medical Systems GmbH, Austria; cosponsored by SPIE--the International Society for Optical Engineering, ISLD--the International Society for Lasers in Dentistry, SPIE Russia Chapter. Published/Created: Bellingham, Wash., USA: SPIE, c1995. Related Authors: Altshuler, Grigori B. Blankenau, Richard J. Wigdor, Harvey A. St. Petersburg Institute of Fine Mechanics and Optics. Laser Center. Laser Medical Systems. Society of Photo-optical Instrumentation Engineers. International Society for Lasers in Dentistry. Society of Photo-optical Instrumentation Engineers. Russian Chapter. Description: x, 300 p.: ill.; 28 cm. ISBN: 0819412317 (pbk.) Notes: Includes bibliographical references and index. Subjects: Lasers in dentistry--Congresses. Series: Proceedings of SPIE--the International Society for Optical Engineering; v. 1984. Variant Series: SPIE proceedings series; v. 1984 LC Classification: RK685.L37 I57 1995 Dewey Class No.: 617.6/0028 20

International Conference on Advanced Laser Technologies (8th: 1999: Potenza, Italy, and Lecce, Italy) ALT '99 International Conference on Advanced Laser

Technologies: 20-24 September 1999, Potenza-Lecce, Italy / Vladimir I. Pustovoy, Vitally I. Konov, editors; Alexander M. Prokhorov, chair; organized by General Physics Institute (Russia) ... [et al.]; sponsored by Russian Foundation for Basic Research ... [et al.]. Published/Created: Bellingham, Wash., USA: SPIE, c2000. Related Authors: Pustovoy, Vladimir. Konov, V. I. Prokhorov, A. M. (Aleksandr Mikhailovich), 1916- Institut obshchei fiziki (Rossiiskaia akademiia nauk) Rossiiskii fond fundamental′nykh issledovanii. Society of Photo-optical Instrumentation Engineers. Description: xi, 486 p.: ill.; 28 cm. ISBN: 0819437077 Notes: Includes bibliographical references and index. Subjects: Lasers--Industrial applications--Congresses. Series: Proceedings of SPIE--the International Society for Optical Engineering; v. 4070. Variant Series: Proceedings of SPIE; v. 4070 LC Classification: TA1673 .I55762 1999 Dewey Class No.:

International Congress on Applications of Lasers and Electro-optics (1991: San Jose, Calif.) ICALEO '91: laser materials processing / chairs, Edward A. Metzbower, Eckhard Beyer, Akira Matsunawa. Published/Created: Orlando, Fla.: LIA--Laser Institute of America; Bellingham, Wash: SPIE--the International Society for Optical Engineering, c1992. Related Authors: Metzbower, Edward A. Beyer, Edkhard. Matsunawa, Akira. Laser Institute of America. Socissety of Photo-optical Instrumentation Engineers. Description: 452 p.: ill.; 28 cm. Cancelled ISBN: 0912035457 Notes: "3-8 November 1991 ... San Jose, California"--Cover. Includes bibliographical references and index. Subjects: Lasers--Industrial applications--Congresses. Manufacturing processes--Congresses. Laser welding--Congresses. Series: Proceedings of SPIE--the International Society for Optical Engineering; v. 1722. Variant Series: Proceedings / SPIE; v. 1722 LC Classification: TA1632 .I558 1991 Dewey Class No.: 621.36/6 20

International Congress on Applications of Lasers and Electro-optics (1992: Orlando, Fla.) ICALEO '92, laser materials processing: 25-29 October 1992, Orlando, Florida / Dave Farson, William Steen, Isamu Miyamoto, chairs/editors; sponsored by Laser Institute of America. Published/Created: Orlando, FL: The Institute; [Bellingham, Wash.]: SPIE--the International Society for Optical Engineering, c1993. Related Authors: Farson, Dave. Steen, W. M. Miyamoto, Isamu. Laser Institute of America. Society of Photo-optical Instrumentation Engineers. Description: 738 p.: ill.; 28 cm. ISBN: 0912035498 Notes: Includes bibliographical references and index. Subjects: Lasers--Industrial applications--Congresses. Manufacturing processes--Congresses. Laser welding--Congresses. Series: Proceedings of SPIE--the International Society for Optical Engineering; v. 1990. Variant Series: Proceedings / SPIE--the International Society for Optical Engineering; v. 1990 LC Classification: TA1673 .I566 1992

International Congress on Applications of Lasers and Electro-optics (1993: Orlando, Fla.) ICALEO '93: laser materials processing: proceedings: 24-28 October 1993, Orlando, Florida / Paul Denney, Isamu Miyamoto, B.L. Mordike, chairs/editors; sponsored by Laser Institute of America. Published/Created: Orlando, FL: Laser Institute of America; [Bellingham, Wash.]: SPIE--the International Society for Optical Engineering, c1994. Related Authors: Denney, Paul. Miyamoto, Isamu. Mordike, Barry L. Description: x, 1019 p.: ill.; 28 cm. ISBN: 0912035501 (pbk.) Notes: Includes bibliographical references and author index. Subjects: Lasers--Industrial applications--Congresses. Laser beam cutting--Congresses. Laser welding--Congresses. Series: Proceedings of SPIE--the International Society for Optical Engineering; v. 2306. Variant Series: SPIE proceedings series; v. 2306 LC Classification: TA1673 .I566 1993 Dewey Class No.: 671.5/028 20

International Congress on Applications of Lasers and Electro-optics (7th: 1988: Santa Clara, Calif.) Laser materials processing: proceedings of the 7th International Congress on Applications of Lasers and Electrooptics, ICALEO '88, 30 October-4 November, 1988, Santa Clara, CA, USA / Gerald Bruck, editor. Published/Created: Berlin; New York: Springer-Verlag, c1989. Related Authors: Bruck, Gerald, 1950- Description: vii, 386 p.: ill.; 28 cm. ISBN: 0387515372 (U.S.: alk. paper) Notes: Includes bibliographical references. Subjects: Lasers--Industrial applications--Congresses. LC Classification: TA1673 .I566 1988 Dewey Class No.: 621.36/6 20

International Congress on Applications of Lasers and Electro-optics (7th: 1988: Santa Clara, Calif.) Optical sensing and measurement: proceedings of the 7th International Congress on Applications of Lasers and Electrooptics ICALEO '88, 30 October-4 November, 1988, Santa Clara, CA, USA / Aaron D. Gara (editor). Published/Created: Berlin; New York: Springer-Verlag, c1989. Related Authors: Gara, Aaron D., 1935- Description: vi, 147 p.: ill.; 28 cm. ISBN: 0387515933 (U.S.: alk. paper) Notes: Includes bibliographical references. Subjects: Lasers--Congresses. Optical measurements--Congresses. Remote sensing--Congresses. LC Classification: TA1673 .I566 1988a Dewey Class No.: 681/.2 20

International Congress on Applications of Lasers and Electro-optics (8th: 1989: Orlando, Fla.) ICALEO '89: optical methods in flow and particle diagnostics: proceedings / chair, Marshall B. Long; [sponsored by Laser Institute of America]. Published/Created: Orlando, Fla.: Laser Institute of America; Bellingham, Wash., USA: SPIE--the International Society for Optical Engineering, c1989. Related Authors: Long, Marshall B. Description: 190 p.: ill.; 28 cm. ISBN: 0912035390 Notes: "October 15-20, 1989, Orange County Convention Center, Orlando, Florida"--Cover. Includes bibliographical references and indexes. Subjects: Laser Doppler velocimeter--Particles--Measurement--Flow visualization--Congresses. Series: Proceedings of SPIE--the International Society for Optical Engineering; v. 1404. Variant Series: SPIE proceedings series; v. 1404 LC Classification: TA357 .I569 1989 Dewey Class No.: 681/.2 20

International Free Electron Laser Conference (18th: 1996: Rome, Italy) Free electron lasers 1996: proceedings of the Eighteenth International Free Electron Laser Conference, Rome, Italy, August 26-31, 1996 / editors G. Dattoli, A. Renieri. Published/Created: New York: Elsevier, c1997. Related Authors: Dattoli, G. Renieri, A. Description: xxv, 569 p.: ill.; 27 cm. ISBN: 0444828192 (alk. paper) Notes: Includes bibliographical references and index. Subjects: Free electron lasers--Congresses. LC Classification: TA1693 .I58 1996 Dewey Class No.: 621.36/6 21

International Free Electron Laser Conference (19th: 1997: Beijing, China) Free electron lasers 1997: proceedings of the Nineteenth International Free Electron Laser Conference and Fourth FEL Users' Workshop, Beijing, China, August 18-22, 1997 / editors, Jialin Xie, Xiangwan Du. Published/Created: Amsterdam; New York: Elsevier, 1998. Related Authors: Xie, Jialin. Du, Xiangwan. FEL Users' Workshop (4th: 1997: Beijing, China) Description: xxvi, 527, 147 p.: ill.; 27 cm. ISBN: 0444829784 (acid-free paper) Notes: Includes bibliographical references and index. Subjects: Free electron lasers--Congresses. LC Classification: TA1693 .I58 1997 Dewey Class No.: 621.36/6 21

International Free Electron Laser Conference (20th: 1998: : Williamsburg, Va.) Free electron lasers 1998: proceedings of the Twentieth International Free Electron Laser Conference, Williamsburg, Virginia, USA, August 16-21, 1998 / editors, G.R. Neil, S.V. Benson. Edition Information: 1st ed. Published/Created: Amsterdam, Netherlands; New York: Elsevier, 1999. Related Authors: Neil, G. R. (George R.) Benson, S. V. (Stephen V.) Description: 506 p.: ill. (some col.); 27 cm. ISBN:

0444502483 Subjects: Free electron lasers--Congresses. LC Classification: TA1693 .I58 1998 Dewey Class No.: 621.36/6 21

International Free Electron Laser Conference (21st: 1999: Deutsches Elektronen-Synchrotron DESY, Hamburg, Germany) Free electron lasers 1999: proceedings of the Twenty-first International Free Electron Laser Conference, DESY, Hamburg, Germany. August 23-26, 1999 / editors: J. Feldhaus, H. Weise. Published/Created: Amsterdam: North-Holland, 2000. Related Authors: Feldhaus, J. Weise, Hans-Peter, 1942- Description: xxvi, 486 p.: ill., ports.; 27 cm. ISBN: 0444504818 Notes: Includes bibliographical references and index. Subjects: Free electron lasers--Congresses. National Bib. No.: GBA0-47240

International Free Electron Laser Conference (23rd: 2001: Darmstadt, Germany) Free electron lasers 2001: proceedings of the twenty-third International Free Electron Laser Conference and the eighth FEL Users Workshop, Darmstadt, Germany, August 20-24, 2001 / editors, M. Brunken, H. Genz, A. Richter. Edition Information: 1st ed. Published/Created: Boston: Elsevier, 2002. Projected Pub. Date: 0206 Related Authors: Brunken, M. Genz, H. Richter, A. FEL Users' Workshop (8th: 2001: Darmstadt, Germany) Description: p. cm. ISBN: 0444510567 (alk. paper) Notes: Includes index. Subjects: Free electron lasers--Congresses. LC Classification: TA1693 .I58 2001 Dewey Class No.: 621.36/6 21

International Laser Science Conference (3rd: 1987: Atlantic City, N.J.) Advances in laser science-III: proceedings of the third International Laser Science Conference, Atlantic City, NJ, 1987 / editors, Andrew C. Tam, James L. Gole, William C. Stwalley. Published/Created: New York: American Institute of Physics, 1988. Related Authors: Tam, Andrew C. Gole, James L., 1945- Stwalley, William C., 1942- Description: 784 p.: ill.; 25 cm. ISBN: 0883183722 Notes: Held Nov. 1-4, 1987. Includes bibliographies and index. Subjects: Lasers--Congresses. Series: AIP conference proceedings; no. 172. AIP conference proceedings. Optical science and engineering series; 9. Variant Series: American Institute of Physics conference proceedings; no. 172. Optical science and engineering series; 9 LC Classification: TA1673 .I568 1987 Dewey Class No.: 621.36/6 19

International Laser Science Conference (4th: 1988: Atlanta, Ga.) Advances in laser science-IV: proceedings of the Fourth International Laser Science Conference, Atlanta, GA, 1988 / editors, James L. Gole ... [et al.]. Published/Created: New York: American Institute of Physics, c1989. Related Authors: Gole, James L., 1945- Description: xviii, 777 p.: ill.; 25 cm. ISBN: 0883183919 Notes: Conference held Oct. 2-7, 1988. "DOE CONF 8810399"--T.p. verso. Includes bibliographical references. Subjects: Lasers--Congresses. Series: AIP conference proceedings; no. 191. AIP conference proceedings. Optical science and engineering series; 10. Variant Series: AIP conference proceedings; no. 191. Optical science and engineering series; 10 LC Classification: TA1673 .I568 1988 Dewey Class No.: 621.36/6 20

International Photodynamic Association. Meeting (5th: 1994: Amelia Island, Florida) 5th international photodynamic association biennial meeting: 21-24 September 1994, Amelia Island, Florida / Denis. A. Cortese, chair/editor. Published/Created: Bellingham, Wash.: SPIE, c1995. Related Authors: Cortese, Denis A. Society of Photo-optical Instrumentation Engineers. Description: xvii, 612 p.: ill.; 28 cm. ISBN: 0819417165 Subjects: Cancer--Photochemotherapy--Photochemotherapy--Lasers in medicine--Congresses. Series: Proceedings of SPIE--the International Society for Optical Engineering; v. 2371. Variant Series: SPIE proceedings series; v. 2371 LC Classification: RC271.P43 I576 1994 Dewey Class No.: 616.99/40631 20

International Quantum Electronics Conference (17th: 1990: Anaheim, Calif.) Digest of technical papers / XVII International Conference on Quantum Electronics, 21-25 May 1990, Anaheim, California; cosponsored by American Physical Society, IEEE/Lasers and Electro-Optics Society, Optical Society of America, in cooperation with Quantum Electronics Division of the European Physical Society, International Union of Pure and Applied Physics, Japanese Quantum Electronics Joint Group. Edition Information: Conference ed. Published/Created: Washington, DC: Optical Society of America, c1990. Related Authors: American Physical Society. Lasers and Electro-optics Society (Institute of Electrical and Electronics Engineers) Optical Society of America. Description: xxii, 322 p.: ill.; 28 cm. ISBN: 1557521336 (Conference ed.) 155752145X (Post conference ed.) Notes: "IQEC '90"--Cover. "IEEE catalog number 90CH2851-4"--T.p. verso. Includes bibliographical references and index. Subjects: Quantum electronics--Congresses. Series: Technical digest series (Optical Society of America) (Conference ed.); 1990, v. 8. Variant Series: Technical digest series; 1990, v. 8 LC Classification: QC685 .I57 1990 Dewey Class No.: 537.5 20

International Quantum Electronics Conference (2000: Nice, France) 2000 International Quantum Electronics Conference: conference digest: Nice Acropolis, Nice, France, 10-15 September 2000. Published/Created: Piscataway, NJ: Institute of Electrical and Electronics Engineers, c2000. Related Authors: European Physical Society. Description: xii, 242 p.: ill.; 30 cm. ISBN: 0780363183 Notes: Includes bibliographical references and index. Subjects: Quantum electronics--Congresses. Nonlinear optics--Congresses. Lasers--Congresses. LC Classification: QC685 .I5645 2000 Dewey Class No.: 537.5 21

International Quantum Electronics Conference (21st: 1994: Anaheim, Calif.) IQEC '94: summaries of papers presented at the International Quantum Electronics Conference, May 8-13, 1994, Anaheim Convention Center, Anaheim, California / sponsored by Optical Society of America, IEEE/Lasers and Electro-Optics Society, American Physical Society, in cooperation with U.S. Joint Council on Quantum Electronics ... [et al.]. Edition Information: Conference ed. Published/Created: Washington, DC: Optical Society of America, c1994. Related Authors: Optical Society of America. Lasers and Electro-optics Society (Institute of Electrical and Electronics Engineers) American Physical Society. Description: xvi, 324 p.: ill.; 28 cm. ISBN: 1557523428 (pbk.) Notes: The twenty-first conference. Includes bibliographical references and index. Subjects: Quantum electronics--Congresses. Nonlinear optics--Congresses. Lasers--Congresses.

International Workshop on Cell and Biotissue Optics (1993: Alexander Suvorov) Cell and biotissue optics: applications in laser diagnostics and therapy: CBO '93 international workshop: 27 June-4 July 1993, Moscow--Nizhny Novgorod / Valery V. Tuchin, chair/editor; organized by Saratov State University ... [et al.]; co-sponsored by SPIE/Russia--the International Society for Optical Engineering/Russian Chapter ... [et al.]. Published/Created: Bellingham, Wash., USA: SPIE--the International Society for Optical Engineering, c1994. Related Authors: Tuchin, V. V. (Valerii Viktorovich) Saratovskii gosudarstvennyi universitet im. N.G. Chernyshevskogo. Society of Photo-optical Instrumentation Engineers. Russian Chapter. Related Tssitles: CBO '93 International Workshop. Description: x, 338 p.: ill.; 28 cm. ISBN: 0819413836 (pbk.) Notes: "Held 27 June-4 July 1993 on board the ship Alexander Suvorov while cruising on the Volga River."--P. ix. Includes bibliographical references and author index. Subjects: Lasers in medicine--Congresses. Lasers--Diagnostic use--Congresses. Lasers--Therapeutic use--Congresses. Series: Proceedings of SPIE--the International Society for Optical Engineering; v. 2100.

Variant Series: Proceedings / SPIE--the International Society for Optical Engineering; v. 2100 LC Classification: R857.L37 I58 1993 Dewey Class No.: 610/.28 20

International Workshop on Iodine Lasers and Applications (4th: 1995: Trest' Castle, Czech Republic) Fourth International Workshop on Iodine Lasers and Applications: 18-22 September, 1995, Trest' Castle, Czech Republic / Karel Rohlena, Jarmila Kodymová, Bozena Králiková, chairs/editors; organized by the Institute of Physics, Academy of Sciences of the Czech Republic; in cooperation with SPIE Czech Republic Chapter; published by SPIE--the International Society for Optical Engineering Published/Created: Bellingham, Wash., USA: SPIE, c1996. Related Authors: Rohlena, Karel. Kodymová, Jarmila. Králiková, Bozena. Description: x, 256 p.: ill.; 28 cm. ISBN: 0819421510 Notes: Includes bibliographic references and author index. Subjects: Iodine lasers--Congresses. Chemical lasers--Congresses. Series: Proceedings of SPIE--the International Society for Optical Engineering; v. 2767. Variant Series: Proceedings / SPIE--the International Society for Optical Engineering; v. 2767 LC Classification: TA1673 .I588 1995 Dewey Class No.: 621.36/6 21

International Workshop on Laser and Fiber-Optical Networks Modeling (2nd: 2000: Kharkiv, Ukraine) Proceedings of LFNM'2000 / 2-nd International Workshop on Laser and Fiber-Optical Networks Modeling; Kharkiv State University of Radio Electronics, Ukraine, May 23, 2000. Published/Created: Piscataway, NJ: IEEE, 2000. Related Authors: Kharkiv State University of Radio Electronics. Lasers and Electro-optics Society (Institute of Electrical and Electronics Engineers). Ukraine Chapter. Description: vii, 136 p.: ill.; 29 cm. ISBN: 0780363809 (softbound edition) Notes: "Laser and Electro-optical Society, Ukraine Chapter"--Cover. "IEEE catalog number 00EX419"--T.p. verso. Includes bibliographical references and author index. Subjects: Laser communication systems--Congresses. Lasers--Congresses. LC Classification: TK5103.6 .I58 2000 Dewey Class No.: 621.382/7 21

International Workshop on Nonlinear Dynamics and Structures in Biology and Medicine: Optical and Laser Technologies (1996: Saratov, Russia) International Workshop on Nonlinear Dynamics and Structures in Biology and Medicine: Optical and Laser Technologies, 8-14 July 1996, Saratov, Russia / Valery V. Tuchin, editor; organized by Saratov State University, Institute of Precision Mechanics and Control, Russian Academy of Sciences; cosponsored by SPIE Russia Chapter ... [et al.]; in cooperation with SPIE--The International Society for Optical Engineering ... [et al.]. Published/Created: Bellingham, WA: SPIE, 1997. Related Authors: Tuchin, V. V. (Valerii Viktorovich) Description: x, 200 p.: ill.; 28 cm. ISBN: 0819424684 (pbk.) Notes: Includes bibliographical references and index. Subjects: Tissues--Optical properties--Lasers in medicine--Light--Physiological effect--Light--Scattering--Congresses. Series: Proceedings of SPIE--the International Society of Optical Engineering; v. 3053. Variant Series: SPIE proceedings series; v. 3053 LC Classification: QH642 .I58 1996 Dewey Class No.: 610/.28 21

Intersubband transitions in quantum wells: physics and devices / edited by Sheng S. Li, Yan-Kuin Su. Published/Created: Boston: Kluwer Academic Publishers, c1998. Related Authors: Li, Sheng S., 1938- Su, Yan-Kuin. International Workshop on Intersubband Transitions in Quantum Wells: Physics and Applications (1997: Tainan-sh¯u, Taiwan) Description: vii, 214 p.: ill.; 27 cm. ISBN: 0792381645 (acid-free paper) Notes: Based on the International Workshop on Intersubband Transitions in Quantum Wells: Physics and Applications, which was held at National Cheng Kung University, in Tainan, Taiwan, December 15-18, 1997. Includes bibliographical references and index. Subjects: Quantum wells--Congresses.

Lasers--Congresses. Photoelectronic devices--Congresses. LC Classification: QC176.8.Q35 I58 1998 Dewey Class No.: 537.6/226 21

Intracavity laser spectroscopy / Eduard A. Sviridenkov, Leonid N. Sinitsa, editors; sponsored by SPIE Russia Chapter. Published/Created: Bellingham, Wash., USA: SPIE, c1998. Related Authors: Sviridenkov, E. A. (Eduard Alekseevich) Sinitsa, L. N. (Leonid Nikiforovich) Society of Photo-optical Instrumentation Engineers. Society of Photo-optical Instrumentation Engineers. Russian Chapter. Description: vii, 270 p.: ill.; 28 cm. ISBN: 0819427896 Notes: Includes bibliographical references and index. Subjects: Laser spectroscopy--Congresses. Dye lasers--Congresses. Absorption spectra--Congresses. Gases--Analysis--Congresses. Series: Proceedings of SPIE--the International Society for Optical Engineering; v. 3342. Variant Series: SPIE proceedings series; v. 3342 LC Classification: QC454.L3 I592 1998 Dewey Class No.: 621.36/6 21

Introduction to nitride semiconductor blue lasers and light emitting diodes / edited by Shuji Nakamura and Shigefusa F. Chichibu. Published/Created: London; New York: Taylor & Francis, 2000. Related Authors: Nakamura, Shuji, 1954- Chichibu, Shigefusa F., 1963- Description: 372 p.: ill.; 25 cm. ISBN: 0748408363 (alk. paper) Notes: Includes bibliographical references and index. Subjects: Semiconductor lasers. Gallium nitride. Diodes, Semiconductor. Light emitting diodes. Blue light. LC Classification: TA1700 .I58 2000 Dewey Class No.: 621.36/6 21

In-vitro diagnostic instrumentation: 26-27 January 2000, San Jose, California / Gerald E. Cohn, chair/editor; sponsored by SPIE--the International Society for Optical Engineering [and] IBOS--the International Biomedical Optics Society. Published/Created: Bellingham, Wash., USA: SPIE, c2000. Related Authors: Cohn, Gerald E. International Biomedical Optics Society. Society of Photo-optical Instrumentation Engineers. Description: ix, 228 p.: ill.; 28 cm. ISBN: 0819435295 Notes: Errata p. inserted. Includes bibliographical references and index. Subjects: Diagnostic imaging--Congresses. Diagnosis, Noninvasive--Congresses. Lasers in medicine--Congresses. Cytodiagnosis--Congresses. Biosensors--Congresses. Series: Progress in biomedical optics and imaging, 1605-7422; vol. 1, no. 7 Proceedings of SPIE--the International Society for Optical Engineering; v. 3913. Variant Series: Proceedings of SPIE; v. 3913 LC Classification: RC78.7.D53 I5 2000 Dewey Class No.: 616.07/54 21

Ivanov, I. G. (Igor′ Grigor′evich) Metal vapour ion lasers: kinetic processes and gas discharges / I.G. Ivanov, E.L. Latush, M.F. Sem; edited by C.E. Little; translated by D.N. Astadjov and C.E. Little. Published/Created: Chichester; New York: Wiley, c1996. Related Authors: Latush, E. L. (Evgenii Leonidovich) Sem, M. F. (Miroslav Frantsevich) Little, Chris E. Description: xi, 285 p.: ill.; 24 cm. ISBN: 0471955639 (cloth: alk. paper) Notes: Includes bibliographical references and index. Subjects: Metal vapor lasers. LC Classification: TA1695 .I8813 1996 Dewey Class No.: 621.36/63 20

Jain, Kanti, 1948- Excimer laser lithography / Kanti Jain. Published/Created: Bellingham, Wash., USA: SPIE Optical Engineering Press, c1990. Description: x, 212 p.: ill.; 26 cm. ISBN: 0819402710: 0819402729 (hard): Notes: Includes bibliographical references (p. 193-207). Subjects: Excimer lasers--Industrial applications. Microlithography. LC Classification: TA1695 .J35 1990 Dewey Class No.: 621.381/531 20

Johnson, Charles S. (Charles Sidney), 1936- Laser light scattering / Charles S. Johnson, Jr., Don A. Gabriel. Published/Created: New York: Dover, 1994. Related Authors: Gabriel, Don A. Description: 96 p.: ill.; 24 cm. ISBN: 0486683281: Notes: An unabridged, corrected republication of the work first published as chapter 5 of the book Spectroscopy in biochemistry (volume II), edited by J. Ellis Bell, CRC Press, Boca Raton, Florida, 1981, with a new preface. Includes bibliographical references (p. 93-96). Subjects: Laser spectroscopy. Laser beams--Scattering. Lasers in biochemistry. Series: Dover classics of science and mathematics LC Classification: QP519.9.L37 J64 1994 Dewey Class No.: 674.19/285 20

Joint International Symposium on Optical memory and Optical Data Storage (1993: Maui, Hawaii) Conference digest / Joint International Symposium on Optical Memory and Optical Data Storage 1993, July 5-9, 1993, Hyatt Regency Maui, Maui, Hawaii; sponsored by IEEE Lasers and Electro-Optics Society (IEEE/LEOS) ... [et al.]; in cooperation with the Institute of Electronics, Information and Communication Engineers (IEICE), the Magnetics Society of Japan (MSJ), Optoelectronic Industry and Technology Development Association (OITDA) Published/Created: [New York]: Institute of Electrical and Electronics Engineers, c1993. Related Authors: Lasers and Electro-optics Society (Institute of Electrical and Electronics Engineers) Description: x, 178 p.: ill.; 27 cm. ISBN: 0780312864 0780312872 Notes: "IEEE catalog number: 93TH0548-8"--T.p. verso. Includes bibliographical references and index. Subjects: Optical storage devices--Congresses. Magnetooptical devices--Congresses. Data disk drives--Congresses. CD-ROMs--Congresses. LC Classification: TK7895.M4 J65 1993 Dewey Class No.: 621.39/7 20

Journal of biomedical optics. Published/Created: Bellingham, WA: Published by SPIE--the International Society for Optical Engineering in cooperation with International Biomedical Optics Society, c1996-Description: v.: ill.; 29 cm. Vol. 1, no. 1 (Jan. 1996)- Current Frequency: Quarterly ISSN: 1083-3668 Cancel/Invalid LCCN: sn 95007415 CODEN: JBOPFO Notes: Title from cover. SERBIB/SERLOC merged record Indexed entirely by: Index medicus 0019-3879 v5n1, Jan. 2000- Subjects: Imaging systems in medicine--Lasers in medicine--Optical fibers in medicine--Biomedical Engineering--Optics--Technology, Medical--Periodicals. LC Classification: R857.O6 J68 Dewey Class No.: 610 12

Journal of laser applications. Published/Created: [Toledo, Ohio]: Laser Institute of America, [1988-] Description: v.: ill.; 28 cm. Issues for Oct. 1988- called also: Fall 1988- . Vol. 1, no. 1 called also: Inaugural issue. Vol. 1, no. 1 (Oct. 1988)- Current Frequency: Quarterly ISSN: 1042-346X Cancel/Invalid LCCN: sn 89006583 CODEN: JLAPEN Notes: Title from cover. Official publication of: Laser Institute of America. SERBIB/SERLOC merged record Additional Form Avail.: Also available via World Wide Web; OCLC FirstSearch Electronic Collections Online; Subscription required for access to abstracts and full text. Subjects: Lasers--Lasers--Periodicals. LC Classification: TA1671 .J68 Dewey Class No.: 621.36/6/05 20

Journal of optics. B, Quantum and semiclassical optics: journal of the European Optical Society. Published/Created: Bristol, UK: Institute of Physics Pub., c1998- Related Authors: European Optical Society. Description: v.: ill.; 30 cm. Vol. 1, no. 1 (Feb. 1999)- Current Frequency: Bimonthly Continues: Journal of the European Optical Society. Part B, Quantum and semiclassical optics 1355-5111 (DLC) 95659087 (OCoLC)32218950 ISSN: 1464-4266 CODEN: JOBOFD Notes: Title from cover. Articles in English, French, or German. Indexed by: Chemical abstracts 0009-2258 Additional Form Avail.: Online version available via the World Wide Web to institutions with a print subscription and/or a site license; articles in Acrobat and Gzipped PostScript formats. Subjects: Optics--Quantum optics--Lasers--Nonlinear optics--Periodicals. LC Classification: QC446.15 .J68

Journal of Russian laser research. Published/Created: New York: Consultants Bureau, c1994- Related Authors: Fizicheskii institut imeni P.N. Lebedeva. Consultants Bureau. Description: v.: ill.; 28 cm. Vol. 15, no. 1 (Jan.-Feb. 1994)- Current Frequency: Bimonthly Continues: Journal of Soviet laser research 0270-2010 (DLC) 81640429 (OCoLC)6353310 ISSN: 1071-2836 Cancel/Invalid LCCN: sn 93005778 CODEN: JRLREO Notes: Title from cover. SERBIB/SERLOC merged record Translated from the Russian, principally from the publications of the Lebedev Physics Institute. Indexed entirely by: Computer & control abstracts 0036-8113 Electrical & electronics abstracts 0036-8105 Physics abstracts 0036-8091 Indx'd selectively by: Electronics and communications abstracts journal (Riverdale) 0361-3313 Energy research abstracts 0160-3604 Engineering index annual (1968) 0360-8557 Engineering index bioengineering abstracts 0736-6213 Engineering index energy abstracts 0093-8408 Engineering index monthly (1984) 0742-1974 International aerospace abstracts 0020-5842 ISMEC bulletin 0306-0039 Pollution abstracts with indexes 0032-3624 Safety science abstracts journal 0160-1342 Additional Form Avail.: Also available via World Wide Web; OCLC FirstSearch Electronic Collections Online; Subscription required for access to abstracts and full text. Subjects: Lasers--Russia (Federation)--Lasers--Periodicals. LC Classification: TA1501 .J68 Dewey Class No.: 621.36/6/0947

Journal of the European Optical Society. Part B, Quantum and semiclassical optics. Published/Created: Bristol, UK: Institute of Physics Pub., c1995-c1998. Related Authors: European Optical Society. Description: 4 v.: ill.; 25 cm. Vol. 7, no. 1 (Feb. 1995)-v. 10, no. 6 (Dec. 1998). Current Frequency: Bimonthly Continues: Journal of the European Optical Society. Part B, Quantum optics (DLC) 95659088 (OCoLC)25991501 Continued by: Journal of optics. B, Quantum and semiclassical optics 1464-4266 (DLC)sn 99023030 (OCoLC)41013469 ISSN: 1355-5111 CODEN: QUSOEC Notes: Title from cover. SERBIB/SERLOC merged record Indx'd selectively by: Chemical abstracts 0009-2258 Additional Form Avail.: Online version available via the World Wide Web to institutions with a print subscription and/or a site license; articles in Acrobat and Gzipped PostScript formats. Subjects: Optics--Quantum optics--Lasers--Nonlinear optics--Periodicals. LC Classification: QC446.15 .Q34 Dewey Class No.: 535 20

Large lenses and prisms: 27-30 March 2001, London, UK / Richard G. Bingham, David D. Walker, editors; sponsored by University College London (UK) ... [et al.]. Published/Created: Bellingham, Wash., USA: SPIE, c2002. Related Authors: Bingham, Richard G. Walker, David D. Society of Photo-optical Instrumentation Engineers. University College, London. Description: vii, 204 p.: ill.; 28 cm. ISBN: 0819441147 Notes: Includes bibliographical references and index. Subjects: Lenses--Telescopes--Design and construction--Congresses. Prisms--Lasers--Congresses. Series: Proceedings of SPIE--the International Society for Optical Engineering; v. 4411. Variant Series: SPIE proceedings series, 0277-786X; v. 4411 LC Classification: QC385.2.D47 L37 2002 Dewey Class No.: 681/.42 21

Laser ablation for materials synthesis: symposium held April 19-20, 1990, San Francisco, California, U.S.A. / editors, David C. Paine, John C. Bravman. Published/Created: Pittsburgh, Pa.: Materials Research Society, c1990. Related Authors: Paine, David C. Bravman, J. C. (John C.) Description: 239 p.: ill.; 24 cm. ISBN: 1558990801 Notes: Includes bibliographical references and indexes. Subjects: Lasers--Industrial applications--Materials--Manufacturing processes--Laser ablation--Congresses. Series: Materials Research Society symposia proceedings; v. 191. Variant Series: Materials Research Society symposium proceedings, 0272-9172; v. 191 LC Classification: TA1673 .L334 1990 Dewey Class No.: 621.36/6 20

Laser ablation in materials processing: fundamentals and applications: symposium held December 1-4, 1992, Boston, Massachusetts, U.S.A. / editors, B. Braren, J.J. Dubowski, D. P. Norton. Published/Created: Pittsburgh, Pa.: Materials Research Society, c1993. Related Authors: Braren, Bodil. Dubowski, J. J. Norton, D. P. (David P.) Description: xv, 612 p.: ill.; 24 cm. ISBN: 1558991808 Notes: Includes bibliographical references and indexes. Subjects: Laser ablation--Congresses. Lasers--Industrial applications--Congresses. Materials--Congresses. Manufacturing processes--Congresses. Series: Materials Research Society symposia proceedings; v. 285. Variant Series: Materials Research Society symposium proceedings; v. 285 LC Classification: TA1673 .L3343 1993 Dewey Class No.: 621.36/6 20

Laser ablation of electronic materials: basic mechanisms and applications / edited by E. Fogarassy, S. Lazare. Published/Created: Amsterdam; New York: North-Holland, 1992. Related Authors: Fogarassy, E. (Eric) Lazare, S. (Sylvain) Description: xi, 394 p.: ill.; 25 cm. ISBN: 0444892346 (alk. paper) Notes: Proceedings of the 1991 Summer School on Laser Ablation of Electronic Materials, held in Gironde, France, Sept. 16-19, 1991. Includes bibliographical references and index. Subjects: Electronics--Materials--Effect of radiation on--Lasers--Industrial applications--Laser ablation--Congresses. Series: European Materials Research Society monographs; v. 4 LC Classification: TK7871 .L37 1992 Dewey Class No.: 621.381 20

Laser ablation: mechanisms and applications: proceedings of a workshop, held in Oak Ridge, Tennessee, USA, 8-10 April, 1991 / J.C. Miller, R.F. Haglund, Jr. (eds.). Published/Created: Berlin; New York: Springer-Verlag, c1991. Related Authors: Miller, J. C. (John C.), 1949- Haglund, R. F. (Richard F.), 1942- Description: ix, 362 p.: ill.; 25 cm. ISBN: 0387977317 (New York: alk. paper): 3540977317 (Berlin: alk. paper) Notes: Includes bibliographical references. Subjects: Lasers--Industrial applications--Lasers in medicine--Laser ablation--Congresses. Series: Lecture notes in physics; 389 LC Classification: TA1673 .L335 1991

Laser and electron beam material processing: handbook / N. Rykalin ... [et al.]. Published/Created: Moscow: Mir Publishers, c1988. Related Authors: Rykalin, N. N. Description: 591 p.; 23 cm. ISBN: 5030000232 Notes: Translation of: Lazernaia i elektronno-luchevaia obrabotka materialov. Includes bibliographical references and index. Subjects: Lasers--Electron beams--Industrial applications. Manufacturing processes. LC Classification: TA1677 .L38813 1988 Dewey Class No.: 621.36/6 20

Laser and noncoherent light ocular effects: epidemiology, prevention, and treatment: 22 January 2001, San Jose, USA / Bruce E. Stuck, Michael Belkin, chairs/editors; sponsored by U.S. Air Force Office of Scientific Research [and] SPIE--the International Society for Optical Engineering. Published/Created: Bellingham, Wash., USA: SPIE, c2001. Related Authors: Stuck, Bruce E. Belkin, Michael. Description: v, 186 p.: ill.; 28 cm. ISBN: 081943924X Notes: Earlier conference has Laser and noncoherent ocular effects. Includes bibliographical references and index. Subjects: Eye--Wounds and injuries--Eye--Effect of radiation on--Lasers in ophthalmology--Lasers--Physiological effect--Eye--Radiation injuries--Congresses. Series: Progress in biomedical optics and imaging, 1605-7422; vol. 2, no. 3 Proceedings of SPIE--the International Society for Optical Engineering; v. 4246. Variant Series: Proceedings of SPIE; v. 4246 LC Classification: RE837 .L37 2001 Dewey Class No.: 617.7/13 21

Laser and particle-beam chemical processing for microelectronics: symposium held December 1-3, 1987, Boston, Massachusetts, USA / editors, Daniel J. Ehrlich, Gregg S. Higashi, Modest M. Oprysko. Published/Created: Pittsburgh,

Pa.: Materials Research Society, c1988. Related Authors: Ehrlich, Daniel J. Higashi, Gregg S. Oprysko, Modest Michael, 1957- Description: xv, 509 p.: ill.; 24 cm. ISBN: 0931837693 Notes: Includes bibliographies and indexes. Subjects: Integrated circuits--Design and construction--Lasers--Industrial applications--Lasers in chemistry--Congresses. Series: Materials Research Society symposia proceedings; v. 101. Variant Series: Materials Research Society symposium proceedings, 0272-9172; v. 101 LC Classification: TK7874 .L297 1988 Dewey Class No.: 621.381/7 19

Laser angioplasty / edited by Timothy A. Sanborn. Published/Created: New York: Liss, 1989. Related Authors: Sanborn, Timothy A. Description: xi, 121 p.: ill.; 29 cm. ISBN: 0845142801 Notes: Includes bibliographical references and index. Subjects: Laser angioplasty. Angioplasty, Transluminal. Coronary Disease--therapy. Lasers--therapeutic use. LC Classification: RD598.5 .S26 1989 Dewey Class No.: 617/.413059 19

Laser applications engineering (LAE-96): 3-5 July, 1996, St. Petersburg-Pushkin, Russia / Vadim P. Veiko, editor; organized by S.I. Vavilov State Optical Institute, St. Petersburg ... [et al.]; published by SPIE--the International Society for Optical Engineering. Published/Created: Bellingham, Wash.: SPIE, c1997. Related Authors: Veiko, V. P. (Vadim Pavlovich) Description: ix, 158 p.: ill.; 28 cm. ISBN: 0819425060 Notes: "This volume contains selected papers from the 8th International Conference on Laser Applications Engineering (LAE-96)."--Introduction. Includes bibliographic references and index. Subjects: Lasers--Industrial applications--Industrial equipment--Congresses. Series: Proceedings of SPIE--the International Society for Optical Engineering; v. 3091. Variant Series: Proceedings / SPIE--the International Society for Optical Engineering; v. 3091 LC Classification: TA1673 .L345 1997 Dewey Class No.: 621.36/6 21

Laser applications for mechanical industry / edited by S. Martellucci, A.N. Chester, A.M. Scheggi. Published/Created: Dordrecht; Boston: Kluwer Academic, c1993. Related Authors: Martellucci, S. Chester, A. N. Verga Scheggi, A. M. (Anna Maria) North Atlantic Treaty Organization. Scientific Affairs Division. NATO Advanced Study Institute on Laser Applications for Mechanical Industry (1992: Erice, Italy) Description: x, 436 p.: ill.; 25 cm. ISBN: 0792323033 (alk. paper) Notes: "Published in cooperation with NATO Scientific Affairs Division." "Proceedings of the NATO Advanced Study Institute on Laser Applications for Mechanical Industry Erice, Trapani, Italy 4-16 April, 1992"--T.p. verso. Includes bibliographical references and index. Subjects: Manufacturing processes--Equipment and supplies Congresses. Lasers--Industrial applications--Congresses. Series: NATO ASI series. Series E, Applied sciences; no. 238. Variant Series: NATO ASI series. Series E, Applied sciences; vol. 238 LC Classification: TS183 .L37 1993 Dewey Class No.: 670.42 20

Laser applications in combustion and combustion diagnostics II: 25-26 January 1994, Los Angeles, California / Randy J. Locke, chair/editor; sponsored and published by SPIE--the International Society for Optical Engineering. Published/Created: Bellingham, Wash., USA: SPIE, c1994. Related Authors: Locke, Randy J. Society of Photo-optical Instrumentation Engineers. Description: vii, 250 p.: ill.; 28 cm. ISBN: 0819414158 (pbk.) Notes: Includes bibliographical references and index. Subjects: Combustion engineering--Congresses. Lasers--Industrial applications--Congresses. Series: Proceedings of SPIE--the International Society for Optical Engineering; v. 2122. Variant Series: SPIE proceedings series; vol. 2122 LC Classification: TJ254.5 .L34 1994 Dewey Class No.: 621.402/3 20

Laser applications in combustion and combustion diagnostics: 19-20 January

1993, Los Angeles, California / Larry C. Liou, chair/editor; sponsored and published by SPIE--the International Society for Optical Engineering. Published/Created: Bellingham, Wash., USA: SPIE, c1993. Related Authors: Liou, Larry C. Society of Photo-optical Instrumentation Engineers. Description: ix, 323 p.: ill.; 28 cm. ISBN: 0819410896 Notes: Includes bibliographical references and index. Subjects: Combustion engineering--Congresses. Lasers--Industrial applications--Congresses. Series: Proceedings of SPIE--the International Society for Optical Engineering; v. 1862. Variant Series: Proceedings / SPIE--the International Society for Optical Engineering; v. 1862 LC Classification: TJ254.5 .L35 1993 Dewey Class No.: 621.402/3 20

Laser applications in life sciences / Sergei A. Akhmanov, Marina Yu. Poroshina, Chairs/Editors, 27-31 August 1990 Moscow, USSR; organized by International Laser Center of Moscow University USSR Academy of Sciences Scientific Research Center for Technological Lasers; sponsored by International Laser Center, Moscow State University and CMEA ...[et al.]. Published/Created: Bellingham, Wash.: SPIE, c1991. Related Authors: Akhmanov, S.A. (Sergei Aleksandrovich) Poroshina, Marina Yu. Description: 2 v.: ill.; 28 cm. ISBN: 0819404861 (pbk.) Contents: v. 1. Laser diagnostics of biological molecules and living cells, linear and nonlinear methods -- v. 2. Lasers in biophysics and biomedicine. Notes: Includes bibliographical references and index. Subjects: Laser spectroscopy--Congresses. Lasers in biology--Congresses. Lasers in medicine--Congresses. Series: Proceedings of SPIE--the International Society for Optical Engineering; v. 1403. Variant Series: Proceedings SPIE -the International Society for Optical Engineering; v. 1403 LC Classification: QP519.9.L37 L34 1991 Dewey Class No.: 574/.028 20

Laser applications in meteorology and earth and atmospheric remote sensing: 16-18 January, 1989, Los Angeles, California / Martin M. Sokoloski, chair/editor; sponsored by SPIE--the International Society for Optical Engineering; cooperating organizations, Applied Optics Laboratory/New Mexico State University ... [et al.]. Published/Created: Bellingham, Wash., USA: SPIE, c1989. Related Authors: Sokoloski, Martin M. Society of Photo-optical Instrumentation Engineers. Description: viii, 305 p.: ill.; 28 cm. ISBN: 0819400971 Notes: Includes bibliographical references and index. Subjects: Atmosphere--Laser observations--Congresses. Atmospheric physics--Remote sensing--Congresses. Remote sensing--Congresses. Lasers--Congresses. Series: Proceedings of SPIE--the International Society for Optical Engineering; v. 1062. Variant Series: SPIE proceedings series; v. 1062 LC Classification: QC976.L36 L36 1989 Dewey Class No.: 621.36/78 20

Laser applications in microelectronic and optoelectronic manufacturing II: 10-12 February, 1997, San Jose, California / Jan J. Dubowski, chair/editor; sponsored and published by SPIE--the International Society for Optical Engineering. Published/Created: Bellingham, Washington: SPIE, c1997. Related Authors: Dubowski, J. J. Society of Photo-optical Instrumentation Engineers. Description: ix, 294 p.: ill.; 28 cm. ISBN: 0819424021 Notes: Includes bibliographical references and author index. Subjects: Microelectronics--Congresses. Lasers--Industrial applications--Congresses. Manufacturing processes--Congresses. Optoelectronic devices--Design and construction Congresses. Series: Proceedings of SPIE--the International Society for Optical Engineering; v. 2991. Variant Series: Proceedings / SPIE--the International Society for Optical Engineering; v. 2991 LC Classification: TK7874 .L2975 1997 Dewey Class No.: 621.381 21

Laser applications in microelectronic and optoelectronic manufacturing III: 26-28 January 1998, San Jose, California / Jan J.

Dubowski, Peter E. Dyer, chairs/editors; sponsored ... by SPIE--the International Society for Optical Engineering. Published/Created: Bellingham, Wash., USA: SPIE, c1998. Related Authors: Dubowski, J. J. Dyer, Peter E. Society of Photo-optical Instrumentation Engineers. Description: ix, 344 p.: ill.; 28 cm. ISBN: 0819427136 Notes: Includes bibliographical references and index. Subjects: Microelectronics industry--Congresses. Lasers--Industrial applications--Congresses. Manufacturing processes--Congresses. Optoelectronics industry--Congresses. Series: Proceedings of SPIE--the International Society for Optical Engineering; v. 3274. Variant Series: SPIE proceedings series; v. 3274 LC Classification: TK7836 .L37 1998 Dewey Class No.: 621.381 21

Laser applications in microelectronic and optoelectronic manufacturing IV: 25-27 January 1999, San Jose, California / Jan J. Dubowski ... [et al.], chairs/editors; sponsored by AFSOR [i.e. AFOSR]--U.S. Air Force Office of Scientific Research [and] SPIE--the International Society for Optical Engineering. Published/Created: Bellingham, Wash., USA: SPIE, c1999. Related Authors: Dubowski, J. J. United States. Air Force. Office of Scientific Research. Society of Photo-optical Instrumentation Engineers. Description: xi, 534 p.: ill. (some col.); 28 cm. ISBN: 0819430889 Notes: Includes bibliographical references and index. Subjects: Microelectronics industry--Equipment and supplies Congresses. Lasers--Industrial applications--Congresses. Manufacturing processes--Congresses. Laser ablation--Congresses. Optoelectronic devices--Design and construction Congresses. Series: Proceedings of SPIE--the International Society for Optical Engineering; v. 3618. Variant Series: SPIE proceedings series; v. 3618 LC Classification: TK7836 .L38 1999 Dewey Class No.: 621.381 21

Laser applications in microelectronic and optoelectronic manufacturing V: 24-26 January, 2000, San Jose, USA / Henry Helvajian, ... [et al.], chairs/editors; sponsored by AFOSR--U.S. Air Force Office of Scientific Research [and] SPIE--the International Society for Optical Engineering. Published/Created: Bellingham, Washington: SPIE, c2000. Related Authors: Helvajian, Henry United States. Air Force. Office of Scientific Research. Society of Photo-optical Instrumentation Engineers. Description: xi, 514 p.: ill.; 28 cm. ISBN: 0819435503 Notes: Includes bibliographic references and author index. Subjects: Microelectronics industry--Equipment and supplies Congresses. Lasers--Industrial applications--Congresses. Manufacturing processes--Congresses. Laser ablation--Congresses. Optoelectronic devices--Design and construction Congresses. Series: Proceedings of SPIE--the International Society for Optical Engineering; v. 3933. Variant Series: Proceedings of SPIE; v. 3933 LC Classification: TK7836 .L383 2000 Dewey Class No.: 621.381 21

Laser applications in microelectronic and optoelectronic manufacturing VI: 22-24 January 2001, San Jose, USA / Malcolm C. Gower ... [et al.], chairs/editors; sponsored ... by SPIE--the International Society for Optical Engineering. Published/Created: Bellingham, Wash.: SPIE, c2001. Related Authors: Gower, M. (Malcolm), 1946- Society of Photo-optical Instrumentation Engineers. Description: x, 506 p.: ill.; 28 cm. ISBN: 0819439525 Notes: Includes bibliographical references and index. Subjects: Microelectronics industry--Congresses. Lasers--Industrial applications--Congresses. Manufacturing processes--Congresses. Optoelectronics industry--Congresses. Series: Proceedings of SPIE--the International Society for Optical Engineering; v. 4274. Variant Series: SPIE proceedings series; v. 4274 LC Classification: TK7836 .L385 2001 Dewey Class No.: 621.31 21

Laser applications in physical chemistry / edited by D.K. Evans. Published/Created: New York: M. Dekker, c1989. Related Authors: Evans, D. Keith. Description: x,

428 p.: ill.; 24 cm. ISBN: 0824780620 (alk. paper) Notes: Includes bibliographical references. Subjects: Lasers in chemistry. Laser spectroscopy. Series: Optical engineering (Marcel Dekker, Inc.); v. 20. Variant Series: Optical engineering; v. 20 LC Classification: QD715 .L365 1989 Dewey Class No.: 542 20

Laser applications to chemical and environmental analysis: February 11-13, 2000, Eldorado Hotel, Santa Fe, New Mexico / sponsored by Optical Society of America. Edition Information: Postconference ed. Published/Created: Washington, DC: Optical Society of America, c2000. Description: xiii, 213 p.: ill.; 28 cm. ISBN: 1557526265 Notes: Includes bibliographical references and index. Subjects: Lasers in chemistry--Congresses. Chemistry, Analytic--Methodology--Congresses. Environmental chemistry--Methodology--Congresses. Series: OSA trends in optics and photonics; 36. Technical digest series (Optical Society of America); 2000. Variant Series: Trends in optics and photonics series, 1094-5695; v. 36 Technical digest; 2000. LC Classification: QD63.L3 L355 2000 Dewey Class No.: 543/.085 21

Laser assisted processing: ECO1, 19-20 September 1988, Hamburg, Federal Republic of Germany: proceedings / Lucien D. Laude, Gerhard Rauscher, chairs/editors; sponsored by EPS--European Physical Society, Europtica--the European Federation for Applied Optics, SPIE--the International Society for Optical Engineering. Published/Created: Bellingham, Wash.: SPIE, c1989. Related Authors: Laude, Lucien D. Rauscher, Gerhard. European Physical Society. European Federation for Applied Optics. Society of Photo-optical Instrumentation Engineers. Description: viii, 160 p.: ill.; 28 cm. ISBN: 0819400572 Notes: Includes bibliographical references. Subjects: Lasers--Industrial applications--Congresses. Manufacturing processes--Congresses. Series: Proceedings of SPIE--the international society for optical engineering; v. 1022. Variant Series: SPIE proceedings series; v. 1022 LC Classification: TA1677 .L362 1989 Dewey Class No.: 621.36/6 20

Laser cathode ray tubes / [edited by] Yu. M. Popov. Published/Created: Commack, N.Y.: Nova Science Publishers, 1995. Projected Pub. Date: 9501 Related Authors: Popov, IU. M. Description: p. cm. ISBN: 1560722169 Notes: Includes bibliographical references and index. Subjects: Cathode ray tubes. Lasers. Series: Trudy Fizicheskogo instituta. English; v. 221. Variant Series: Proceedings of the Lebedev Physics Institute; v. 221 LC Classification: QC1 .A4114 vol. 221 Dewey Class No.: 530 s 621.3815/42 20

Laser chemical processing for microelectronics / edited by K.G. Ibbs, R.M. Osgood. Published/Created: Cambridge [England]; New York: Cambridge University Press, 1989. Related Authors: Ibbs, K. G. Osgood, R. M. Description: 172 p.: ill.; 24 cm. ISBN: 0521322545 Notes: Includes bibliographies and index. Subjects: Integrated circuits--Design and construction. Lasers--Industrial applications. Series: Cambridge studies in modern optics; 7 LC Classification: TK7874 .L298 1989 Dewey Class No.: 621.381/73 19

Laser chemistry, biophysics, and biomedicine: ICONO '95: 27 June-1 July 1995, St. Petersburg, Russia / Victor N. Zadkov, editor; organized by Scientific Council on Coherent and Nonlinear Optics of the Russian Academy of Sciences ... [et al.]. Published/Created: Bellingham, Wash.: SPIE--the International Society for Optical Engineering, c1996. Related Authors: Zadkov, V. N. (Viktor Nikolaevich) Scientific Council for Coherent and Nonlinear Optics (Rossiiskaia akademiia nauk) ICONO '95 (1995: Saint Petersburg, Russia) Description: viii, 224 p.: ill.; 28 cm. ISBN: 0819421901 Notes: Includes bibliographic references and author index. Subjects: Lasers in chemistry--Congresses. Lasers in biophysics--Congresses. Lasers in medicine--

Congresses. Series: Proceedings of SPIE--the International Society for Optical Engineering; v. 2802. Variant Series: Proceedings / SPIE--the International Society for Optical Engineering; v. 2802 LC Classification: QD63.L3 L36 1996

Laser cleaning in conservation: an introduction / edited by Martin Cooper. Published/Created: Woburn, MA: Butterworth-Heinemann, c1998. Related Authors: Cooper, Martin, Ph. D. Description: x, 98 p.: ill. (some col.); 26 cm. ISBN: 0750631171 Notes: Includes bibliographical references and index. Subjects: X-ray lasers. Art--Conservation and restoration. LC Classification: N8560 .L38 1998 Dewey Class No.: 702/.8/8 21

Laser control and manipulation of molecules / A.D. Bandrauk, editor, Y. Fujimura, editor, R.J. Gordon, editor. Published/Created: Washington, D.C.: American Chemical Society, 2002. Projected Pub. Date: 0207 Related Authors: Bandrauk, André D. Fujimura, Y. (Yuichi) Gordon, R. J. (Robert J.), 1944- Pacifichem 2000 (2000: Honolulu, Hawaii) Description: p. cm. ISBN: 0841237867 (alk. paper) Notes: Includes bibliographical references and index. Subjects: Lasers in chemistry--Congresses. Laser manipulation (Nuclear physics)--Congresses. Molecular dynamics--Congresses. Series: ACS symposium series; 821 LC Classification: QD461 .L38 2002 Dewey Class No.: 542 21

Laser dimensional metrology: recent advances for industrial application: proceedings: 5-7 October 1993, Brighton, United Kingdom / M.J. Downs, chair/editor; organized by Sira Communications, Ltd.; sponsored by Advanced Optics Group of the Institute of Physics ... [et al.]. Published/Created: Bellingham, Wash., USA: SPIE--the International Society for Optical Engineering, c1994. Related Authors: Downs, M. J. Sira Communications Ltd. Institute of Physics (Great Britain). Advanced Optics Group. International Conference on Laser Dimensional Metrology, Photonex '93 (1993: Brighton, England) Description: ix, 216 p.: ill.; 28 cm. ISBN: 0819413593 (pbk.) Notes: "International Conference on Laser Dimensional Metrology, Photonex '93, SSSwas held at the Brighton Centre in October 1993"--P. ix. Includes bibliographical references and index. Subjects: Mensuration--Congresses. Lasers--Industrial applications--Congresses. Optical instruments--Congresses. Series: Proceedings of SPIE--the International Society for Optical Engineering; v. 2088. Variant Series: SPIE proceedings series; v. 2088 LC Classification: T50 .L37 1994 Dewey Class No.: 681/.2 20

Laser diode and LED applications III: 10-11 February, 1997, San Jose, California / Kurt J. Linden, chair/editor; sponsored and published by SPIE--the International Society for Optical Engineering; cooperating organization ARPA--Advanced Research Projects Agency. Published/Created: Bellingham, Washington,: SPIE, c1997. Related Authors: Linden, Kurt J. Society of Photo-optical Instrumentation Engineers. United States. Advanced Research Projects Agency. Description: ix, 216 p.: ill.; 28 cm. ISBN: 0819424110 Notes: Previous volume published under Laser diodes and applications II. Includes bibliographic references and author index. Subjects: Semiconductor lasers--Congresses. Diodes, Semiconductor--Congresses. Light emitting diodes--Congresses. Optical fiber detectors--Congresses. Series: Proceedings of SPIE--the International Society for Optical Engineering; v. 3000. Variant Series: Proceedings / SPIE--the International Society for Optical Engineering; v. 3000 LC Classification: TA1700 .L387 1997

Laser diode technology and applications. Published/Created: Bellingham, Wash.: SPIE--the International Society for Optical Engineering, c1989- Related Authors: Society of Photo-optical Instrumentation Engineers. Description: v.: ill.; 28 cm. [1] (18-20 Jan. 1989)- Current Frequency: Annual Cancel/Invalid LCCN: sn

93042094 Notes: SERBIB/SERLOC merged record Subjects: Semiconductor lasers--Congresses. Series: Proceedings of SPIE--the International Society for Optical Engineering. Variant Series: Proceedings / SPIE--the International Society for Optical Engineering LC Classification: TA1700 .L364 Dewey Class No.: 621.36/61 20

Laser diodes and applications II / Kurt J. Linden, Prasad R. Akkapeddi, editors; sponsored and published by SPIE--the International Society for Optical Engineering; cooperating organization, ARPA--Advanced Research Projects Agency. Published/Created: Bellingham, WA: SPIE, 1996. Related Authors: Linden, Kurt J. Akkapeddi, Prasad R. Society of Photo-optical Instrumentation Engineers. United States. Advanced Research Projects Agency. Description: x, 306 p.: ill.; 28 cm. ISBN: 0819420565 (pbk.) Notes: Includes bibliographical references and index. Subjects: Semiconductor lasers--Congresses. Diodes, Semiconductor--Congresses. High power lasers--Congresses. Far infrared lasers--Congresses. Series: Proceedings of SPIE--the International Society for Optical Engineering; v. 2682. Variant Series: Proceedings / SPIE--the International Society for Optical Engineering; 2682 LC Classification: TA1700 .L378 1996 Dewey Class No.: 621.36/6 21

Laser diodes and applications III: 15-16 July 1998, Québec, Canada / Pierre Galarneau, chair/editor; sponsored by SPIE--the International Society for Optical Engineering; co-sponsored by Government of Canada ... [et al.]; cooperating organizations, Canadian Association of Physicists [and] Defence Research Establishment of Valcartier (Canada). Published/Created: Bellingham, Wash., USA: SPIE, c1998. Related Authors: Galarneau, Pierre, 1958- Society of Photo-optical Instrumentation Engineers. Canadian Association of Physicists. Defence Research Establishment Valcartier (Québec) Description: vii, 200 p.: ill.; 28 cm. ISBN: 0819428698 Notes: Includes bibliographical references and index. Subjects: Semiconductor lasers--Congresses. Diodes, Semiconductor--Congresses. Semiconductor lasers--Industrial applications--Congresses. Series: Proceedings of SPIE--the International Society for Optical Engineering; v. 3415. Variant Series: SPIE proceedings series, 0277-786X; v. 3415 LC Classification: TA1700 .L362 1998 Dewey Class No.: 621.36/6 21

Laser diodes and applications: 8-10 February 1995, San Jose, California / Kurt J. Linden, Prasad R. Akkapeddi, chairs/editors; sponsored and published by SPIE--the International Society for Optical Engineering. Published/Created: Bellingham, Wash., USA: SPIE, c1995. Related Authors: Linden, Kurt J. Akkapeddi, Prasad R. Society of Photo-optical Instrumentation Engineers. Description: ix, 314 p.: ill.; 28 cm. ISBN: 0819417297 (pbk.) Notes: Includes bibliographical references and author index. Subjects: Semiconductor lasers--Congresses. Diodes, Semiconductor--Congresses. High power lasers--Congresses. Series: Proceedings of SPIE--the International Society for Optical Engineering; v. 2382. Variant Series: Proceedings / SPIE--the International Society for Optical Engineering; v. 2382 LC Classification: TA1700 .L385 1995 Dewey Class No.: 621.36/6 20

Laser diodes and LEDs in industrial, measurement, imaging, and sensors applications II: Testing, packaging, and reliability of semiconductor lasers V: 26-26[sic], January, 2000, San Jose, California / Geoffrey T. Burnham ... [et al.], chairs/editors; sponsored and published by SPIE--the International Society for Optical Engineering. Published/Created: Bellingham, Washington: SPIE, c2000. Related Authors: Burnham, Geoffrey T. Society of Photo-optical Instrumentation Engineers. Description: viii, 320 p.: ill.; 28 cm. ISBN: 0819435627 Notes: Includes bibliographic references and author index. Subjects: Semiconductor lasers--Congresses. Diodes, Semiconductor--Congresses. Semiconductor lasers--

Industrial applications--Congresses. Series: Proceedings of SPIE--the International Society for Optical Engineering; v. 3945. Variant Series: SPIE proceedings series; v. 3945

Laser experiments for beginners / Richard N. Zare ... [et al.]. Published/Created: Sausalito, Calif.: University Science Books, c1995. Related Authors: Zare, Richard N. Description: xvi, 232 p.: ill.; 26 cm. ISBN: 0935702369 (acid-free paper) Notes: Includes bibliographical references and index. Subjects: Lasers--Experiments. LC Classification: TA1675 .L363 1995 Dewey Class No.: 621.36/6/078 20

Laser Florence 2000: a window on the laser medicine world: 18-22 October 2000, Florence, Italy / Leonardo Longo ... [et al.], editors; organized by ILM--Institute for Laser Medicine of Florence (Italy) ... [et al.]; cooperating organizations, WHO--World Health Organization ... [et al.]. Published/Created: Bellingham, Wash., USA: SPIE, c2001. Related Authors: Longo, Leonardo. Society of Photo-optical Instrumentation Engineers. Institute for Laser Medicine (Florence, Italy) World Health Organization. Description: x, 154 p.: ill.; 28 cm. ISBN: 081944345X Notes: Includes bibliographical references and index. Subjects: Lasers in medicine--Congresses. Lasers in surgery--Congresses. Lasers in dentistry--Congresses. Laser beams--Therapeutic use--Congresses. Series: Progress in biomedical optics and imaging, 1605-7422; vol. 2, no. 35 Proceedings of SPIE--the International Society for Optical Engineering; v. 4606. Variant Series: Proceedings of SPIE, 0277-786X; v. 4606 LC Classification: R857.L37 L373 2000 Dewey Class No.: 610/.28 21

Laser Florence '99: a window on the laser medicine world: 28-31 October 1999, Florence, Italy / Leonardo Longo ... [et al.], editors; organized by ILM--Institute for Laser Medicine of Florence (Italy) ... [et al.]; cooperating organizations, WHO--World Health Organization ... [et al.]. Published/Created: Bellingham, Wash., USA: SPIE, c1999. Related Authors: Longo, Leonardo. Society of Photo-optical Instrumentation Engineers. Description: xii, 328 p.: ill.; 28 cm. ISBN: 0819438227 Notes: Includes bibliographical references and index. Subjects: Lasers in medicine--Congresses. Lasers in surgery--Congresses. Lasers in dentistry--Congresses. Laser beams--Therapeutic use--Congresses. Series: Progress in biomedical optics and imaging, 1605-7422; vol. 1, no. 37 Proceedings of SPIE--the International Society for Optical Engineering; v. 4166. Variant Series: Proceedings of SPIE; v. 4166 LC Classification: R857.L37 L3728 1999 Dewey Class No.: 610/.28 21

Laser focus world. European supplement. Published/Created: Westford, MA: Advanced Technology Group, PennWell Pub. Co., 1990. Description: 1 v.: ill. (some col.); 28 cm. Issue for autumn 1990 called: Premier issue. Autumn 1990. Continued by: European electro-optics 1057-4956 (DLC) 91650388 (OCoLC)24021631 Notes: Title from cover. SERBIB/SERLOC merged record Supplement to: Laser focus world (OCoLC)19045940 (DLC) 89642029 Subjects: Lasers--Europe--Periodicals. Electrooptics--Periodicals. Fiber optics--Periodicals. LC Classification: TA1501 .L375 Dewey Class No.: 621.36/6 20

Laser focus world. Published/Created: [Tulsa, OK: PennWell Pub. Co., c1989- Description: v.: ill., ports.; 28 cm. Issue for Aug. 1993 called v. 20, no. 20 but constitutes v. 29, no. 8. [Vol. 25, no. 1] (Jan. 1989)- Current Frequency: Monthly (except two issues in Dec.) Continues: Laser focus (Littleton, Mass.) 0740-2511 (DLC) 83648163 (OCoLC)9902932 ISSN: 1043-8092 Incorrect ISSN: 0740-2511 Cancel/Invalid LCCN: sn 89007483 CODEN: LFWOE8 Summary: "Global electro-optic technology and markets." Notes: Title from cover. Each issue has also a distinctive title. Includes: Fiberoptics world, as a separate section within each issue, 1989- SERBIB/SERLOC merged record Laser focus world buyers' guide separately issued annually in Dec. 1989-

Indx'd selectively by: Chemical abstracts 0009-2258 Computer & control abstracts 0036-8113 Jan. 1989- Electrical & electronic abstracts 0036-8105 Jan. 1989- Physics abstracts 0036-8091 Jan. 1989- Has Supplement: Laser focus world. European supplement (DLC) 91650334 (OCoLC)23748491 European electro-optics 1057-4956 (DLC) 91650388 (OCoLC)24021631 Laser focus world buyers' guide (DLC)sn 90023247 (OCoLC)18977457 WDM solutions Sept. 1999-Aug. 2001 1536-0032 (DLC) 2001213991 (OCoLC)46429565 Subjects: Lasers--Electrooptics--Fiber optics--Fiber Optics--periodicals. Lasers--Periodicals. LC Classification: TA1501 .L37 Dewey Class No.: 621.36/6 20

Laser frequency stabilization and noise reduction: 9-10 February 1995, San Jose, California / Yaakov Shevy, chair/editor; sponsored and published by SPIE--the International Society for Optical Engineering. Published/Created: Bellingham, Wash.: SPIE, c1995. Related Authors: Shevy, Yaakov. Society of Photo-optical Instrumentation Engineers. Description: ix, 256 p.: ill.; 28 cm. ISBN: 0819417254 Notes: Includes bibliographical references and index. Subjects: Lasers--Semiconductor lasers--Noise--Frequency stability--Congresses. Series: Proceedings of SPIE--the International Society for Optical Engineering; v. 2378. Variant Series: Proceedings / SPIE--the International Society for Optical Engineering; v. 2378 LC Classification: TA1673 .L3355 1995

Laser frequency stabilization, standards, measurement, and applications: 24-26 January, 2001, San Jose, [California] USA / John L. Hall, Jun Ye, chairs/editors; sponsored and published by SPIE--the International Society for Optical Engineering. Published/Created: Bellingham, Washington: SPIE, c2001. Related Authors: Hall, J. L. (John L.), 1934- Ye, Jun.Description: vii, 280 p.: ill.; 28 cm. ISBN: 0819439479 Notes: Includes bibliographic references and author index. Subjects: Lasers-- Semiconductor lasers--Noise--Frequency stability--Congresses. Series: Proceedings of SPIE--the International Society for Optical Engineering; v. 4269. Variant Series: Proceedings / SPIE--the International Society for Optical Engineering; v. 4269

Laser interaction with tissue: 11-13 January 1988, Los Angeles, California / Michael W. Berns, chair/editor; sponsored by SPIE--the International Society for Optical Engineering; cosponsored by University of California/Irvine, California College of Medicine; cooperating organizations, American Academy of Otolaryngology--Head and Neck Surgery ... [et al.]. Published/Created: Bellingham, Wash., USA: SPIE, c1988. Related Authors: Berns, Michael W., 1942- Description: viii, 166 p.: ill.; 28 cm. ISBN: 0892529431 Notes: Includes bibliographical references and index. Subjects: Lasers--Therapeutic use--Lasers--Physiological effect--Congresses. Series: Proceedings of SPIE--the International Society for Optical Engineering; v. 908 LC Classification: RM841.5 .L37 1988 Dewey Class No.: 615.8/3 20

Laser interactions with atoms, solids, and plasmas / edited by Richard M. More. Published/Created: New York: Plenum Press, c1994. Related Authors: More, Richard M. Description: viii, 477 p.: ill.; 26 cm. ISBN: 0306448017 Notes: "Published in cooperation with NATO Scientific Affairs Division." "Proceedings of a NATO Advanced Study Institute on Laser Interactions with Atoms, Solids, and Plasmas, held August 17-25, 1992, in Cargèse, Corsica, France"--T.p. verso. Includes bibliographical references and index. Subjects: Laser manipulation (Nuclear physics)--Congresses. Atoms--Solids--Effect of radiation on--Laser-plasma interactions--Laser pulses, Ultrashort--High power lasers--Congresses. Series: NATO ASI series. Series B, Physics; v. 327 The language of science LC Classification: QC689.5.L35 L37 1994 Dewey Class No.: 539.7/23 20

Laser interferometry, quantitative analysis of interferograms: third in a series: 7-9 August 1989, San Diego, California / Ryszard J. Pryputniewicz, chair/editor; sponsored by SPIE--the International Society for Optical Engineering; cooperating organizations, Applied Optics Laboratory/New Mexico State University ... [et al.]. Published/Created: Bellingham, Wash., USA: SPIE, c1990. Related Authors: Pryputniewicz, Ryszard J. Description: ix, 468 p.: ill.; 28 cm. ISBN: 0819401986 Notes: "Part of a four-conference program o n Interferometry, Microscopy, and Testing held at SPIE's 33rd Annual International Symposium on Optical & Optoelectronic Applied Science & Engineering, 6-11-August 1989, in San Diego, California"--P. vii. Includes bibliographical references and index. Subjects: Lasers--Industrial applications--Laser interferometers--Industrial applications--Congresses. Series: Proceedings of SPIE--the International Society for Optical Engineering; v. 1162. Variant Series: Proceedings / SPIE--the International Society for Optical Engineering; v. 1162 LC Classification: TA1673 .L36453 1990 Dewey Class No.: 621.36/6 20

Laser isotope separation: 19-20 January 1993, Los Angeles, California / Jeffrey A. Paisner, chair/editor; sponsored and published by SPIE--the International Society for Optical Engineering. Published/Created: Bellingham, Wash., USA: SPIE, c1993. Related Authors: Paisner, Jeffrey A., 1948- Description: ix, 288 p.: ill.; 28 cm. ISBN: 0819410861 (pbk.) Notes: Includes bibliographical references and author index. Subjects: Lasers in isotope separation--Congresses. Series: Proceedings of SPIE--the International Society for Optical Engineering; v. 1859. Variant Series: Proceedings / SPIE--the International Society for Optical Engineering; v. 1859 LC Classification: TP156.I7 L37 1993 Dewey Class No.: 621.48/335 20

Laser materials processing / edited by Leonard Migliore. Published/Created: New York: M. Dekker, c1996. Related Authors: Migliore, Leonard R. Description: vii, 319 p.: ill.; 24 cm. ISBN: 0824797140 (hardcover: alk. paper) Notes: Includes bibliographical references and index. Subjects: Manufacturing processes--Equipment and supplies. Lasers--Industrial applications. Series: Manufacturing engineering and materials processing; 46 LC Classification: TS183 .L38 1996 Dewey Class No.: 621.36/6 20

Laser materials processing and machining: 20-21 June 1994, Frankfurt, FRG / Rolf-Jürgen Ahlers ... [et al.], chairs/editors; sponsored by the Commission of the European Communities, Directorate General for Science, Research, and Development, EOS--the European Optical Society, SPIE--the International Society for Optical Engineering. Published/Created: Bellingham, Wash., USA: SPIE, c1994. Related Authors: Ahlers, R.-J. (Rolf-Jürgen) Commission of the European Communities. Directorate-General for Science, Research, and Development. European Optical Society. Society of Photo-optical Instrumentation Engineers. Description: v, 206 p.: ill.; 28 cm. ISBN: 0819415529 Notes: Includes bibliographical references and index. Subjects: Lasers--Industrial applications--Congresses. Series: Proceedings EurOpt series Proceedings of SPIE--the International Society for Optical Engineering; v. 2246. Variant Series: SPIE proceedings series; v. 2246 LC Classification: TA1673 .L36467 1994 Dewey Class No.: 621.36/6 20

Laser materials processing III: proceedings of the third symposium on laser materials processing, sponsored by the TMS Physical Metallurgy, Solidification and Electronics Materials Committees, and held at the TMS Fall Meeting, Chicago, Illinois, September 26-28, 1988 / edited by J. Mazumder, K.N. Mukherjee. Published/Created: Warrendale, Pa.: Minerals, Metals & Materials Society, c1989. Related Authors: Mazumder, J. Mukherjee, K. Description: viii, 255 p.: ill.; 24 cm. ISBN: 0873391047 Notes:

Includes bibliographical references. Subjects: Lasers--Industrial applications--Surfaces (Technology)--Laser welding--Congresses. LC Classification: TA1673 .L3646 1989 Dewey Class No.: 621.36/6 20

Laser materials processing: industrial and microelectronics applications: 5-8 April 1994, Vienna, Austria / Eckhard Beyer ... [et al.], chairs/editors; sponsored by the Commission of the European Communities, Directorate General for Science, Research, and Development ... [et al.]. Published/Created: Bellingham, Wash., USA: SPIE--the International Society for Optical Engineering, c1994. Related Authors: Beyer, Eckhard. Description: xiv, 850 p.: ill.; 28 cm. ISBN: 0819415081 (pbk.) Notes: Includes bibliographical references and author index. Subjects: Lasers--Industrial applications--Laser beam cutting--Laser welding--Process control--Congresses. Series: Proceedings EurOpt series Proceedings of SPIE--the International Society for Optical Engineering; v. 2207. Variant Series: SPIE proceedings series; v. 2207 LC Classification: TA1673 .L3647 1994 Dewey Class No.: 671/.028 20

Laser metrology and inspection: 14-15 June 1999, Munich, Germany / Hans J. Tiziani, Pramod K. Rastogi, chairs/editors; sponsored by EOS, SPIE, WLT. Published/Created: Bellingham, Wash.: SPIE, c1999. Related Authors: Tiziani, Hans J. Rastogi, P. K. (Pramod K.) European Optical Society. Society of Photo-optical Instrumentation Engineers. Wissenschaftliche Gesellschaft Lasertechnik. Description: vii, 298 p.: ill.; 28 cm. Notes: Includes bibliographical references and index. Subjects: Lasers--Industrial applications--Mensuration--Engineering inspection--Congresses. Series: Proceedings EurOpt series Proceedings of SPIE--the International Society for Optical Engineering; v. 3823. Variant Series: SPIE proceedings series; v. 3823 LC Classification: TA1673 .L36475 1999 Dewey Class No.: 621.36/6 21

Laser metrology and machine performance III / editors, D.G. Ford, S.R. Postlethwaite. Published/Created: Southampton; Boston: Computational Mechanics Publications, c1997. Related Authors: Ford, D. G. Postlethwaite, S. R. Description: 547 p.: ill.; 24 cm. ISBN: 1853125369 Notes: "Third International Conference on Laser Metrology and Performance, LAMDAMAP 97. Organised by University Huddersfield"--[3rd] prelim. p. Includes bibliographical references and indexes. Subjects: Machine-tools--Monitoring--Numerical control--Lasers--Industrial applications--Mensuration--Congresses. LC Classification: TJ1180 .L38 1997 Dewey Class No.: 621.9/02 21

Laser metrology and machine performance IV / editors: V. Chiles, D. Jenkinson. Published/Created: Southampton: WIT Press; Boston: Computational Mechanics, c1999. Related Authors: Chiles, Vic. Jenkinson, D. (Des) International Conference on Laser Metrology and Machine Performance (4th: 1999: University of Northumbria) Description: 500 p.: ill.; 24 cm. ISBN: 1853126616 Notes: "Fourth International Conference on Laser Metrology and Machine Performance, LAMDAMAP 99 ... organized by the University of Northumbria"--Facing t.p. Includes bibliographical references and index. Subjects: Machine-tools--Monitoring--umerical control--Lasers--Industrial applications--Mensuration--Congresses. LC Classification: TJ1180 .L383 1999 Dewey Class No.: 621.9/02 21

Laser metrology and machine performance V / editor, G.N. Peggs. Published/Created: Southampton; Boston: WIT Press, 2001. Related Authors: Peggs, G. N. Description: 376 p.: ill.; 24 cm. ISBN: 1853128902 Notes: "Fifth International Conference on Laser Metrology, Machine Tool, CMM, and Robot Performance, LAMDAMAP 2001 ... organised by: National Physical Laboratory"--Facing t.p. Includes bibliographical references and index. Subjects: Machine-tools--Monitoring--Numerical control--Lasers--Industrial applications--Mensuration--Congresses. LC Classification: TJ1180 .L384 2001 Dewey Class No.: 621.9/02 21

Laser microfabrication: thin film processes and lithography / edited by Daniel J. Ehrlich, Jeffrey Y. Tsao. Published/Created: Boston: Academic Press, c1989. Related Authors: Ehrlich, Daniel J. Tsao, Jeffrey Y. Description: xii, 587 p.: ill.; 24 cm. ISBN: 0122334302 Notes: Includes bibliographies and index. Subjects: Lasers--Industrial applications. Thin film devices--Design and construction. Microlithography. Microfabrication. LC Classification: TA1677 .L366 1989 Dewey Class No.: 621.36/6 19

Laser microscopy: 7-8 July 2000, Amsterdam, Netherlands / Karsten König, Hans J. Tanke, Herbert Schneckenburger, chairs/editors; sponsored by EOS--the European Optical Society, SPIE--the International Society for Optical Engineering, [and] ELA--European Laser Association; cooperating organizations, NMLA--Netherlands Medical Laser Association ... [et al.]. Published/Created: Bellingham, Wash., USA: SPIE, c2000. Related Authors: König, Karsten. Tanke, H. J. Schneckenburger, Herbert. Description: v, 134 p.: ill.; 28 cm. ISBN: 0819438200 Notes: Includes bibliographical references and index. Subjects: Fluorescence microscopy--Medical microscopy--Imaging systems in medicine--Lasers in medicine--Congresses. Series: Progress in biomedical optics and imaging, 1605-7422; vol. 1, no. 35 Proceedings of SPIE--the International Society for Optical Engineering; v. 4164. Variant Series: SPIE proceedings series; v. 4164 LC Classification: QH212.F55 L37 2000 Other

Laser noise: 5-6 November 1990, Boston, Massachusetts / Rajarshi Roy, chair/editor; sponsored and published by SPIE--the International Society for Optical Engineering. Published/Created: Bellingham, Wash., USA: SPIE, c1991. Related Authors: Roy, Rajarshi. Description: vii, 295 p.: ill.; 28 cm. ISBN: 0819404438 Notes: "Part of a five-conference symposium on Laser Science and Optics Applications, a part of OE/Boston '90, 4-9 November 1990"--P. v. Includes bibliographical references and index. Subjects: Lasers--Noise--Congresses. Series: Proceedings of SPIE--the International Society for Optical Engineering; v. 1376. Variant Series: Proceedings / SPIE--the International Society for Optical Engineering; v. 1376 LC Classification: TA1673 .L3648 1991 Dewey Class No.: 621.36/6 20

Laser non-surgical medicine: new challenges for an old application / edited by Leon Goldman. Published/Created: Lancaster, Pa., U.S.A.: Technomic Pub. Co., c1991. Related Authors: Goldman, Leon, 1905- Technomic Publishing Company. Description: xii, 334 p.: ill.; 27 cm. ISBN: 0877627924 Notes: "A Technomic Publishing Company book"--T.p. verso. Includes bibliographical references and index. Subjects: Lasers--Therapeutic use. LC Classification: RM841.5 .L38 1991 Dewey Class No.: 615.8/31 20

Laser optics for intracavity and extracavity applications / Philippe M. Fauchet, Karl H. Guenther, chairs/editors; sponsored by SPIE--the International Society for Optical Engineering; cooperating organizations, American Academy of Otolaryngology--Head and Neck Surgery ... [et al.]. Published/Created: Bellingham, Wash., USA: SPIE, c1988. Related Authors: Fauchet, Philippe Max. Guenther, Karl H. Society of Photo-optical Instrumentation Engineers. Description: viii, 289 p.: ill.; 28 cm. ISBN: 089252930X Notes: "11-13 January 1988, Los Angeles, California." Includes bibliographies and index. Subjects: Optics--Congresses. Lasers--Congresses. Series: Proceedings of SPIE--the International Society for Optical Engineering; v. 895 LC Classification: TA1505 .L34 1988 Dewey Class No.: 621.36/6 20

Laser physics and photonics: and spectroscopy and molecular modeling: 3-7 October 2000, Saratov, Russia / Vladimir L.

Derbov, Leonid A. Melnikov, Lev M. Babkov, editors; organized by Saratov State University (Russia) ... [et al.]; in cooperation with Ministry of Education of the Russian Federation ... [et al.]; sponsored by SPIE Russia Chapter ... [et al.]. Published/Created: Bellingham, Wash., USA: SPIE, c2001. Related Authors: Derbov, Vladimir L. Melnikov, Leonid A. Babkov, L. M. (Lev Mikhailovich) Saratov, Russia) Description: x, 216 p.: ill.; 28 cm. ISBN: 0819439215 Notes: "Contributions presented at the Workshops on Laser Physics and Photonics (LLP) and on Spectroscopy and Molecular Modeling (SMM), International School for Young Scientists and Students in Optics, Lasers [sic] Physics and Biophysics"--P. ix. Includes bibliographical references and index. Subjects: Lasers--Congresses. Nonlinear optics--Congresses. Quantum optics--Congresses. Laser spectroscopy--Congresses. Molecules--Models--Congresses. Series: Proceedings of SPIE--the International Society for Optical Engineering; v. 4243. Variant Series: SPIE proceedings series, 0277-786X; v. 4243 LC Classification: QC685 .L35 2001 Dewey Class No.: 621.36/6 21

Laser physics and spectroscopy: Saratov Fall Meeting '99: International Workshop and Fall School for Young Scientists and Students on Optics, Laser Physics, and Biophysics: 5-8 October, 1999, Saratov, Russia / Vladimir L. Derbov, Leonid A. Melnikov, Vladimir P. Ryabukho, editors; organized by Saratov State University (Russia) ... [et al.]; in cooperation with Ministry of Education of the Russian Federation ... [et al.]; sponsored by Russian Foundation for Basic Research. Published/Created: Bellingham, Wash.: SPIE, c2000. Related Authors: Derbov, Vladimir L. Melnikov, Leonid A. Ryabukho, Vladimir P. Description: x, 280 p.: ill.; 28 cm. ISBN: 0819436275 Notes: Includes bibliographic references and author index. Subjects: Laser spectroscopy--Lasers--Nonlinear theories--Congresses. Series: Proceedings of SPIE--the International Society for Optical Engineering; v. 4002. Variant Series: Proceedings / SPIE--the International Society for Optical Engineering, 0277-786X; v. 4002 LC Classification: QC454.L3 L338 2000 Dewey Class No.: 621.36/6 21

Laser physics at relativistic intensities / A.V. Borovsky ... [et al.]. Published/Created: New York: Springer, 2002. Projected Pub. Date: 0207 Related Authors: Borovskii, A. V. (Andrei Viktorovich) Description: p. cm. ISBN: 3540434461 (acid-free paper) Notes: Includes bibliographical references and index. Subjects: Laser-plasma interactions. Laser pulses, Ultrashort. High power lasers. Series: Springer series on atomic, optical, and plasma physics, 1615-5653; 34 LC Classification: QC718.5.L3 L37 2002 Dewey Class No.: 530/.4/46 21

Laser physics at the limits / Hartmut Figger, Dieter Meschede, Claus Zimmermann, eds. Published/Created: Berlin; New York: Springer, c2002. Related Authors: Figger, Hartmut, 1939- Meschede, Dieter, 1954- Zimmermann, Claus, 1958- Description: xxxiv, 522 p.: ill.; 24 cm. ISBN: 3540424180 (alk. paper) Notes: Includes bibliographical references and index. Subjects: Lasers. Laser spectroscopy. Atomic clocks. LC Classification: QC689 .L375 2002 Dewey Class No.: 621.36/6 21

Laser physics. Published/Created: Lawrence, KS: Pleiades Pub., c1991- Description: v.: ill.; 28 cm. Vol. 1, no. 1 (Jan.-Feb. 1991)- Current Frequency: Bimonthly ISSN: 1054-660X Cancel/Invalid LCCN: sn 91001055 CODEN: LAPHEJ Notes: Title from cover. Issues for Jan.-Feb. 1991- published in cooperation with the USSR Academy of Sciences; issues for published in Moscow by Interperiodica Pub., in cooperation with the Russian Academy of Sciences. SERBIB/SERLOC merged record Subjects: Lasers--Periodicals. LC Classification: QC685 .L29 Dewey Class No.: 621.36/6 20

Laser plasma generation and diagnostics: 27 January 2000, San Jose, California / Richard F. Haglund, Jr., Richard F. Wood, chairs/editors; sponsored ... by SPIE--the International Society for Optical Engineering. Published/Created: Bellingham, Wash., USA: SPIE, c2000. Related Authors: Haglund, R. F. (Richard F.), 1942- Wood, Richard F. Society of Photo-optical Instrumentation Engineers. Description: vi, 158 p.: ill.; 28 cm. ISBN: 081943552X Notes: Includes bibliographical references and index. Subjects: Laser plasmas--Plasma generators--Lasers--Diagnostic use--Congresses. Series: Proceedings of SPIE--the International Society for Optical Engineering; v. 3935. Variant Series: SPIE proceedings series, 0277-786X; v. 3935

Laser power beaming II: 8-9 February, 1995, San Jose, California / Harold E. Bennett, Richard D. Doolittle, chairs/editors; sponsored and published by SPIE--the International Society for Optical Engineering. Published/Created: Bellingham, Wash., USA: SPIE, c1995. Related Authors: Bennett, Harold Earl, 1929- Doolittle, Richard D. Society of Photo-optical Instrumentation Engineers. Description: xi, 330 p.: ill.; 28 cm. ISBN: 0819417238 Notes: Includes bibliographic references and author index. Subjects: Laser beams--Free electron lasers--Laser beams--Atmospheric effects--Microtrons--Congresses. Series: Proceedings of SPIE--the International Society for Optical Engineering; v. 2376. Variant Series: Proceedings / SPIE--the International Society for Optical Engineering; v. 2376 LC Classification: TA1673 .L36496 1995 Dewey Class No.: 621.382/7 20

Laser power beaming: 27-28 January 1994, Los Angeles, California / Jack V. Walker, Edward E. Montgomery IV, chairs/editors; sponsored and published by SPIE--the International Society for Optical Engineering. Published/Created: Bellingham, Wash., USA: SPIE, c1994. Related Authors: Walker, Jack V. Montgomery, Edward E. Description: xiv, 304 p.: ill.; 28 cm. ISBN: 081941414X Notes: Includes bibliographical references and author index. Subjects: High power lasers--Congresses. Laser beams--Congresses. Series: Proceedings of SPIE--the International Society for Optical Engineering; v. 2121. Variant Series: Proceedings / SPIE--the International Society for Optical Engineering; v. 2121 LC Classification: TA1673 .L36497 1994 Dewey Class No.: 621.36/6 20

Laser processing in manufacturing / edited by R.C. Crafer and P.J. Oakley. Edition Information: 1st ed. Published/Created: London; New York: Chapman & Hall, 1993. Related Authors: Crafer, R. C. (Roger C.) Oakley, P. J. (Peter J.) Description: x, 292 p.: ill.; 24 cm. ISBN: 0412415208 Notes: Includes bibliographical references and index. Subjects: Lasers--Industrial applications. Production engineering. Manufacturing processes. Materials Processing Use of Lasers Series: Engineering aspects of lasers series LC Classification: TA1677 .L368 1993 Dewey Class No.: 621.36/6 20

Laser processing of materials and industrial applications II: 16-19 September, 1998, Beijing, China / Shu-Sen Deng, S.C. Wang, chairs/editors; sponsored by SPIE--the International Society for Optical Engineering, COEMA--China Optics & Optoelectronic Manufacturers Association, COS--Chinese Optical Society; cooperating organizations, National Natural Science Foundation of China ... [et al.]. Published/Created: Bellingham, Washington: SPIE, c1998. Related Authors: Deng, Shu-Sen. Wang, S. C. (Shing Chung), 1934- Society of Photo-optical Instrumentation Engineers. Chung-kuo kuang hsüeh hsüeh hui. Kuo chia tzu jan k`o hsüeh chi chin wei yüan hui (China) Description: ix, 528 p.: ill.; 28 cm. ISBN: 0819430110 Notes: Includes bibliographical references and author index. Subjects: Lasers--Congresses. Lasers--Industrial applications--Congresses. Series: Proceedings of SPIE--the International Society for Optical Engineering; v. 3550. Variant Series: Proceedings / SPIE--the International Society for Optical Engineering; v. 3550

Laser processing of materials and industrial applications: 6-7 November 1996, Beijing, China / Shu-Sen Deng, S.C. Wang, chairs/editors; sponsored by SPIE--the International Society for Optical Engineering, COEMA--China Optics & Optoelectronic Manufacturers Association, COS--Chinese Optical Society; cooperating organizations, National Natural Science Foundation of China ... [et al.]. Published/Created: Bellingham, Wash.: SPIE, c1996. Related Authors: Deng, Shu-Sen. Wang, S. C. (Shing Chung), 1934- Description: xi, 426 p.: ill.; 28 cm. ISBN: 0819422894 Notes: Includes bibliographical references and index. Subjects: Lasers--Congresses. Lasers--Industrial applications--Congresses. Series: Proceedings of SPIE--the International Society for Optical Engineering; v. 2888. Variant Series: Proceedings / SPIE--the International Society for Optical Engineering; v. 2888 LC Classification: TA1673 .L3655 1996

Laser processing: surface treatment and film deposition / edited by J. Mazumder ... [et al.]. Published/Created: Dordrecht; Boston: Kluwer Academic Publishers, c1996. Related Authors: Mazumder, J. North Atlantic Treaty Organization. Scientific Affairs Division. NATO Advanced Study Institute on "Laser Processing: Surface Treatment and Film Deposition" (1994: Sezimbra, Portugal) Description: xiv, 944 p.: ill.; 25 cm. ISBN: 0792339010 (acid-free paper) Notes: "Published in cooperation with NATO Scientific Affairs Division." "Proceedings of the NATO Advanced Study Institute on 'Laser Processing: Surface Treatment and Film Deposition', Sesimbra, Portugal, July 3-16, 1994." Includes bibliographical references. Subjects: Lasers--Industrial applications--Metals--Surfaces--Thin films--Laser ablation--Congresses. Series: NATO ASI series. Series E, Applied sciences; no. 307. Variant Series: NATO ASI series. Series E, Applied sciences; vol. 307 LC Classification: TA1677 .N42 1996 Dewey Class No.: 620/.44 20

Laser radar V: 18-19 January 1990, Los Angeles, California / Richard J. Becherer, chair/editor; sponsored by SPIE--the International Society for Optical Engineering. Published/Created: Bellingham, Wash., USA: SPIE, c1990. Related Authors: Becherer, Richard, 1941- Society of Photo-optical Instrumentation Engineers. Symposium on High-Power Lasers and Optical Computing (1990: Los Angeles, Calif.) Description: viii, 207 p.: ill.; 28 cm. ISBN: 081940263X Notes: Papers presented at a technical conference held at the Symposium on High-Power Lasers and Optical Computing, held 14-19 Jan. 1990, in Los Angeles, Calif. Includes bibliographical references and index. Subjects: Optical radar--Congresses. Series: Proceedings of SPIE--the International Society for Optical Engineering; v. 1222. Variant Series: Proceedings / SPIE--the International Society for Optical Engineering; v. 1222 LC Classification: TK6592.O6 L384 1990 Dewey Class No.: 621.384/8 20

Laser resonators and coherent optics: modeling, technology, and applications: 18-20 January 1993, Los Angeles, California / Anup Bhowmik, chair/editor; sponsored and published by SPIE--the International Society for Optical Engineering. Published/Created: Bellingham, Wash., USA: SPIE, c1993. Related Authors: Bhowmik, Anup. Description: x, 440 p.: ill.; 28 cm. ISBN: 0819410950 (pbk.) Notes: Includes bibliographical references and author index. Subjects: Lasers--Resonators--Congresses. Coherence (Optics)--Congresses. Series: Proceedings of SPIE--the International Society for Optical Engineering; v. 1868. Variant Series: Proceedings / SPIE--the International Society for Optical Engineering; v. 1868 LC Classification: TA1673 .L3673 1993 Dewey Class No.: 621.36/6 20

Laser resonators II: 27-29 January 1999, San Jose, California / Alexis V. Kudryashov, chair/editor. Published/Created: Bellingham, Wash.: SPIE, c1999. Related Authors: Kudryashov, Alexis V.

Description: viii, 346 p.: ill.; 28 cm. Notes: Includes bibliographical references and index. Subjects: Lasers--Resonators--Congresses. Series: Proceedings of SPIE--the International Society for Optical Engineering v. 3611. Variant Series: Proceedings / SPIE--the International Society of Optical Engineering; v. 3611 LC Classification: TA1673 .L3672 1999 Dewey Class No.: 621.36/6 21

Laser resonators III: 26-28 January, 2000, San Jose, California / Alexis V. Kudryashov, Alan H. Paxton, chairs/editors; sponsored and published by SPIE--the International Society for Optical Engineering. Published/Created: Bellingham, Washington: SPIE, c2000. Related Authors: Kudryashov, Alexis V. Paxton, Alan H. Society of Photo-optical Instrumentation Engineers. Description: ix, 238 p.: ill.; 28 cm. ISBN: 0819435473 Notes: Includes bibliographic references and author index. Subjects: Lasers--Resonators--Congresses. Series: Proceedings of SPIE--the International Society for Optical Engineering; v. 3930. Variant Series: Proceedings of SPIE--the International Society for Optical Engineering; v. 3930 LC Classification: TA1673 .L36723 2000 Dewey Class No.: 621.36/6 21

Laser resonators IV: 23-25 January, 2001, San Jose, [California] USA / Alexis V. Kudryashov, Alan H. Paxton, chairs/editors; sponsored and published by SPIE--the International Society for Optical Engineering. Published/Created: Bellingham, Washington: SPIE, c2001. Related Authors: Kudryashov, Alexis V. Paxton, Alan H. Description: viii, 274 p.: ill.; 28 cm. ISBN: 0819439487 Notes: Includes bibliographic references and author index. Subjects: Lasers--Resonators--Congresses. Series: Proceedings of SPIE--the International Society for Optical Engineering v. 4270. Variant Series: Proceedings / SPIE--the International Society of Optical Engineering; v. 4270

Laser resonators: novel design and development / Alexis V. Kudryashov, Horst Weber, editors. Published/Created: Bellingham, Wash.: SPIE Optical Engineering Press, 1999. Related Authors: Kudryashov, Alexis V. Weber, Horst, 1935- Society of Photo-optical Instrumentation Engineers. Description: xiii, 301 p.: ill.; 25 cm. ISBN: 0819433179 Notes: "A publication of SPIE--the International Society for Optical Engineering." Includes bibliographical references. Subjects: Lasers--Resonators. LC Classification: TA1675 .L3763 1999 Dewey Class No.: 621.36/6 21

Laser safety guide / prepared by LIA Laser Safety Committee; edited by Wesley Marshall & David Sliney. Edition Information: 10th ed. Published/Created: Orlando, FL: Laser Institute of America, c2000. Related Authors: Marshall, Wesley. Sliney, David H. Description: ii, 48 p.: ill.; 23 cm. ISBN: 0912035064 Notes: Includes bibliographical references. Subjects: Lasers--Safety measures. LC Classification: TA1677 .L369 2000

Laser safety, eyesafe laser systems, and laser eye protection: 16-17 January 1990, Los Angeles, California / Penelope K. Galoff, David H. Sliney, chairs/editors; sponsored by SPIE--the International Society for Optical Engineering. Published/Created: Bellingham, Wash., USA: SPIE, c1990. Related Authors: Galoff, Penelope K. Sliney, David H. Description: vii, 241 p.: ill.; 28 cm. ISBN: 0819402486 Notes: Papers submitted to a technical conference held at the Symposium on High-Power Lasers and Optical Computing, held 14-19 Jan. 1990, in Los Angeles, Calif. Includes bibliographical references and index. Subjects: Eye--Protection--Lasers--Safety measures--Health aspects--Congresses. Series: Proceedings of SPIE--the International Society for Optical Engineering; v. 1207. Variant Series: Proceedings / SPIE--the International Society for Optical Engineering; v. 1207 LC Classification: RE840 .L37 1990 Dewey Class No.: 617.7 20

Laser surgery and medicine: principles and practice / edited by Carmen A. Puliafito. Published/Created: New York: Wiley-Liss, c1996. Related Authors: Puliafito, Carmen A., 1951- Description: x, 447 p., [20] p. of plates: ill. (some col.); 29 cm. ISBN: 0471120707 (cloth: alk. paper) Notes: Collection of review articles previously published in Lasers in surgery and medicine. Includes bibliographical references and index. Subjects: Lasers in medicine. Lasers in surgery. Laser Surgery--methods--collected works. Lasers--therapeutic use--collected works. LC Classification: R857.L37 L416 1996 Dewey Class No.: 610/.28 20

Laser surgery in children / H.-P. Berlien, P.P. Schmittenbecher (eds.). Published/Created: Berlin; New York: Springer, c1998. Projected Pub. Date: 1111 Related Authors: Berlien, H.-P. (Hans-Peter) Schmittenbecher, P.P. (Peter P.), 1958- Description: p. cm. ISBN: 3540626336 (hardcover: alk. paper) Notes: Includes bibliographical references and index. Subjects: Children--Surgery. Lasers in surgery. Laser Surgery--in infancy & childhood. LC Classification: RD137 .L324 1998 Dewey Class No.: 617.9/8 21

Laser surgery in gynecology and obstetrics / [edited by] William R. Keye, Jr. Edition Information: 2nd ed. Published/Created: Chicago: Year Book Medical Publishers, c1990. Related Authors: Keye, William R., 1943- Description: xxv, 279 p.: ill. (some col.); 26 cm. ISBN: 0815150334 Notes: Includes bibliographical references. Subjects: Gynecology, Operative. Obstetrics--Surgery. Lasers in surgery. Genitalia, Female--surgery. Laser Surgery. Pregnancy Complications--surgery. LC Classification: RG104 .L37 1990 Dewey Class No.: 618/.0459 20

Laser surgery in ophthalmology: practical applicalications / edited by Thomas A. Weingeist, Scott R. Sneed; foreword by J. Donald M. Gas s. Published/Created: Norwalk, Conn.: Appleton & Lange, c1992. Related Authors: Weingeist, Thomas A. Sneed, Scott R. Description: xv, 206 p.: ill.; 29 cm. ISBN: 0838579035 Notes: Includes bibliographical references and index. Subjects: Lasers in ophthalmology. Eye--Surgery. Eye Diseases--surgery. Laser Surgery--methods LC Classification: RE86 .P73 1992 Dewey Class No.: 617.7/1 20

Laser surgery: characterization and therapeutics: 16-17 January 1988, Los Angeles, California / Stephen N. Joffe, Kazuhiko Atsumi, chairs/editors; sponsored by SPIE--the International Society for Optical Engineering; cosponsored by University of California/Irvine, California College of Medicine; cooperating organizations, American Academy of Otolaryngology--Head and Neck Surgery ... [et al.]. Published/Created: Bellingham, Wash., USA: The Society, c1988. Related Authors: Joffe, Stephen N. Atsumi, Kzuhiko, 1928- Description: viii, 167 p.: ill.; 28 cm. ISBN: 0892529423 (pbk.) Notes: "One of the six conferences comprising the Symposium on Medical Applications of Lasers, Fiber Optics, and Electro-Optics at SPIE's O-E/LASE '88, 10-17 January 1988, Los Angeles, California"--P. vi. Includes bibliographies and index. Subjects: Lasers in surgery--Congresses. Series: Proceedings of SPIE--the International Society for Optical Engineering; v. 907 LC Classification: RD73.L3 L36 1988 Dewey Class No.: 617/.05 19

Laser tech briefs. Published/Created: New York, NY: Associated Business Publications, c1993- Description: v.: ill.; 28 cm. Vol. 1 complete in one issue. Vol. 1, no. 1 (Sept. 1993)- Current Frequency: Quarterly ISSN: 1077-2324 Notes: Title from cover. SERBIB/SERLOC merged record Subjects: Lasers--Periodicals. LC Classification: TA1671 .L378 Dewey Class No.: 621.36/6 20

Laser techniques and applications in fluid mechanics: proceedings of the 6th international symposium, Lisbon, Portugal, 20-23 July 1992 / R.J. Adrian ... [et al.], eds. Published/Created: Berlin; New York:

Springer-Verlag, c1993. Related Authors: Adrian, R. J. (Ronald J.) International Symposium on Applications of Laser Techniques to Fluid Mechanics (6th: 1993: Lisbon, Portugal) Description: viii, 534 p.: ill. (some col.); 25 cm. ISBN: 3540568794 (Berlin: acid-free paper) 0387568794 (New York: acid-free paper) Notes: Papers presented at the Sixth Symposium on the Applications of Laser Techniques to Fluid Mechanics. Includes bibliographical references. Subjects: Fluid dynamic measurements--Congresses. Lasers--Congresses. LC Classification: TA357.5.M43 L38 1993 Dewey Class No.: 681/.2 20

Laser techniques and systems in art conservation: 18-19 June 2001, Munich, Germany / Renzo Salimbeni, chair/editor; sponsored ... by SPIE--the International Society for Optical Engineering; cosponsored by European Optical Society [and] WLT--Wissenschaftliche Gesellschaft Lasertechnik e.V. (Germany). Published/Created: Bellingham, Wash., USA: SPIE, c2001. Related Authors: Salimbeni, Renzo. Society of Photo-optical Instrumentation Engineers. European Optical Society. Wissenschaftliche Gesellschaft Lasertechnik. Description: x, 244 p.: ill.; 28 cm. ISBN: 0819440973 Notes: Includes bibliographical references and index. Subjects: Art--Conservation and restoration--Congresses. Architecture--Conservation and restoration--Congresses. Art--Expertising--Congresses. Lasers in art--Congresses. Series: Proceedings of SPIE--the International Society for Optical Engineering; v. 4402. Variant Series: SPIE proceedings series; v. 4402

Laser techniques applied to fluid mechanics: selected papers from the 9th international symposium, Lisbon, Portugal, July 13-16, 1998 / R.J. Adrian ... [et al.] (eds.). Published/Created: Berlin; New York: Springer-Verlag, 2000. Related Authors: Adrian, R. J. (Ronald J.) International Symposium on Applications of Laser Techniques to Fluid Mechanics (9th: 1998: Lisbon, Portugal) Description: xi, 638 p.: ill.; 25 cm. ISBN: 3540667385 (hc: alk. paper) Notes: Includes revised versions of selected papers presented at the Ninth International Symposium on Applications of Laser Techniques to Fluid Mechanics. Includes bibliographical references and index. Subjects: Fluid mechanics--Fluid dynamic measurements--Flow meters--Lasers--Congresses. LC Classification: TA357 .L375 2000 Dewey Class No.: 620.1/06 21

Laser techniques for condensed-phase and biological systems: 29-31 January 1998, San Jose, California / Norbert F. Scherer, Janice M. Hicks, chairs/editors; sponsored and published by SPIE--the International Society for Optical Engineering. Published/Created: Bellingham, Wash., USA: SPIE, c1998. Related Authors: Scherer, Norbert F. Hicks, Janice M. Society of Photo-optical Instrumentation Engineers. Description: vii, 312 p.: ill.; 28 cm. ISBN: 0819427128 Notes: Includes bibliographical references and index. Subjects: Lasers in biology--Congresses. Lasers in chemistry--Congresses. Picosecond pulses--Congresses. Laser spectroscopy--Congresses. Molecular spectroscopy--Congresses. Series: Proceedings of SPIE--the International Society for Optical Engineering; v. 3273. Variant Series: SPIE proceedings series; v. 3273 LC Classification: QH324.9.L37 Lss375 1998 Dewey Class No.: 570/.28 21

Laser techniques for state-selected and state-to-state chemistry. Published/Created: Bellingham, Wash.: SPIE, c1993- Description: v.: ill.; 28 cm. Vol. for 21-23 Jan. 1993 lacks numeric designation. 21-23 Jan. 1993- Current Frequency: Annual ISSN: 1090-9885 Notes: Sponsored by: SPIE--the International Society for Optical Engineering. SERBIB/SERLOC merged record Subjects: Lasers in chemistry--Congresses. Photochemistry--Congresses. Series: Proceedings of SPIE--the International Society for Optical Engineering. Variant Series: Proceedings / SPIE--the International Society for Optical Engineering LC Classification: QD63.L3 L377 Dewey Class No.: 621 12

Laser techniques for surface science: 27-29 January 1994, Los Angeles, California / Hai-Lung Dai, Steven J. Sibener, chairs/editors; sponsored and published by SPIE--the International Society for Optical Engineering. Published/Created: Bellingham, Wash.: SPIE, c1994. Related Authors: Dai, Hai-Lung. Sibener, Steven J. Society of Photo-optical Instrumentation Engineers. Description: vii, 390 p.: ill.; 28 cm. ISBN: 0819414182 Notes: Includes bibliographical references and index. Subjects: Surfaces (Technology)--Congresses. Lasers--Congresses. Nonlinear optics--Congresses. Series: Proceedings of SPIE--the International Society for Optical Engineering; v. 2125. Variant Series: SPIE proceedings series, 0277-786X; v. 2125 LC Classification: TA418.7 .L36 1994 Dewey Class No.: 620/.44 20

Laser technologies in industry: proceedings, 6-8 June 1988, Porto, Portugal / Olivério D.D. Soares, chair/editor; Silvério P. Almeida, L.M. Bernardo, editors; supported by Commission of the European Communities. Published/Created: Bellingham, Wash., USA: SPIE--the International Society for Optical Engineering, c1989- Related Authors: Soares, O. D. D. (Olivério D. D.) Almeida, Silvério P. Bernardo, L. M. Society of Photo-optical Instrumentation Engineers. Description: v. <1: ill.; 28 cm. ISBN: 0892529873 Notes: Papers presented at a meeting sponsored by the Society of Photo-optical Instrumentation Engineers. Includes bibliographies. Subjects: Lasers--Industrial applications--Congresses. Series: Proceedings of SPIE--the International Society for Optical Engineering; v. 952, etc. Variant Series: SPIE; v. 952- LC Classification: TA1673 .L368 1989 Dewey Class No.: 621.36/6 20

Laser technology II: 7-10 September 1987, Szczecin, Poland / Wieslaw Woli´nski ... [et al.], editors; organized by Polish Academy of Sciences, Committee of Electronics and Telecommunications ... [et al.]. Published/Created: Bellington, Wash., USA: SPIE--the International Society for Optical Engineering, c1988. Related Authors: Woli´nski, Wieslaw. Polska Akademia Nauk. Komitet Elektroniki i Telekomunikacji. Society of Photo-optical Instrumentation Engineers. Description: viii, 278 p.: ill.; 28 cm. ISBN: 089252894X Notes: Includes bibliographical references. Subjects: Lasers--Congresses. Series: Proceedings of SPIE--the International Society for Optical Engineering; v. 859. Variant Series: Proceedings / SPIE; v. 859 LC Classification: TA1673 .L369 1988 Dewey Class No.: 621.36/6 20

Laser technology III: 24-27 September 1990, Szczecin-Swinoujscie, Poland / Wieslaw Woli´nski ... [et al.], editors; organized by Polish Academy of Sciences/Committee of Electronics and Telecommunications ... [et al.]. Published/Created: Bellingham, Wash.: SPIE, c1991. Related Authors: Woli´nski, Wieslaw. Polsak Akademia Nauk. Komitet Elektroniki i Telekomunikacji. Description: x, 393 p.: ill.; 28 cm. ISBN: 0819404586 Notes: Includes bibliographical references and index. Subjects: Lasers--Congresses. Series: Proceedings of SPIE--the International Society for Optical Engineering; v. 1391. Variant Series: Proceedings / SPIE; v. 1391 LC Classification: TA1673 .L3692 1991 Dewey Class No.: 621.36/6 20

Laser technology in ophthalmology / edited by John Marshall. Published/Created: Amsterdam; Berkeley: Kugler & Ghedini; Berkeley, CA, U.S.A.: Distributor for the U.S.A. and Canada, Kugler Publications, c1988. Related Authors: Marshall, John, 1943- Description: vii, 281 p.: ill.; 24 cm. ISBN: 9062990401: Notes: Includes bibliographies and index. Subjects: Lasers in ophthalmology. LC Classification: RE86 .L37 1988 Dewey Class No.: 617.7/1 19

Laser technology IV: applications in medicine: 26-30 September 1993, Szczecin-Swinoujscie, Poland / Wieslaw Woli´nski, Tadeusz Kecik, editors; Danuta Gajda, Bohdan K. Wolczak, co-editors; organized by Technical University of Szczecin ... [et al.]; sponsored by State Committee for

Scientific Research, Poland, SPIE--the International Society for Opticval Engineering in association with SPIE/Poland Chapter. Published/Created: Bellingham, Wash.: SPIE, c1995. Related Authors: Woli'nski, Wieslaw. Kecik, Tadeusz. Politechnika Szczeci'nska. Description: x, 186 p.: ill.; 28 cm. ISBN: 0819415006 Notes: Includes bibliographical references and indexes. Subjects: Lasers in medicine--Congresses. Series: SPIE Poland Chapter proceedings; 15 Proceedings of SPIE--the International Society for Optical Engineering; v. 2203. Variant Series: Proceedings / SPIE--the International Society for Optical Engineering; v. 2203 LC Classification: R857.L37 L375 1995 Dewey Class No.: 610/.28 20

Laser technology IV: research trends, instrumentation, and applications in metrology and materials processing: 26-30 September 1993, Szczecin-Swinoujscie, Poland / Wieslaw Woli'nski, Zdzislaw Jankiewicz, editors; Jerzy K. Gajda, Bohdan K. Wolczak, co-editors; organized by Technical University of Szczecin ... [et al.]; sponsors, State Committee for Scientific Research, Poland, SPIE--the International Society for Optical Engineering in association with the SPIE/Poland Chapter. Published/Created: Bellingham, Wash.: SPIE, c1995. Related Authors: Woli'nski, Wieslaw. Jankiewicz, Zdzislaw. Description: xviii, 626: ill.; 28 cm. ISBN: 0819414999 Notes: Includes bibliographical references and indexes. Subjects: Lasers--Congresses. Lasers--Industrial applications--Congresses. Laser materials--Congresses. Measuring instruments--Congresses. Series: SPIE Poland Chapter proceedings; 14 Proceedings of SPIE--the International Society for Optical Engineering; v. 2202. Variant Series: Proceedings / SPIE--the International Society for Optical Engineering; v. 2202 LC Classification: TA1673 .L3693 1995 Dewey Class No.: 621.36/6 20

Laser technology V. Applications in materials sciences and engineering: 23-27 September, 1996, Szczecin-'Swinouj'scie, Poland / Wieslaw Woli'nski, Jerzy Kusi'nski, editors; organized by Technical University of Szczecin ... [et al.]; sponsored by State Committee for Scientific Research (Poland), SPIE--the International Society for Optical Engineering in association with the SPIE Poland Chapter.Published/Created: Bellingham, Wash.: SPIE, c1996. Related Authors: Woli'nski, Wieslaw. Kusi'nski, Jerzy. Politechnika Szczeci'nska. Komitet Bada'n Naukowych (Poland) Society of Photo-optical Instrumentation Engineers. Society of Photo-optical Instrumentation Engineers. Poland Chapter. Description: vii, 158 p.: ill.; 28 cm. ISBN: 0819426172 Notes: Includes bibliographical references and indexes. Subjects: Lasers--Congresses. Lasers--Industrial applications--Congresses. Lasers in engineering--Congresses. Materials science--Instruments--Congresses. Measuring instruments--Congresses. Series: SPIE Poland Chapter proceedings; 35 Proceedings of SPIE--the International Society for Optical Engineering; v. 3187. Variant Series: Proceedings of SPIE, 0277-786X; v. 3187 LC Classification: TA1673 .L36938 1996 Dewey Class No.: 621.36/6 21

Laser technology V. Applications in medicine and ecology: 23-27 September 1996, Szczecin-'Swinouj'scie, Poland / Wieslaw Woli'nski, Alfreda Graczyk, editors; organized by Technical University of Szczecin (Poland) ... [et al.]; sponsored by State Committee for Scientific Research, Poland, SPIE Poland Chapter. Published/Created: Bellingham, Wash.: SPIE, c1997. Related Authors: Woli'nski, Wieslaw. Graczyk, Alfreda. Politechnika Szczeci'nska. Komitet Bada'n Naukowych (Poland) Society of Photo-optical Instrumentation Engineers. Poland Chapter. Description: x, 198 p.: ill.; 28 cm. ISBN: 0819426180 Notes: Includes bibliographical references and indexes. Subjects: Lasers in medicine--Congresses. Series: SPIE Poland Chapter proceedings; 36 Proceedings of SPIE--the International Society for Optical Engineering; v. 3188.

Variant Series: Proceedings of SPIE, 0277-786X; v. 3188 LC Classification: R857.L37 L428 1997 Dewey Class No.: 610/.28 21

Laser technology V. Physics and research and development trends: 23-27 September, 1996, Szczecin-'Swinouj'scie, Poland / Wieslaw Woli'nski, Michal Malinowski, editors; organized by Technical University of Szczecin ... [et al.]; sponsors, State Committee for Scientific Research (Poland), SPIE--the International Society for Optical Engineering. Published/Created: Bellingham, Wash.: SPIE, c1997. Related Authors: Woli'nski, Wieslaw. Malinowski, Michal. Politechnika Szczeci'nska. Komitet Bada'n Naukowych (Poland) Society of Photo-optical Instrumentation Engineers. Description: xx, 428: ill.; 28 cm. ISBN: 0819426024 Notes: Includes bibliographical references and indexes. Subjects: Lasers--Industrial applications--Laser materials--Measuring instruments--Congresses. Series: SPIE Poland Chapter proceedings; 34 Proceedings of SPIE--the International Society for Optical Engineering; v. 3186. Variant Series: Proceedings of SPIE, 0277-786X; v. 3186 LC Classification: TA1673 .L3694 1997 Dewey Class No.: 621.36/6 21

Laser technology VI. Applications: 27 September-1 October, 1999, Szczecin-'Swinouj'scie, Poland / Wieslaw Woli'nski, Zdzislaw Jankiewicz, editors; organized by Technical University of Szczecin (Poland) ... [et al.]; sponsored by State Committee for Scientific Research (Poland), SPIE--the International Society for Optical Engineering in association with the SPIE Poland Chapter. Published/Created: Bellingham, Washington: SPIE, c2000. Related Authors: Woli'nski, Wieslaw. Jankiewicz, Zdzislaw. Description: xvi, 274 p.: ill.; 28 cm. ISBN: 0819439126 Notes: Includes bibliographic references and author index. Subjects: Lasers--Congresses. Lasers--Industrial applications--Congresses. Lasers in engineering--Congresses. Materials science--Instruments--Congresses. Measuring instruments--Congresses. Series: Proceedings of SPIE--the International Society for Optical Engineering; v. 4238. Variant Series: Proceedings of SPIE; v. 4238

Laser technology VI: progress in lasers: 27 September-1 October 1999, Szczecin-'Swinouj'scie, Poland / Wieslaw L. Woli'nski, Zdzislaw Jankiewicz, editors; organized by Technical University of Szczecin (Poland) ... [et al.]; sponsored by State Committee for Scientific Research (Poland) [and] SPIE--the International Society for Optical Engineering in association with SPIE Poland Chapter. Published/Created: Bellingham, Wash., USA: SPIE, c2000. Related Authors: Woli'nski, Wieslaw. Jankiewicz, Zdzislaw. Politechnika Szczeci'nska. Komitet Bada'n Naukowych (Poland) Society of Photo-optical Instrumentation Engineers. Society of Photo-optical Instrumentation Engineers. Poland Chapter. Description: xix, 236 p.: ill.; 28 cm. ISBN: 0819439118 Notes: "STL'99"--Cover. Includes bibliographical references and index. Subjects: Lasers--Congresses. Lasers--Industrial applications--Congresses. Series: SPIE Poland Chapter proceedings; 54 Proceedings of SPIE--the International Society for Optical Engineering; v. 4237. Variant Series: SPIE proceedings series; v. 4237 LC Classification: TA1673 .L36943 2000 Dewey Class No.: 621.36/6 21

Laser testing and reliability: 7 November 1991, San Jose, California / David L. Begley, S.C. Wang, chairs/editors; sponsored and published by SPIE--the International Society for Optical Engineering. Published/Created: Bellingham, Wash.: SPIE, c1992. Related Authors: Begley, David L. Wang, S. C. (Shing Chung), 1934- Society of Photo-optical Instrumentation Engineers. Description: v, 104 p.: ill.; 28 cm. ISBN: 0819407585 Notes: Includes bibliographical references and index. Subjects: Semiconductor lasers--Reliability--Semiconductor lasers--Testing--Congresses. Series: Proceedings of SPIE--the International Society for Optical Engineering; v. 1620. Variant

Series: Proceedings / SPIE--the International Society for Optical Engineering; v. 1620 LC Classification: TA1700 .L39 1992 Dewey Class No.: 621.36/6 20

Laser use in oncology / edited by Andrei V. Ivanov, Mishik A. Kazaryan. Published/Created: Bellingham, Wash., USA: SPIE--the International Society of Optical Engineering in cooperation with SPIE Russia chapter, c1996. Related Authors: Ivanov, Andrei V. Kazaryan, Mishik A. Society of Photo-optical Instrumentation Engineers. Society of Photo-optical Instrumentation Engineers. Russian Chapter. Description: vii, 252 p.: ill.; 28 cm. ISBN: 0819421049 (pbk.) Notes: Includes bibliographical references and author index. Subjects: Tumors--Diagnosis--Equipment and supplies--Congresses. Tumors--Treatment--Equipment and supplies--Congresses. Lasers--Diagnostic use--Congresses. Lasers in surgery--Congresses. Series: Proceedings of SPIE--the International Society for Optical Engineering; v. 2728. Variant Series: SPIE proceedings series; v. 2728 LC Classification: RC270 .L365 1996 Dewey Class No.: 616.99/2/0028 20

Laser use in oncology II: selected research papers on laser use in oncology, 1997-1999 / Andrei V. Ivanov, Mishik A. Kazaryan, editors; sponsored by SPIE Russia Chapter. Published/Created: Bellingham, Wash., USA: SPIE, c2000. Related Authors: Ivanov, Andrei V. Kazaryan, Mishik A. Society of Photo-optical Instrumentation Engineers. Society of Photo-optical Instrumentation Engineers. Russian Chapter. Description: viii, 230 p.: ill.; 28 cm. ISBN: 0819436887 Notes: Includes bibliographical references and index. Subjects: Cancer--Photochemotherapy--Congresses. Lasers--Therapeutic use--Congresses. Series: Proceedings of SPIE--the International Society for Optical Engineering; v. 4059. Variant Series: SPIE proceedings series, 0277-786X; v. 4059 LC Classification: RC271.P43 L374 2000 Dewey Class No.: 616.99/40631 21

Laser weapons technology II: 16-17 April, 2001, Orlando, [Fla.] USA / William E. Thompson, Paul H. Merritt, chairs/editors; sponsored ... by SPIE--the International Society for Optical Engineering. Published/Created: Bellingham, Wash.: SPIE, c2001. Related Authors: Thompson, William E. Merritt, Paul H. Society of Photo-optical Instrumentation Engineers. Description: viii, 198 p.: ill.; 28 cm. ISBN: 081944071X Notes: Includes bibliographical references and index. Subjects: Lasers--Military applications--Congresses. Series: Proceedings of SPIE--the International Society for Optical Engineering; v. 4376. Variant Series: SPIE proceedings series; v. 4376

Laser/optical processing of electronic materials, 10-11 October 1989, Santa Clara, California / J. Narayan, chair/editor; sponsored by SPIE--the International Society for Optical Engineering; cooperating organizations, SEMATECH [and] Center for Advanced Electronic Materials Processing, North Carolina State University [and] Engineering Research Center for Plasma-Aided Manufacturing, University of Wisconsin-Madison. Published/Created: Bellingham, Wash., USA: SPIE, c1990. Related Authors: Narayan, J. (Jagdish) Society of Photo-optical Instrumentation Engineers. Description: vi, 221 p.: ill.; 28 cm. ISBN: 0819402265 Notes: Includes bibliographical references and index. Subjects: Semiconductor industry--Laser use in--Congresses. Lasers--Industrial applications--Congresses. Semiconductors--Etching--Congresses. Annealing of crystals--Congresses. Series: Proceedings of SPIE--the International Society for Optical Engineering; v. 1190. Variant Series: Proceedings / SPIE--the International Society for Optical Engineering; v. 1190 LC Classification: TK7871.85 .L276 1990 Dewey Class No.: 621.381/52 20

Laser-6 / subject editors, B. Mordike, A.B. Vannes. Published/Created: Gournay-sur-Marne, France: IITT-International, [1990] Related Authors: Mordike, Barry L.

Vannes, A. B. IITT-International. Description: 180 p.: ill.; 24 cm. ISBN: 2907669125 Notes: Includes bibliographical references. Subjects: Lasers--Industrial applications--Congresses. Surfaces (Technology)--Congresses. Series: Technology transfer series (Gournay-sur-Marne, France) Variant Series: Technology transfer series LC Classification: TA1673 .L315 1990 Dewey Class No.: 621.36/6 20

Laser-assisted fabrication of thin films and microstructures: 17-19 August 1993, Québec, Canada / Ian W. Boyd, chair/editor; Masamitsu Haruna ... [et al.], cochairs; sponsored and published by SPIE--the International Society for Optical Engineering; cosponsored by Government of Canada ... [et al.]; cooperating organization, American Physical Society. Published/Created: Bellingham, Wash., USA: SPIE, c1994. Related Authors: Boyd, Ian W., 1958- Haruna, Masamitsu, 1945- Society of Photo-optical Instrumentation Engineers. American Physical Society. Description: ix, 366 p.: ill.; 28 cm. ISBN: 0819413046 (pbk.) Notes: Includes bibliographical references and author index. Subjects: Lasers--Industrial applications--Congresses. Pulsed laser deposition--Congresses. Thin film devices--Design and construction--Congresses. Microstructure--Congresses. Series: Proceedings of SPIE--the International Society for Optical Engineering; v. 2045. Variant Series: Proceedings / SPIE--the International Society for Optical Engineering; v. 2045 LC Classification: TA1673 .L3533 1994 Dewey Class No.: 621.3815/2 20

Laser-assisted microtechnology 2000: 23-25 August 2000, St. Petersburg-Pushkin, Russia / Vadim P. Veiko, editor; organized by St. Petersburg Institute of Fine Mechanics and Optics (Russia) ... [et al.]; sponsored by Ministry of Education of the Russian Federation ... [et al.]; cooperating organizations, General Physics Institute, Russian Academy of Sciences ... [et al.]. Published/Created: Bellingham, Wash.: SPIE, c2001. Related Authors: Veiko, V. P. (Vadim Pavlovich) Society of Photo-optical Instrumentation Engineers. St. Petersburg Institute of Fine Mechanics and Optics. Russia (Federation). Ministerstvo obrazovaniia. Institut obshchei fiziki (Rossiiskaia akademiia nauk) Description: x, 306 p.: ill.; 25 cm. ISBN: 0819438138 Notes: Includes bibliographical references and index. Subjects: Electronic industries--Technological innovations Congresses. Lasers--Industrial applications--Congresses. Laser ablation--Congresses. Manufacturing processes--Congresses. Micromachining--Congresses. Series: Proceedings of SPIE--the International Society for Optical Engineering; v. 4157. Variant Series: SPIE proceedings series; v. 4157 LC Classification: TK7836 .L387 2001 Dewey Class No.: 621.381 21

Laser-assisted processing II: proceedings: ECO3, the Congress of EPS--European Physical Society, EUROPTICA--the European Federation for Applied Optics, SPIE--the International Society for Optical Engineering / Lucien D. Laude, chair/editor; cooperating organizations, ANRT--Association nationale de la recherche technique ... [et al.]. Published/Created: Bellingham, Wash., USA: SPIE, c1990. Related Authors: Laude, Lucien D. European Physical Society. European Federation for Applied Optics. Society of Photo-optical Instrumentation Engineers. Association nationale de la recherche technique. European Congress on Optics (3rd: 1990: Hague, Netherlands) Description: vii, 220 p.: ill.; 28 cm. ISBN: 0819403261 Notes: Includes bibliographical references and index. Subjects: Lasers--Industrial applications--Congresses. Manufacturing processes--Congresses. Series: Proceedings of SPIE--the International Society for Optical Engineering; v. 1279. Variant Series: SPIE proceedings series; v. 1279 LC Classification: TA1677 .L362 1990 Dewey Class No.: 621.36/6 20

Laser-Doppler blood flowmetry / edited by A.P. Shepherd, P.Å. Öberg. Published/Created: Boston: Kluwer Academic Publishers, c1990. Related

Authors: Shepherd, A. P. (Albert P.) Öberg, P. Åke. Description: xv, 395 p.: ill.; 25 cm. ISBN: 0792305086 Notes: Includes bibliographical references and index. Subjects: Blood flow--Measurement. Laser Doppler blood flowmetry. Blood Flow Velocity. Echocardiography, Doppler. Lasers--diagnostic use. Ultrasonic Diagnosis. Series: Developments in cardiovascular medicine; v. 107. Variant Series: Developments in cardiovascular medicine; DICM 107 LC Classification: RC691.6.B55 L37 1990 Dewey Class No.: 616.1/07543 20

Laser-induced interstitial thermotherapy / editors, Gerhard J. Müller, André Roggan. Published/Created: Bellingham, Wash.: SPIE Optical Engineering Press, 1995. Related Authors: Müller, Gerhard J. Roggan, André. Description: xvi, 549 p.: ill.; 26 cm. ISBN: 0819418595 (hard cover) Notes: Includes bibliographical references. Subjects: Thermotherapy. Lasers in medicine. LC Classification: RM865 .L37 1995 Dewey Class No.: 615.8/32 20

Laser-induced plasmas and applications / edited by Leon J. Radziemski, David Asss. Cremers. Published/Created: New York: M. Dekker, c1989. Related Authors: Radziemski, Leon J., 1937- Cremers, David A. Description: xiv, 445 p.: ill.; 24 cm. ISBN: 0824780787 (alk. paper) Notes: Includes bibliographies. Subjects: Plasma engineering. High power lasers. Series: Optical engineering (Marcel Dekker, Inc.); v. 21. Variant Series: Optical engineering; 21 LC Classification: TA2020 .L37 1989 Dewey Class No.: 620.044 20

Laser-induced thin film processing: 8-10 February 1995, San Jose, California / Jan J. Dubowski, chair/editor; sponsored and published by SPIE--the International Society for Optical Engineering. Published/Created: Bellingham, Wash., USA: SPIE, c1995. Related Authors: Dubowski, J. J. Society of Photo-optical Instrumentation Engineers. Description: xi, 476 p.: ill.; 28 cm. ISBN: 0819417505 (pbk.) Notes: Includes bibliographical references and index. Subjects: Thin films--Thin film devices--Microelectronics--Lasers--Industrial applications--Congresses. Series: Proceedings of SPIE--the International Society for Optical Engineering; v. 2403. Variant Series: SPIE proceedings series; v. 2403 LC Classification: TA418.9.T45 L37 1995 Dewey Class No.: 621.3815/2 20

Lasers and Electro-optics Society (Institute of Electrical and Electronics Engineers). Meetings (1994: Lake Tahoe, Nev.) LEOS 1994, Summer Topical Meeting Digest on Integrated Optoelectronics, July 6-8, 1994; Smart Pixels, July 11-13, 1994; Optical Networks and Their Enabling Technologies, July 11-13, 1994; Optoelectronic Materials Growth and Processing, July 11-13, 1994, Hyatt Regency Lake Tahoe, Lake Tahoe, NV / sponsored by the IEEE Lasers and Electro-Optics Society in cooperation with IEEE Electron Devices Society. Published/Created: New York: Institute of Electronics and Electrical Engineers, c1994. Description: 1 v. (various pagings): ill.; 28 cm. ISBN: 0780317521 078031753X (microfiche) Notes: Cover title. "IEEE catalog number: 94TH0606-4." Includes bibliographical references and index. Subjects: Integrated optics--Optical communications--Optoelectronic devices--Materials--Congresses. LC Classification: TA1660 .L372 1994 Dewey Class No.: 621.36/93 20

Lasers and mass spectrometry / edited by David M. Lubman. Published/Created: New York: Oxford University Press, 1990. Related Authors: Lubman, David M. Description: xiii, 545 p.: ill.; 24 cm. ISBN: 0195059298 (alk. paper) Notes: Includes bibliographies and index. Subjects: Laser spectroscopy. Mass spectrometry. Series: Oxford series on optical sciences; 1 LC Classification: QD96.L3 L365 1990 Dewey Class No.: 543/.0858 19

Lasers in Manufacturing--S.P.O.T. '88 (1988: Cleveland, Ohio) Lasers in Manufacturing--S.P.O.T. '88: May 2-4, 1988, Cleveland, Ohio. Published/Created: Dearborn, Mich.

(1 SME Dr., Dearborn 48121): Society of Manufacturing Engineers, c1988. Description: 1 v. (various pagings): ill.; 28 cm. Notes: Cover title. "For presentation at a creative manufacturing engineering program." Contains technical papers MS88-166-173 of the Society of Manufacturing Engineers. Includes bibliographies. Subjects: Lasers--Industrial applications--Congresses. LC Classification: TA1677 .L363 1988 Dewey Class No.: 621.36/6 20

Lasers in neurosurgery / edited by Jon H. Robertson, W. Craig Clark. Published/Created: Boston: Kluwer Academic Publishers, c1988. Related Authors: Robertson, Jon H. Clark, W. Craig. Description: xiii, 182 p.: ill.; 26 cm. ISBN: 0898389666: Notes: Includes bibliographies and index. Subjects: Nervous system--Laser surgery. Laser Surgery. Nervous System--surgery. Series: Foundations of neurological surgery; FONS1 LC Classification: RD593 .L35 1988 Dewey Class No.: 617/.48 19

Lasers in neurosurgery / editors, E.F. Downing (editor-in-chief) ... [et al.]. Published/Created: Wien; New York: Springer-Verlag, c1989. Related Authors: Downing, E. F. (Edward F.) Description: 129 p.: ill.; 25 cm. ISBN: 0387820671 (U.S.) Notes: Includes bibliographies and index. Subjects: Nervous system--Laser surgery. Lasers--therapeutic use. Neurosurgery--methods. LC Classification: RD593 .L36 1989 Dewey Class No.: 617/.48059 19

Lasers in ophthalmic surgery / [edited by] David B. Karlin. Published/Created: Cambridge, Mass., USA: Blackwell Science, c1995. Related Authors: Karlin, David B. Description: x, 237 p.: ill. (some col.); 29 cm. ISBN: 0865422605 Notes: Includes bibliographical references and index. Subjects: Lasers in ophthalmology. Eye--Eye Diseases--Surgery. Laser Surgery--methods. LC Classification: RE86 .L374 1995 Dewey Class No.: 617.7/1 20

Lasers in orthopaedics / edited by Henry H. Sherk. Published/Created: Philadelphia: Lippincott, c1990. Related Authors: Sherk, Henry H., 1930- Description: xvii, 221 p.: ill.; 26 cm. ISBN: 0397509626 Notes: Includes index. Includes bibliographical references. Subjects: Lasers in orthopedics. Laser Surgery. Orthopedics. LC Classification: RD732 .L37 1990 Dewey Class No.: 617.3 20

Lasers in otolaryngology / edited by J.A.S. Carruth and G.T. Simpson. Published/Created: Chicago: Year Book Medical Publishers, c1988. Related Authors: Carruth, J. A. S. (John A. S.) Simpson, George T. Description: xiv, 181 p.: ill.; 24 cm. ISBN: 081511494X Notes: Includes bibliographies and index. Subjects: Lasers in otolaryngology. Laser Surgery. Otorhinolaryngologic Diseases--surgery. LC Classification: RF51.5 .L37 1988 Dewey Class No.: 617/.51059 19

Lasers in otolaryngology--head and neck surgery / edited by R. Kim Davis. Published/Created: Philadelphia: Saunders, 1990. Related Authors: Davis, R. Kim. Description: x, 208 p.: ill. (some col.); 27 cm. ISBN: 072163124X Notes: Includes bibliographical references and index. Subjects: Lasers in otolaryngology. Head--Surgery. Neck--Surgery. Head--surgery. Laser Surgery. Neck--surgery. Otorhinolaryngologic Diseases--surgery. LC Classification: RF51.5 .L38 1990 Dewey Class No.: 617.5/10592 20

Lasers in otorhinolaryngology, and in head and neck surgery: 4th international symposium, Kiel, January 14-16, 1994 / volume editors, H. Rudert, J.A. Werner. Published/Created: Basel; New York: Karger, 1995. Related Authors: Rudert, H. (Heinrich), 1935- Werner, J. A. (Jochen A.), 1958- Description: xii, 264 p.: ill. (some col.); 25 cm. ISBN: 3805560877 (acid-free paper) Notes: Includes bibliographical references and index. Subjects: Lasers in otolaryngology--Head--Laser surgery--Neck--Laser surgery—Otorhino-laryngologic Diseases--surgery--Laser Surgery--Congresses. Series: Advances in oto-rhino-laryngology; vol. 49 LC Classification: RF51.5 .L374 1995 Dewey Class No.: 617.5/1059 20

Lasers in polymer science and technology: applications / editors, Jean-Pierre Fouassier, Jan F. Rabek. Published/Created: Boca Raton, Fla.: CRC Press, c1990. Related Authors: Fouassier, Jean-Pierre, 1947- Rabek, J. F. Description: 4 v.: ill.; 26 cm. ISBN: 0849348447 (v. 1) 0849348455 (v. 2) 0849348463 (v. 3) 0849348471 (v. 4) Notes: Includes bibliographical references and indexes. Subjects: Polymers--Analysis. Laser spectroscopy. LC Classification: TP1140 .L37 1990 Dewey Class No.: 668.9 20

Lasers in surface engineering / edited by Narendra B. Dahotre. Published/Created: Materials Park, OH: ASM International, 1998. Description: 599 p.; 27 cm. ISBN: 0871706652 Series: Surface engineering series; v. 1

Lasers in surgery: advanced characterization, therapeutics, and systems X: 22-23, 25 January 2000, San Jose, California / R. Rox Anderson ... [et al.], chairs/editors; sponsored by SPIE--the International Society for Optical Engineering [and] IBOS--the International Biomedical Optics Society. Published/Created: Bellingham, Wash., USA: SPIE, c2000. Related Authors: Anderson, Rox. Description: xvi, 638 p.: ill. (some col.); 28 cm. ISBN: 0819435236 Notes: Earlier vols. have Proceedings of lasers in surgery: advanced characterization, therapeutics, and systems. Includes bibliographical references and index. Subjects: Lasers in surgery--Congresses. Lasers in medicine--Congresses. Lasers--Therapeutic use--Congresses. Series: Progress in biomedical optics and imaging, 1605-7422; vol. 1, no. 1 Proceedings of SPIE--the International Society for Optical Engineering; v. 3907. Variant Series: Proceedings of SPIE; v. 3907 LC Classification: RD73.L3 L347 2000 Dewey Class No.: 617/.05 21

Lasers in surgery: advanced characterization, therapeutics, and systems XI: 20-23 January 2001, San Jose, USA / R. Rox Anderson ... [et al.], chairs/editors. Published/Created: Bellingham, Wash., USA: SPIE, c2001. Related Authors: Anderson, Rox. Society of Photo-optical Instrumentation Engineers. Description: xxi, 606 p.: ill.; 28 cm. ISBN: 0819439223 Notes: Earlier vols. have Proceedings of lasers in surgery: advanced characterization, therapeutics, and systems. Includes bibliographical references and index. Subjects: Lasers in surgery--Lasers in medicine--Lasers--Therapeutic use--Congresses. Series: Progress in biomedical optics and imaging, 1605-7422; vol. 2, no. 1 Proceedings of SPIE--the International Society for Optical Engineering; v. 4244. Variant Series: Proceedings of SPIE; v. 4244 LC Classification: RD73.L3 L365 2001 Dewey Class No.: 617/.05 21

Lasers in synthesis, characterization, and processing of diamond: 6-9 October 1997, Tashkent, Uzbekistan / Alexander M. Prokhorov, chair; Vitaly I. Konov, Mukhsin Kh. Ashurov, cochairs; Vitaly I. Konov, Victor G. Ralchenko, editors; sponsored by General Physics Institute, Russian Academy of Sciences (Russia) ... [et al.]; organized by General Physics Institute, Russian Academy of Sciences, Phonon Scientific Industrial Association (Uzbekistan), [and] SPIE Russia Chapter. Published/Created: Bellingham, Wash.: SPIE, c1997. Related Authors: Prokhorov, A. M. (Aleksandr Mikhailovich), 1916- Konov, V. I. Ralchenko, Victor G. Description: x, 246 p.: ill.; 28 cm. ISBN: 0819429422 Notes: Includes bibliographical references and index. Subjects: Diamonds, Artificial--Diamond thin films--lasma-enhanced chemical vapor disposition--Lasers--Industrial applications--Congresses. Series: Proceedings of SPIE--the International Society for Optical Engineering; v. 3484. Variant Series: SPIE proceedings series; v. 3484 LC Classification: TP873.5.D5 L37 1997 Dewey Class No.: 666/.88 21

Lasers in urologic surgery / [edited by] Joseph A. Smith, Jr., Barry S. Stein, Ralph C. Benson. Edition Information: 3rd ed. Published/Created: St. Louis: Mosby, c1994. Related Authors: Smith, Joseph A., 1949- Stein, Barry S. (Barry Stephen), 1948- Benson, Ralph C., 1942- Description: xiv, 295 p.: ill.; 28 cm. ISBN: 080167736X Notes: Includes bibliographical references and index. Subjects: Genitourinary organs--Laser surgery. Laser Surgery. Urogential System--surgery. Urogential Diseases--surgery. Urologic Diseases--surgery. LC Classification: RD571 .L37 1993 Dewey Class No.: 617.4/6059 20

Lasers in urologic surgery / [edited by] Joseph A. Smith, Jr., Barry S. Stein, Ralph C. Benson, Jr. Edition Information: 2nd ed. Published/Created: Chicago: Year Book Medical Pub., c1989. Related Authors: Smith, Joseph A., 1949- Stein, Barry S. (Barry Stephen), 1948- Benson, Ralph C., 1942- Description: xxiv, 194 p.: ill. (some col.); 27 cm. ISBN: 0815178441 Notes: Includes bibliographical references and index. Subjects: Genitourinary organs--Laser surgery. Laser Surgery. Urologic Diseases--surgery. LC Classification: RD571 .L37 1989 Dewey Class No.: 617/.46/059 19

Lasers in urological surgery / Alfons G. Hofstetter(ed.); with contributions by R. Baumgartner ... [et al.]. Published/Created: Berlin; New York: Springer, c1997. Projected Pub. Date: 9706 Related Authors: Hofstetter, Alfons. Baumgartner, R. Description: p. cm. ISBN: 354062452X (alk. paper) Notes: Includes bibliographical references and index. Subjects: Genitourinary organs--Laser surgery. Urogenital Diseases--surgery. Laser Surgery. LC Classification: RD571 .L36813 1997 Dewey Class No.: 617.4/6059 21

Lasers in urology: principles and practice / T.A. McNicholas (ed.). Published/Created: London; New York: Springer-Verlag, c1990. Related Authors: McNicholas, T. A., 1952- Description: xii, 168 p., [2] leaves of plates: ill. (some col.); 25 cm. ISBN: 3540195173 0387196153 (alk. paper) Notes: Includes bibliographical references and index. Subjects: Urinary organs--Laser surgery. Lasers--therapeutic use. Urologic Diseases--radiotherapy. Series: The Bloomsbury series in clinical science LC Classification: RD571 .L38 1990 Dewey Class No.: 617.4/61059 20

Lasers, molecules, and methods / edited by Joseph O. Hirschfelder, Robert E. Wyatt, Rob D. Coalson. Published/Created: New York: Wiley, c1989. Related Authors: Hirschfelder, Joseph Oakland, 1911- Wyatt, Robert E. (Robert Eugene) Coalson, Rob D. (Rob Duncan) Center for Nonlinear Studies(Los Alamos National Laboratory) Description: xvii, 1022 p.: ill.; 24 cm. Notes: Based on papers presented at a symposium held at the Los Alamos Center for Nonlinear Studies on July 7-11, 1986. "An Interscience publication." Includes bibliographies and indexes. Subjects: Lasers in physics--Congresses. Molecules--Congresses. Series: Advances in chemical physics, 0065-2385; v. 73 LC Classification: QD453 .A27 vol. 73 QC685 Dewey Class No.: 541 s 542 19

Laser-solid interactions for materials processing: symposium held April 25-27, 2000, San Francisco, California, U.S.A. / editors, D. Kumar ... [et al.]. Published/Created: Warrendale, Pa.: Materials Research Society, 2001. Related Authors: Kumar, D. (Dhananjay) Description: 1 v. (various pagings): ill.; 24 cm. ISBN: 1558995250 Notes: Includes bibliographical references and indexes. Subjects: Lasers--Industrial applications--Congresses. Series: Materials Research Society symposia proceedings; . 617. Variant Series: Materials Research Society symposium proceedings; v. 617 LC Classification: TA1673 .L3676 2001 Dewey Class No.: 621.36/6 21

Laser-tissue interaction and tissue optics II: 7-10 September 1996, Vienna, Austria / Hans J. Albrecht ... [et al.] chairs/editors; sponsored by Laser Vision ... [et al.]. Published/Created: Bellingham, WA:

SPIE, 1996. Related Authors: Albrecht, Hans Jörg. Society of Photo-optical Instrumentation Engineers. Description: vii, 204 p.: ill.; 28 cm. ISBN: 0819423254 (pbk.) Notes: Includes bibliographical references and index. Subjects: Tissues--Optical properties--Congresses. Lasers--Physiological effect--Congresses. Series: Progress in biomedical optics Proceedings EurOpt series. Proceedings of SPIE--the International Society for Optical Engineering; v. 2923. Variant Series: EurOpt series SPIE proceedings series; v. 2923 LC Classification: QH642 .L37 1996 Dewey Class No.: 571.5/028 21

Laser-tissue interaction XI: photochemical, photothermal, and photomechanical: 22-27 January 2000, San Jose, USA / Donald D. Duncan, Jeffrey O. Hollinger, Steven L. Jacques, chairs/editors; sponsored by U.S. Air Force Office of Scientific Research [and] SPIE--the International Society for Optical Engineering, International Biomedical Optics Society. Published/Created: Bellingham, Wash., USA: SPIE, c2000. Related Authors: Duncan, Donald D. Hollinger, Jeffrey O. Jacques, Steven L. United States. Air Force. Office of Scientific Research. International Biomedical Optics Society. Society of Photo-optical Instrumentation Engineers. Description: xiii, 652 p.: ill.; 28 cm. ISBN: 0819435309 Notes: Earlier conference proceedings titled: Proceedings of laser-tissue interaction. Includes bibliographical references and index. Subjects: Lasers in medicine--Congresses. Lasers--Diagnostic use--Congresses. Lasers--Therapeutic use--Congresses. Laser ablation--Congresses. Laser spectroscopy--Congresses. Series: Progress in biomedical optics and imaging, 1605-7422; vol. 1, no. 8 Proceedings of SPIE--the International Society for Optical Engineering; v. 3914. Variant Series: Proceedings of SPIE; v. 3914 LC Classification: R857.L37 L4285 2000 Dewey Class No.: 610/.28 21

Laser-tissue interaction XII: photochemical, photothermal, and photomechanical: 21-24 January 2001, San Jose, USA / Donald D. Duncan, Steven L. Jacques, Peter C. Johnson, chairs/editors; sponsored by U.S. Air Force Office of Scientific Research [and] SPIE--the International Society for Optical Engineering. Published/Created: Bellingham, Wash., USA: SPIE, c2001. Related Authors: Duncan, Donald D. Jacques, Steven L. Johnson, Peter C. United States. Air Force. Office of Scientific Research. Society of Photo-optical Instrumentation Engineers. Description: xii, 486 p.: ill.; 28 cm. ISBN: 0819439355 Notes: Earlier conference proceedings titled: Proceedings of laser-tissue interaction. Includes bibliographical references and index. Subjects: Lasers in medicine--Congresses. Lasers--Diagnostic use--Congresses. Lasers--Therapeutic use--Congresses. Laser ablation--Congresses. Laser spectroscopy--Congresses. Series: Progress in biomedical optics and imaging, 1605-7422; vol. 2, no. 14 Proceedings of SPIE--the International Society for Optical Engineering; v. 4257. Variant Series: Proceedings of SPIE, 0277-786X; v. 4257 LC Classification: R857.L37 L377 2001 Dewey Class No.: 610/.28 21

Laser-tissue interactions, therapeutic applications, and photodynamic therapy: 18-21 June 2001, Munich, Germany / Reginald Birngruber, Hubert van den Bergh, chairs/editors; sponsored by OSA--Optical Society of America ... [et al.]. Published/Created: Washington, D.C.: Optical Society of America; Bellingham, Wash.: International Society for Optical Engineering, c2001. Related Authors: Birngruber, R. (Reginald) Bergh, Hubert van den. Optical Society of America. Description: viii, 198 p.: ill.; 27 cm. ISBN: 0819441473 Notes: Includes bibliographical references and index. Subjects: Lasers in medicine--Congresses. Lasers--Diagnostic use--Congresses. Lasers--Therapeutic use--Congresses. Series: Progress in biomedical optics and imaging, 1605-7422; v. 2, no. 33 Proceedings of SPIE--the International Society for Optical Engineering; v. 4433. Variant Series: Proceedings of SPIE, 0277-786X; v. 4433

Lask, Gary P. (Gary Philip) Lasers in cutaneous and cosmetic surgery / Gary P. Lask, Nicholas J. Lowe. Published/Created: Philadelphia: Churchill Livingstone, c2000. Related Authors: Lowe, N. J. (Nicholas J.) Description: xi, 167 p.: ill. (some col.); 29 cm. ISBN: 0443076391 Notes: Includes bibliographical references and index. Subjects: Skin--Surgery. Lasers in surgery. Surgery, Plastic. Skin Diseases--Skin--surgery. Laser Surgery--methods. Lasers--therapeutic use. Surgery, Plastic. LC Classification: RD520 .L374 2000 Dewey Class No.: 617.4/77059 21

Laud, B. B. Lasers and non-linear optics / B.B. Laud. Edition Information: 2nd ed. Published/Created: New York: Wiley, 1991. Description: xii, 262 p.: ill.; 24 cm. ISBN: 0470217316 Notes: Includes bibliographical references (p. [249]-257) and index. Subjects: Lasers. Nonlinear optics. LC Classification: QC688 .L38 1991 Dewey Class No.: 621.36/6 20

Laufer, Gabriel. Introduction to optics and lasers in engineering / Gabriel Laufer. Published/Created: Cambridge; New York: Cambridge University Press, 1996. Description: xvii, 476 p.: ill.; 26 cm. ISBN: 0521452333 (hc) Notes: Includes bibliographical references and index. Subjects: Lasers in engineering. Optics. LC Classification: TA367.5 .L39 1996 Dewey Class No.: 621.36/6 20

LEOS (Conference) Conference digest / Lasers and Electro-optics Society Annual Meeting. Published/Created: New York, N.Y.: Institute of Electrical and Electronics Engineers, [1988?- Related Authors: Lasers and Electro-optics Society (Institute of Electrical and Electronics Engineers) Institute of Electrical and Electronics Engineers. Description: v.: ill.; 28 cm. Began with 1988. Current Frequency: Annual Continued by: LEOS (Conference). LEOS ... conference digest (DLC) 96644741 (OCoLC)29684733 Notes: Description based on: '89. SERBIB/SERLOC merged record Supplement to: LEOS (Conference). Conference proceedings (DLC) 96644738 (OCoLC)19408894 Subjects: Lasers--Electrooptics--Optoelectronic devices--Optical detectors--Congresses. LC Classification: TA1671 .L46a Dewey Class No.: 621.36/6/05 20

LEOS (Conference) Conference proceedings / Lasers and Electro-optics Society, Annual Meeting. Published/Created: [New York, N.Y.?: Institute of Electrical and Electronics Engineers?], c1988- Description: v.: ill.; 28 cm. '88- Current Frequency: Annual Continued by: LEOS (Conference). LEOS ... conference proceedings (DLC) 96644739 (OCoLC)34233597 Cancel/Invalid LCCN: sn 89013157 CODEN: CPISFO Notes: Sponsored by: IEEE Lasers and Electro-optics Society, in conjunction with various other scientific organizations and meetings each year. SERBIB/SERLOC merged record Has Supplement: LEOS (Conference). Conference digest (DLC) 96644740 (OCoLC)21381972 Additional Form Avail.: Also available by subscription, in PDF format, via the World Wide Web. Subjects: Lasers--Electrooptics--Optoelectronic devices--Optical detectors--Congresses. LC Classification: TA1671 .L46a Dewey Class No.: 621.36/6/05 20

LEOS (Conference) Conference proceedings / LEOS ... Annual Meeting. Published/Created: [New York, N.Y.: Institute of Electrical and Electronics Engineers, c1996/ Description: v.: ill.; 28 cm. Vols. for 1996-<1998 also designated as 9th-<11th annual meeting. Issues for 1997-<1998 in 2 vols. '96- Current Frequency: Annual Continues: LEOS (Conference). LEOS ... conference proceedings (DLC) 96644739 (OCoLC)34233597 ISSN: 1092-8081 Notes: Description based on surrogate. Subjects: Lasers--Electrooptics--Optoelectronic devices--Optical detectors--Congresses. LC Classification: TA1671 .L46a Dewey Class No.: 621 13

LEOS (Conference) LEOS ... conference digest / IEEE Lasers and Electro-optics Society ... Annual Meeting. Published/Created: New

York, N.Y.: Institute of Electrical and Electronics Engineers, Related Authors: Lasers and Electro-optics Society (Institute of Electrical and Electronics Engineers). Institute of Electrical and Electronics Engineers. Description: v.: ill.; 28 cm. Current Frequency: Annual Continues: LEOS (Conference). Conference digest (DLC) 96644740 (OCoLC)21381972 Notes: Description based on: '91. SERBIB/SERLOC merged record Supplement to: LEOS (Conference). LEOS ... conference proceedings (DLC) 96644739 (OCoLC)34233597 Subjects: Lasers--Electrooptics--Optoelectronic devices--Optical detectors--Congresses. LC Classification: TA1671 .L46a Dewey Class No.: 621.36/6/05 20

LEOS (Conference) LEOS ... conference proceedings: IEEE Lasers and Electro-Optics Society ... Annual Meeting. Published/Created: [New York, N.Y.: Institute of Electrical and Electronics Engineers, Related Authors: Lasers and Electro-optics Society (Institute of Electrical and Electronics Engineers). Institute of Electrical and Electronics Engineers. Description: v.: ill.; 28 cm. Vols. for 1993-<1995 also designated as 6th-<8th annual meeting. Current Frequency: Annual Continues: LEOS (Conference). Conference proceedings (DLC) 96644738 (OCoLC)19408894 Continued by: LEOS (Conference). Conference proceedings (LEOS (Conference): 1996) 1092-8081 (DLC)sn 970001160 (OCoLC)36437250 Notes: Description based on: '92. SERBIB/SERLOC merged record Has Supplement: LEOS (Conference). LEOS ... conference digest (DLC) 96644741 (OCoLC)29684733 Subjects: Lasers--Electrooptics--Optoelectronic devices--Optical detectors--Congresses. LC Classification: TA1671 .L46a Dewey Class No.: 621.36/6/05 20

LEOS (Conference). Summer Topical Meetings (1999: Sheraton San Diego Hotel & Marina) Nanostructures and quantum dots: 1999 IEEE/LEOS summer topical meeting, 26-27 July 1999, Sheraton San Diego Hotel & Marina, San Diego, CA. Published/Created: Piscataway, NJ: IEEE Service Center, c1999. Related Authors: Lasers and Electro-optics Society (Institute of Electrical and Electronics Engineers) Description: 1 v. (various pagings): ill.; 28 cm. ISBN: 0780356330 (softbound edition) Notes: "ISSN 1099-4742." Includes bibliographical references and indexes. Subjects: Quantum dots--Nanostructures--Congresses. LC Classification: TK7874.88 .L393 1999 Dewey Class No.: 621.3815/2 21

LEOS (Conference). Summer Topical Meetings (2000: Aventura, Fla.) 2000 digest of the LEOS Summer Topical Meetings: electronic-enhances optics, optical sensing in semiconductor manufacturing, electro-optics in space, broadband optical networks, 24-28 July, 2000, Turnberry Isle Resort & Club, Aventura, FL / IEEE Laser and Electro-optics Society. Published/Created: Piscataway, NJ: IEEE, c2000. Related Authors: Lasers and Electro-Optics Society (Institute of Electrical and Electronics Engineers) Institute of Electrical and Electronics Engineers. Description: 1 v. (various pagings): ill.; 27 cm. ISBN: 0780362527 0769506453 (microfiche) Notes: "IEEE Catalog #00TH8497"--T.p. Includes bibliographical references and author index. Additional Form Avail.: Also available via the World Wide Web with additional Electronic-enhanced optics, optical sensing in semiconductor manufacturing, electro-optics in space, broadband optical networks, 2000, digest of the LEOS Summer Topical Meetings. Subjects: Optical communications--Optoelectronic devices--Broadband communication systems--Congresses.

LEOS summer topical on broadband analog optoelectronics: devices and systems: July 23-25, 1990, Monterey Sheraton, Monterey, California: conference digest. Published/Created: New York, NY (345 E. 47th St., New York 10017): Institute of Electrical and Electronics Engineers, c1990. Description: 70 p.: ill.; 28 cm. Notes: Spine Title - Broadband analog optoelectronics. "Sponsored by the IEEE Lasers and Electro-optics Society and in cooperation with the Optical Society of America." "IEEE # 90TH0322-8." Includes bibliographical references and index. Subjects: Optical communications--Broadband communication systems--Optoelectronic devices--Fiber optics--Congresses. LC Classification: TK5103.59 .L46 1990 Dewey Class No.: 621.382/7 20

LEOS Summer Topical on Integrated Optoelectronics, July 30-August 1, 1990, Monterey Sheraton, Monterey, California: conference digest / sponsored by the IEEE Lasers and Electro-Optics Society ... Published/Created: New York, N.Y.: The Institute of Electrical and Electronics engineers, c1990. Description: 90 p.; 28 cm. Subjects: Optoelectronic devices--Integrated circuits--Congresses. LC Classification: TA1750 .L46 1990 Dewey Class No.: 621.381/045 20

LEOS summer topical on new semiconductor laser devices and applications, August 1-3, 1990, Monterey Sheraton, Monterey, California: conference digest / sponsored by the IEEE Lasers and Electro-optics Society and in cooperation with the Optical Society of America. Published/Created: New York, N.Y. (345 E. 47th St., New York 10017): Institute of Electrical and Electronics Engineers, c1990. Description: 70 p.: ill.; 28 cm. Notes: Spine Title - New semiconductor laser devices and applications. Papers presented at the Conference on "New Semiconductor Laser Devices and Applications." "IEEE #90TH0323-6." Includes bibliographical references and index. Subjects: Semiconductor lasers--Congresses. LC Classification: TA1700 .L47 1990 Dewey Class No.: 621.36/6 20

LEOS summer topical on optical multiple access networks, July 25-27, 1990, Monterey Sheraton, Monterey, California: conference digest / co-sponsored by IEEE Lasers and Electro-optics Society, IEEE Communications Society, in cooperation with the Optical Society of America. Published/Created: New York, NY (345 E. 47th St., New York 10017): Institute of Electrical and Electronics Engineers, 1990.

L'Esperance, Francis A., 1932- Ophthalmic lasers / Francis A. L'Esperance, Jr.; tone drawings by Virginia Cantarella. Edition Information: 3rd ed. Published/Created: St. Louis: Mosby, 1989- Description: v. <1-: ill.; 29 cm. ISBN: 0801629659 (v. 1) Notes: Includes bibliographies and index. Subjects: Laser coagulation. Eye--Diseases--Radiotherapy. Eye--surgery--atlases. Lasers--therapeutic use--atlases. LC Classification: RE992.P5 L47 1989 Dewey Class No.: 617.7/1 19

Modeling and simulation of higher-power laser systems IV: 12-13 February, 1997, San Jose, California / Usamah O. Farrukh, Santanu Basu, chairs/editors; sponsored and published by SPIE--the International Society for Optical Engineering. Published/Created: Bellingham, Washington: SPIE, c1997. Related Authors: Farrukh, Usamah O. Basu, Santanu. Society of Photo-optical Instrumentation Engineers. Description: x, 272 p.: ill.; 28 cm. ISBN: 0819424005 Notes: Includes bibliographic references and author index. Subjects: Lasers--Mathematical models--High-power lasers--Mathematical models--Congresses. Series: Proceedings of SPIE--the International Society for Optical Engineering; v. 2989 LC Classification: TA1673 .M626 1997 Dewey Class No.: 621.36/6 21

Modeling and simulation of laser systems II: proceedings, 23-24 January 1991, Los Angeles, California / Alvin D. Schnurr, chair/editor; sponsored by SPIE-the International Society for Optical Engineering. Published/Created: Bellingham, Wash., USA: The Society, 1991. Related Authors: Schnurr, Alvin D. Society of Photo-optical Instrumentation Engineers. Description: ix, 351 p.: ill.; 28 cm. ISBN: 0819405051 Notes: Includes bibliographical references and index. Subjects: Lasers--Mathematical models--Congresses. Lasers--Data processing--Congresses. Series: Proceedings of the SPIE--the International Society for Optical

Engineering; v. 1415. Variant Series: SPIE proceedings series; vol. 1415 LC Classification: TA1673 .M629 1991 Dewey Class No.: 621.36/6/015118 20

Modeling and simulation of laser systems. Published/Created: Bellingham, Wash.: SPIE--the International Society for Optical Engineering, Related Authors: Society of Photo-optical Instrumentation Engineers. Description: 3 v.: ill.; 28 cm. Began in 1989. -3 (24-25 Jan. 1994). Current Frequency: Biennial (irregular) Notes: Description based on: 3 (24-25 Jan. 1994). SERBIB/SERLOC merged record Continued by a monograph under Modeling and simulation of higher-power laser systems. Subjects: Lasers--Mathematical models--Congresses. Lasers--Data processing--Congresses. Series: Proceedings of SPIE--the International Society for Optical Engineering. Variant Series: Proceedings / SPIE--the International Society for Optical Engineering LC Classification: TA1673 .M628 Dewey Class No.: 621.36/6/011 20

Modeling and simulation of laser systems: proceedings, 17-18 January, 1989, Los Angeles, California / Donald L. Bullock, chair/editor; sponsored by SPIE-the International Society for Optical Engineering; cooperating organizations, Applied Optics Laboratory/New Mexico State University ... [et al.]. Published/Created: Bellingham, Wash., USA: The Society, c1989. Related Authors: Bullock, Donald L. Society of Photo-optical Instrumentation Engineers. Description: viii, 211 p.: ill.; 28 cm. ISBN: 0819400807 Notes: Includes bibliographical references. Subjects: Lasers--Mathematical models--Data processing--Congresses. Series: Proceedings of SPIE--the International Society for Optical Engineering; v. 1045. Variant Series: SPIE proceedings series; v. 1045 LC Classification: TA1673 .M63 1989 Dewey Class No.: 621.36/6 20

Mode-locked and solid state lasers, amplifiers, and applications: 17-19 August 1993, Québec, Canada / Michel Piché, Paul W. Pace, chairs/editors; sponsored and published by SPIE-The International Society for Optical Engineering. Published/Created: Bellingham, Wash.: The Society, c1994. Related Authors: Piché, Michel. Pace, Paul W. Society of Photo-optical Instrumentation Engineers. Description: vii, 446 p.: ill.; 28 cm. ISBN: 0819413003 Notes: Includes bibliographical references and index. Subjects: Mode-locked lasers--Solid-state lasers--Laser pulses, Ultrashort--Congresses. Series: Proceedings of SPIE--the International Society for Optical Engineering; v. 2041. Variant Series: Proceedings / SPIE--the International Society for Optical Engineering; v. 2041 LC Classification: TA1688 .M63 1994 Dewey Class No.: 621.36/61 20

Modern problems of laser physics: MPLP '95, Novosibirsk, August 28-September 2, 1995 / editors, Bagayev S.N., Denisov V.I.; organized by Institute of Laser Physics ... [et al.]. Published/Created: Novosibirsk: Siberian Division of Russian Academy of Sciences, 1996. Related Authors: Bagayev, S. N. Denisov, V. I. (Vladimir Ivanovich) Institut lazernoi fiziki SO RAN. International Symposium on Laser Physics (1995: Akademgorodok Novosibirsk, Russia) Description: 666 p.: ill. (some col.); 25 cm. Notes: "The International Symposium on Laser Physics was held in Akademgorodok, Novosibirsk, Russia."--Pref. At head of Title - International symposium. Includes bibliographical references. Subjects: Lasers--Congresses. Quantum electronics--Congresses. LC Classification: QC685 .M63 1996 Dewey Class No.: 621.36/6 21

Monitoring of gaseous pollutants by tunable diode lasers: proceedings of the international symposium held in Freiburg, F.R.G. 17-18 October 1988 / organized by the Fraunhofer Institut für Physikalische Messtechnik (Freiburg) under the auspices of the Commission of the European Communities; edited by R. Grisar ... [et al.]. Published/Created: Dordrecht; Boston: Kluwer Academic Publishers, c1989. Related Authors: Grisar, R. Fraunhofer

Institut für Physikalische Messtechnik. Commission of the European Communities. International Symposium on Monitoring of Gaseous Pollutants by Tunable Diode Lasers (2nd: 1988: Freiburg im Breisgau, Germany) Description: x, 305 p.: ill.; 24 cm. ISBN: 0792303342 (alk. paper) Notes: Papers presented at the second International Symposium on Monitoring of Gaseous Pollutants by Tunable Diode Lasers, held 10/17-18, 1988 in Freiburg. Includes bibliographical references. Subjects: Combustion gases--Environmental aspects--Analysis Congresses. Semiconductor lasers--Laser spectroscopy--Congresses. Series: Air pollution research report; 18 EUR (Series); 11956. Variant Series: EUR; 11956 LC Classification: TD885.5.C66 M66 1989 Dewey Class No.: 628.5/3 20

Monitoring of gaseous pollutants by tunable diode lasers: proceedings of the international symposium held in Freiburg, Germany, 17-18 October 1991 / organized by the Fraunhofer Institut für Physikalische Messtechnik (Freiburg) under the auspices of the German Federal Minister of Research and Development [and] the Commission of the European Communities; edited by R. Grisar ... [et al.]. Published/Created: Dordrecht; Boston: Kluwer Academic Publishers, c1992. Related Authors: Grisar, R Description: xxi, 372 p.: ill.; 24 cm. ISBN: 0792318269 (alk. paper) Notes: Papers presented at the Third International Symposium on Monitoring of Gaseous Pollutants by Tunable Diode Lasers. Includes bibliographical references and index. Subjects: Combustion gases--Environmental aspects--Analysis Congresses. Semiconductor lasers--Congresses. Laser spectroscopy--Congresses. LC Classification: TD885.5.C66 M66 1992 Dewey Class No.: 628.5/3/0287 20

Monitoring of gaseous pollutants by tunable diode lasers: proceedings of the international symposium held in Freiburg, F.R.G. 17-18 October 1988 / organized by the Fraunhofer Institut für Physikalische Messtechnik (Freiburg) under the auspices of the Commission of the European Communities; edited by R. Grisar ... [et al.]. Published/Created: Dordrecht; Boston: Kluwer Academic Publishers, c1989. Related Authors: Grisar, R. Fraunhofer Description: x, 305 p.: ill.; 24 cm. ISBN: 0792303342 (alk. paper) Notes: Papers presented at the second International Symposium on Monitoring of Gaseous Pollutants by Tunable Diode Lasers, held 10/17-18, 1988 in Freiburg. Includes bibliographical references. Subjects: Combustion gases--Environmental aspects--Analysis Congresses. Semiconductor lasers--Congresses. Laser spectroscopy--Congresses. Series: Air pollution research report; 18 EUR (Series); 11956. Variant Series: EUR; 11956 LC Classification: TD885.5.C66 M66 1989 Dewey Class No.: 628.5/3 20

Nakamura, Shuji, 1954- The blue laser diode: the complete story / Shuji Nakamura, Stephen Pearton, Gerhard Fasol. Edition Information: 2nd updated and extended ed. Published/Created: Berlin; New York: Springer, 2000. Related Authors: Pearton, S. J. Fasol, Gerhard. Description: xvi, 368 p.: ill. (some col); 24 cm. ISBN: 3540665056 (alk. paper) Notes: Includes bibliographical references (p. 347-360) and index. Subjects: Semiconductor lasers. Light emitting diodes. Gallium nitride. Diodes, Semiconductor. Blue light. LC Classification: TA1700 .N35 2000

Nardo, Don, 1947- Lasers / by Don Nardo. Published/Created: San Diego Calif.: Lucent Books, 2003. Projected Pub. Date: 0301 Description: p. cm. ISBN: 1590181042 Summary: Discusses the scientific discovery and development of the use of high intensity light, called laser, and its use in our daily lives. Notes: Includes bibliographical references and index. Subjects: Lasers--Juvenile literature. Lasers. Series: The Lucent science and technology library LC Classification: TA1682 .N36 2003 Dewey Class No.: 621.36/6 21

Nardo, Don, 1947- Lasers: humanity's magic light / by Don Nardo. Published/Created: San Diego, CA: Lucent Books, c1990. Description: 96 p.: ill. (some col.); 27 cm. ISBN: 1560062002 Summary: Discusses the history of lasers and their uses in such fields as medicine, entertainment, and the military. Notes: Includes bibliographical references (p. 90-91) and index. Subjects: Lasers--Juvenile literature. Lasers. Series: The Encyclopedia of discovery and invention LC Classification: TA1682 .N37 1990 Dewey Class No.: 621.36/6 20

NATO Advanced Research Workshop (ARW) on Pulsed Metal Vapour Lasers, Physics and Emerging Applications in Industry, Medicine, and Science (1995: University of St. Andrews) Pulsed metal vapour lasers / edited by Chris E. Little and Nikola V. Sabotinov. Published/Created: Dordrecht; Boston: Kluwer Academic, 1996. Related Authors: Little, Chris E. Sabotinov, Nikola V. North Atlantic Treaty Organization. Scientific Affairs Division. Description: xiii, 479 p.: ill.; 25 cm. ISBN: 0792340027 (hb: alk. paper) Notes: Collection of papers given at the NATO Advanced Research Workshop (ARW) on Pulsed Metal Vapour Lasers, Physics and Emerging Applications in Industry, Medicine, and Science, held at the University of St. Andrews, 6-10 August, 1995. "Published in cooperation with NATO Scientific Affairs Division." Includes bibliographical references and index. Subjects: Metal vapor lasers. Pulsed radiation. Series: NATO ASI series. Partnership sub-series 1, Disarmament technologies; vol. 5 LC Classification: TA1695 .N37 1995 Dewey Class No.: 621.36/64 20

NATO Advanced Research Workshop on Atomic and Molecular Processes with Short Intense Laser Pulses (1987: Lennoxville, Québec) Atomic and molecular processes with short intense laser pulses / edited by André D. Bandrauk. Published/Created: New York: Plenum Press, c1988. Related Authors: Bandrauk, André D. North Atlantic Treaty Organization. Scientific Affairs Division. Description: x, 481 p.: ill.; 26 cm. ISBN: 0306428261 Notes: "Proceedings of a NATO Advanced Research Workshop on Atomic and Molecular Processes with Short Intense Laser Pulses held July 20-24, 1987, in Lennoxville, Québec, Canada"--T.p. verso. "Published in cooperation with NATO Scientific Affairs Division." Includes bibliographies and indexes. Subjects: Multiphoton processes--Congresses. Laser pulses, Ultrashort--Congresses. Coherence (Nuclear physics)--Congresses. Lasers in chemistry--Congresses. Series: NATO ASI Series. Series B, Physics; v. 171 LC Classification: QC793.5.P427 N38 1987 Dewey Class No.: 535/.2 19

NATO Advanced Study Institute on Instabilities and Chaos in Quantum Optics (1987: Il Ciocco, Italy) Instabilities and chaos in quantum optics II / edited by N.B. Abraham, F.T. Arecchi, L.A. Lugiato. Published/Created: New York: Plenum Press, c1988. Related Authors: Abraham, Neal B. Arecchi, F. T. Lugiato, L. A. (Luigi A.), 1944- North Atlantic Treaty Organization. Scientific Affairs Division. Description: viii, 395 p.: ill.; 26 cm. ISBN: 0306429144 Notes: "Proceedings of a NATO Advanced Study Institute on Instabilities and Chaos in Quantum Optics, held June 28-July 7, 1987, in Il Ciocco, Italy"--T.p. verso. "Published in cooperation with NATO Scientific Affairs Division." Includes bibliographical references and index. Subjects: Quantum optics--Congresses. Lasers--Congresses. Masers--Congresses. Chaotic behavior in systems--Congresses. Nonlinear optics--Congresses. Series: NATO ASI series. Series B, Physics; v. 177 LC Classification: QC446.15 .N35 1987 Dewey Class No.: 535 19

NATO Advanced Study Institute on Solid State Lasers: New Developments and Applications (1992: Tuscany, Italy) Solid state lasers: new developments and applications / edited by Massimo Inguscio and Richard Wallenstein. Published/Created: New York: Plenum Press, c1993. Related Authors: Inguscio, M. Wallenstein, Richard. North Atlantic

Treaty Organization. Scientific Affairs Division. Description: viii, 349 p.: ill.; 26 cm. ISBN: 0306445980 Notes: "Published in cooperation with NATO Scientific Affairs Division." Includes bibliographical references and index. Subjects: Solid-state lasers--Congresses. Laser spectroscopy--Congresses. Quantum electronics--Congresses. Series: NATO ASI series. Series B, Physics; v. 317 LC Classification: TA1705 .N38 1994 Dewey Class No.: 621.36/61 20

NATO Advanced Study Institute/15th Course of the International School of Quantum Electronics on Laser Systems for Photobiology and Photomedicine (1990: Erice, Italy) Laser systems for photobiology and photomedicine / edited by A.N. Chester, S. Martellucci, and A.M. Scheggi. Published/Created: New York: Plenum Press, c1991. Related Authors: Chester, A. N. Martellucci, S. Verga Scheggi, A. M. (Anna Maria) North Atlantic Treaty Organization. Scientific Affairs Division. Description: ix, 311 p.: ill.; 26 cm. ISBN: 0306438860 Notes: "Proceedings of a NATO Advanced Study Institute/15th Course of the International School of Quantum Electronics on Laser Systems for Photobiology and Photomedicine, held May 11-20, 1990, in Erice, Sicily, Italy"--T.p. verso. "Published in cooperation with NATO Scientific Affairs Division." Includes bibliographical references and index. Subjects: Lasers in medicine--Lasers in biology--Lasers--Therapeutic use--Lasers in surgery--Laser Surgery--Lasers--diagnostic use--therapeutic use--Photochemotherapy--Congresses. Series: NATO ASI series. Series B, Physics; v. 252 LC Classification: R857.L37 C68 1990 Dewey Class No.: 610/.28 20

NATO Advanced Study Institute/Ninth Course of the International School of Radiation Damage and Protection on Optical Sources, Lasers, and Synchrotron Radiation: Biological Effects and Hazard Potential (1989: Erice, Italy) Light, lasers, and synchrotron radiation: a health risk assessment / edited by M. Grandolfo, A. Rindi, and D.H. Sliney. Published/Created: New York: Plenum Press, c1991. Related Authors: Grandolfo, M. Rindi, Alessandro. Sliney, David H. Description: ix, 426 p.: ill.; 26 cm. ISBN: 0306437333 Notes: "Published in cooperation with NATO Scientific Affairs Division." Includes bibliographical references and index. Subjects: Light--Health aspects--Congresses. Laser beams--Health aspects--Congresses. Synchrotron radiation--Health aspects--Congresses. Health risk assessment--Congresses. Series: NATO ASI series. Series B, Physics; v. 242 LC Classification: RA569.3 .N38 1991 Dewey Class No.: 612/.01448 20

NDLOS '93 International Workshop (1993: Alexander Suvorov) Nonlinear dynamics in lasers and optical systems: NDLOS '93 International Workshop: 27 June-4 July 1993, Moscow--Nizhny Novgorod / Neal B. Abraham ... [et al.], chairs; Leonid A. Melnikov, editor; organized by Saratov State University ... [et al.]; co-sponsored by Research Center for Control and Exploration of Physical Fields and Radiation, Russian Academy of Sciences, Russian High School Education Committee, SPIE/Russia--the International Society for Optical Engineering/Russia Chapter. Published/Created: Bellingham, Wash., USA: SPIE--the International Society for Optical Engineering, c1994. Related Authors: Abraham, Neal B. Melnikov, Leonid A. Description: vii, 202 p.: ill.; 28 cm. ISBN: 0819413828 Notes: "The First International Workshop on Nonlinear Dynamics in Lasers and Optical Systems was held on 27 June-4 July 1993 as part of the Volga Laser Tour '93 [i.e., on board the ship Alexander Suvorov]."--P. vii. Includes bibliographical references and author index. Subjects: Nonlinear optics--Chaotic behavior in systems--Lasers--Congresses. Series: Proceedings of SPIE--the International Society for Optical Engineering; v. 2099. Variant Series: Proceedings / SPIE--the International Society for Optical Engineering; v. 2099 LC Classification: QC446.15 .N34 1993 Dewey Class No.: 621.36/6 20

New and emerging laser applications: a technical forecast for the 1990s. Published/Created: West Brattleboro, VT: Truett Scientific Co., c1990. Description: 121 p.; 28 cm. Notes: Includes bibliographical references (p. 103-121). Subjects: Lasers--Technological innovations. Lasers--Industrial applications. Series: Report (Truett Scientific Co.); no. 490. Variant Series: Report / Truett Scientific Co.; no. 490 LC Classification: TA1677 .N49 1990 Dewey Class No.: 621.36/6 20

New frontiers in medical device technology / edited by Arye Rosen, Harel D. Rosen. Published/Created: New York: Wiley, c1995. Related Authors: Rosen, Arye. Rosen, Harel D. Description: x, 364 p.: ill.; 24 cm. ISBN: 0471591890 Notes: "A Wiley Interscience publication." Includes bibliographical references and index. Subjects: Medical technology. Diagnostic imaging. Lasers in medicine. Microwave imaging in medicine. Microwave heating. Series: Wiley series in microwave and optical engineering LC Classification: R855.3 .N48 1995 Dewey Class No.: 610/.28 20

New materials for advanced solid state lasers: symposium held November 29-December 1, 1993, Boston, Massachusetts, U.S.A. / editors, B.H.T. Chai ... [et al.]. Published/Created: Pittsburgh, Pa.: Materials Research Society, c1994. Related Authors: Chai, Bruce Huai-Tsu. Description: x, 301 p.: ill.; 24 cm. ISBN: 1558992286 Notes: Includes bibliographical references and indexes. Subjects: Solid-state lasers--Congresses. Laser materials--Congresses. Series: Materials Research Society symposia proceedings; v. 329. Variant Series: Materials Research Society symposium proceedings; v. 329 LC Classification: TA1705 .N48 1994 Dewey Class No.: 621.36/61 20

New technologies in cytometry: 19-20 January 1989, Los Angeles, California / Gary C. Salzman, chair/editor; sponsored by SPIE--the International Society for Optical Engineering; cooperating organization, Society for Analytic Cytology. Published/Created: Bellingham, Wash., USA: SPIE, c1989. Related Authors: Salzman, G. C. (Gary Clyde), 1942- Society of Photo-optical Instrumentation Engineers. Society for Analytic Cytology. Symposium on Medical Applications of Lasers and Optics (1989: Los Angeles, Calif.) Description: viii, 207 p.: ill.; 28 cm. ISBN: 081940098X Notes: Papers from the Symposium on Medical Applications of Lasers and Optics, held in Los Angeles, Calif. Includes bibliographical references. Subjects: Flow cytometry--Congresses. Flow cytometry--Diagnostic use--Congresses. Series: Proceedings of SPIE--the International Society for Optical Engineering; v. 1063. Variant Series: Proceedings / SPIE--The International Society for Optical Engineering; vol. 1063 LC Classification: QH585.5.F56 N48 1989 Dewey Class No.: 574.87/028 20

Niemz, Markolf H., 1964- Laser-tissue interactions: fundamentals and applications / Markolf H. Niemz. Published/Created: Berlin; New York: Springer, c2002. Description: xiv, 303 p.: ill. (some col.); 24 cm. ISBN: 3540427635 Notes: Includes bibliographical references (p. [273]-296) and index. Subjects: Lasers in medicine. Lasers--Physiological effect. Lasers--Therapeutic use. Laser Surgery. Lasers. Photobiology. Safety. Series: Biological and medical physics series LC Classification: R857.L37 N54 2002

Niemz, Markolf H., 1964- Laser-tissue interactions: fundamentals and applications / Markolf H. Niemz; with a foreword by Martin van Gemert. Published/Created: Berlin; New York: Springer, c1996. Description: xii, 297 p.: ill. (some col.); 25 cm. ISBN: 3540603638 (acid-free paper) Notes: Includes bibliographical references (p. [267]-290) and index. Subjects: Lasers in medicine. Lasers--Physiological effect. Lasers--Therapeutic use. Laser Surgery. Lasers. Photobiology. Safety. LC Classification: R857.L37 N54 1996 Dewey Class No.: 610/.28 20

Nonlinear dynamics and quantum phenomena in optical systems: proceedings of the third international workshop, Blanes (Girona, Spain), October 1-3, 1990 / R. Vilaseca, R. Corbalan (eds.). Published/Created: Berlin; New York: Springer-Verlag, c1991. Related Authors: Vilaseca, R. Corbalan, R. (Ramon), 1946 Description: x, 327 p.: ill.; 24 cm. ISBN: 3540536027 (Springer-Verlag Berlin: alk. paper) 0387536027 (Springer-Verlag New York: alk. paper) Notes: The Third International Workshop on Nonlinear Dynamics and Quantum Phenomena in Optical Systems, held in Blanes, Spain, 1-3 Oct. 1990. Includes bibliographical references and index. Subjects: Quantum optics--Congresses. Nonlinear optics--Congresses. Lasers--Congresses. Series: Springer proceedings in physics; v. 55. Variant Series: Springer proceedings in physics; 55 LC Classification: QC446.15 .N64 1992 Dewey Class No.: 535.2 20

Nonlinear dynamics in optical systems: summaries of papers presented at the Nonlinear Dynamics in optical Systems Topical Meeting, June 22-26, 1992, Alpbach, Austria / sponsored by Air Force Office of Science Research, Office of Naval Research for Optical Society of America. Edition Information: Post Conference ed. Published/Created: Washington, DC: The Society, c1992. Related Authors: United States. Air Force. Office of Scientific Research. United States. Office of Naval Research. Optical Society of America. Nonlinear Dynamics in Optical Systems Topical Meeting (1992: Alpbach, Austria) Description: xiv, 365 p.: ill.; 28 cm. ISBN: 1557522596 Notes: Includes bibliographical references and index. Subjects: Semiconductors--Congresses. Dynamics--Congresses. Nonlinear theories--Congresses. Lasers--Congresses. Series: Technical digest series (Optical Society of America); 1992, v. 16. Variant Series: 1992 technical digest series; v. 16 LC Classification: QC610.9 .N65 1992 Dewey Class No.: 621.36/6 20

Nonlinear dynamics of laser and optical systems: CIS selected papers / Valery V. Tuchin, editor; sponsored by SPIE Russia Chapter, State Educational Science Center College [and] Department of Optics, Saratov State University. Published/Created: Bellingham, Wash., USA: SPIE, c1997. Related Authors: Tuchin, V. V. (Valerii Viktorovich) Society of Photo-optical Instrumentation Engineers. Society of Photo-optical Instrumentation Engineers. Russian Chapter. Saratovskii gosudarstvennyi universitet im. N.G. Chernyshevskogo. Dept. of Optics. Description: viii, 170 p.: ill.; 28 cm. ISBN: 0819426032 Notes: "Translation of selected papers from the Russian journal Izvestiya VUZ. Applied nonlinear dynamics, Vol. 3, 1995-Vol. 4, 1996." Includes bibliographical references and index. Subjects: Lasers--Congresses. Nonlinear optics--Congresses. Dynamics--Congresses. Series: Proceedings of SPIE--the International Society for Optical Engineering; v. 3177. Variant Series: SPIE proceedings series; v. 3177 LC Classification: QC685 .N66 1997 Dewey Class No.: 621.36/6 21

Nonlinear effects in optical fibers / E.M. Dianov ... [et al.]. Published/Created: Chur; New York: Harwood Academic Publishers, c1989. Related Authors: Dianov, E. M. Description: vii, 59 p.: ill.; 23 cm. ISBN: 371864889X Notes: Includes bibliographical references and index. Subjects: Fiber optics. Nonlinear optics. Optical fibers. Lasers. Series: Laser science and technology, 0899-2711; v. 6 LC Classification: QC448 .N66 1989 Dewey Class No.: 535.8/9 19

Nonlinear frequency generation and conversion: 29-31 January 1996, San Jose, California / Mool C. Gupta, William J. Kozlovsky, David C. MacPherson, chairs/editors; sponsored and published by SPIE--the International Society for Optical Engineering. Published/Created: Bellingham, Wash.: SPIE, c1996. Related Authors: Gupta, M. C. (Mool Chand) Kozlovsky, William J. MacPherson, David C. Society of Photo-optical Instrumentation Engineers. Description: x, 510 p.: ill.; 28 cm. ISBN: 0819420743

Notes: Includes bibliographical references and index. Subjects: Solid state lasers--Congresses. Semiconductor lasers--Congresses. Nonlinear optics--Congresses. Crystals--Congresses. Optical pumping--Congresses. Raman effect--Congresses. Wave guides--congresses. Series: Proceedings of SPIE--the International Society for Optical Engineering; v. 2700. Variant Series: Proceedings / SPIE--the International Society for Optical Engineering; v. 2700 LC Classification: TA1673 .N66 1996 Dewey Class No.: 621.36/6 21

Nonlinear guided waves and their applications: summaries of papers presented at the topical meeting ... February 23-25, 1995, Dana Point, California / sponsored by Optical Society of America; cosponsored by IEEE/Lasers and Electro-Optics Society Edition Information: Postconference ed. Published/Created: Washington, D.C.: Optical Society of America, 1995. Related Authors: Optical Society of America. Lasers and Electro-Optics Society (Institute of Electrical and Electronics Engineers). Description: xii, 308 p.: ill.; 28 cm. ISBN: 1557523827 Notes: Includes bibliographical references and index. Subjects: Optoelectronic devices--Congresses. Optical wave guides--Congresses. Nonlinear optics--Congresses. Solitons--Congresses. Series: Technical digest series (Optical Society of America); 1995, v 6. Variant Series: Technical digest series; 1995, v 6. LC Classification: TA1750 .N645 1995 Dewey Class No.: 621.36/94 21

Nonlinear Guided-Wave Phenomena Topical Meeting (1991: Cambridge, England) Nonlinear guided-wave phenomena: summaries of papers presented at the Nonlinear Guided-Wave Phenomena Topical Meeting, September 2-4, 1991, Cambridge, England, United Kingdom / sponsored by Optical Society of America, in cooperation with IEEE/Lasers and Electro-Optics Society, the Institute of Physics, the Institution of Electrical Engineers. Edition Information: Postconference ed. Published/Created: Washington, DC: Optical Society of America, c1991. Related Authors: Optical Society of America. Description: xiv, 463 p.: ill.; 29 cm. ISBN: 1557522030 Notes: Includes bibliographical references and index. Subjects: Fiber optics--Congresses. Optical wave guides--Congresses. Solitons--Congresses. Series: Technical digest series (Optical Society of America); 1991, v. 15. Variant Series: 1991 technical digest series; v. 15 LC Classification: QC447.9 .N66 1991 Dewey Class No.: 621.36/92 20

Nonlinear Guided-Wave Phenomena Topical Meeting (1993: Cambridge, England) Nonlinear guided-wave phenomena: summaries of papers presented at the Nonlinear Guided-Wave Phenomena Topical Meeting, September 20-22, 1993, Cambridge, England, United Kingdom / sponsored by Optical Society of America. Edition Information: Postconference ed. Published/Created: Washington, DC: Optical Society of America, c1993. Related Authors: Optical Society of America. Description: xiii, 421 p.: ill.; 28 cm. ISBN: 1557523126 (pbk.) Notes: "In cooperation with IEEE/Lasers and Electro-Optics Society, The Institution of Electrical Engineers, U.K., The Institute of Physics, U.K." Includes bibliographical references and index. Subjects: Solitons--Congresses. Optical wave guides--Congresses. Nonlinear theories--Congresses. Series: Technical digest series (Optical Society of America); 1993, v. 15. Variant Series: 1993 technical digest series; v. 15 LC Classification: QC174.26.W28 N67 1993 Dewey Class No.: 621.36/9 20

Nonlinear optical materials and devices for photonic switching: 16-17 January 1990, Los Angeles, California / Nasser Peyg[h]ambarian, chair/editor; sponsored by SPIE--the International Society for Optical Engineering. Published/Created: Bellingham, Wash., USA: SPIE, c1990. Related Authors: Peyghambarian, Nasser, 1954- Society of Photo-optical Instrumentation Engineers. Symposium on High-Power Lasers and Optical Computing (1990: Los Angeles, Calif.) Description:

viii, 300 p.: ill.; 28 cm. ISBN: 0819402575 Notes: "Part of SPIE's Symposium on High-Power Lasers and Optical Computing held at OE LASE '90, 14-19-January 1990, Los Angeles California"--P. vii. Includes bibliographical references and index. Subjects: Optoelectronic devices--Optical wave guides--Semiconductors--Photorefractive materials--Nonlinear optics--Congresses. Series: Proceedings of SPIE--the International Society for Optical Engineering; v. 1216. Variant Series: Proceedings / SPIE--the International Society for Optical Engineering; v. 1216 LC Classification: TA1750 .N65 1990 Dewey Class No.: 621.381/045 20

Nonlinear optics '98: materials, fundamentals, and applications topical meeting, 10-14 August 1998, Princeville Hotel, Princeville, Kauai, Hawaii. Published/Created: Piscataway, NJ: IEEE Service Center, c1998. Related Authors: Optical Society of America. Lasers and Electro-optics Society (Institute of Electrical and Electronics Engineers) Description: 468 p.: ill.; 28 cm. ISBN: 0780349504 (softbound) 0780349512 (casebound) 0780349520 (microfiche) Notes: "The papers in this book make up the digest of the Nonlinear Optica [i.e. Optics] '98 Materials, Fundamentals and Applications Topical Meeting"--T.p. verso. Includes bibliographical references and indexes. Subjects: Nonlinear optics--Congresses. LC Classification: QC446.15 .N65 1998 Dewey Class No.: 535/.2 21

Nonlinear optics for high-speed electronics and optical frequency conversion: 24-26 January 1994, Los Angeles, California / Nasser Peygambarian ... [et al.], chairs/editors; sponsored and published by SPIE--the International Society for Optical Engineering. Published/Created: Bellingham, Wash., USA: SPIE, c1994. Related Authors: Peyghambarian, Nasser, 1954- Society of Photo-optical Instrumentation Engineers. Description: viii, 356 p.: ill.; 28 cm. ISBN: 0819414409 Notes: Includes bibliographical references and index. Subjects: Optoelectronic devices--Nonlinear optics--Semiconductor lasers--Parametrons--Congresses. Series: Proceedings of SPIE--the International Society for Optical Engineering; v. 2145. Variant Series: Proceedings / SPIE--the International Society for Optical Engineering; v. 2145 LC Classification: TA1750 .N656 1994 Dewey Class No.: 621.3815/2 20

Nonlinear optics in signal processing / edited by Robert W. Eason and Alan Miller. Edition Information: 1st ed. Published/Created: London; New York: Chapman & Hall, 1993. Related Authors: Eason, Robert W. Miller, Alan. Description: xiii, 421 p.: ill.; 25 cm. ISBN: 0442316585 Notes: Includes bibliographical references and index. Subjects: Signal processing. Nonlinear optics. Series: Engineering aspects of lasers series LC Classification: TK5102.5 .N564 1993 Dewey Class No.: 621.382/2 20

Nonlinear optics: materials, fundamentals and applications: technical digest, August 6-10, 2000, Kaua'i-Lihue, Hawaii / sponsored by Optical Society of America, IEEE/Lasers and Electro-Optics Society. Edition Information: Postconference ed. Published/Created: Washington, DC: Optical Soceity of America, c2000. Related Authors: Optical Society of America. Lasers and Electro-optics Society (Institute of Electrical and Electronics Engineers) Description: xx, 422 p.: ill.; 28 cm. ISBN: 155752646X Notes: Includes bibliographical references and index. Subjects: Nonlinear optics--Congresses. Series: OSA trends in optics and photonics; v. 46. Technical digest series (Optical Society of America); 1999. Variant Series: Trends in optics and photonics; TOPS v. 46 Technical digest LC Classification: QC446.15 .N65 2000 Dewey Class No.: 535/.2 21

Nonlinear optics: materials, phenomena, and devices: digest: Stouffer Waiohai Beach, Kauai, Hawaii, July 16-20, 1990 / sponsored by IEEE Lasers and Electro-Optics Society in cooperation with the Optical Society of America.

Published/Created: New York, NY (345 E. 47th, New York 10017): Institute of Electrical and Electronics Engineers, c1990. Related Authors: Lasers and Electro-optics Society (Institute of Electrical and Electronics Engineers) Optical Society of America. International Meeting on Nonlinear Optics (1st: 1990: Kauai, Hawaii) Description: xv, 327 p.: ill.; 28 cm. Notes: At head of Title - NLO '90. Papers from the First International Meeting on Nonlinear Optics. Includes bibliographical references and index. Subjects: Nonlinear optics--Congresses. LC Classification: QC446.15 .N67 1990 Dewey Class No.: 535.2 20

Novel applications of lasers and pulsed power: 6-8 February 1995, San Jose, California / Randy D. Curry, chair/editor; sponsored and published by SPIE--the International Society for Optical Engineering. Published/Created: Bellingham, Wash.: SPIE, c1995. Related Authors: Curry, Randy D. Description: vii, 304 p.: ill.; 28 cm. ISBN: 0819417211 Notes: Includes bibliographical references and author index. Subjects: Lasers--Industrial applications--Congresses. Pulsed power systems--Congresses. Electron beams--Industrial applications--Congresses. Series: Proceedings of SPIE--the International Society for Optical Engineering; v. 2374. Variant Series: Proceedings / SPIE--the International Society for Optical Engineering; v. 2374 LC Classification: sTA1673 .N68 1995 Dewey Class No.: 621.36/6 20

Novel laser sources and applications: proceedings of a workshop held November 12-13, 1993, San Jose, California, USA / Joseph F. Becker ... [et al.], editors. Published/Created: Bellingham, Wash., USA: SPIE Optical Engineering Press, c1994. Related Authors: Becker, Joseph F. (Joseph Frederick) Description: viii, 244 p.: ill.; 26 cm. ISBN: 081941512X Notes: Includes bibliographical references. Subjects: Lasers--Congresses. LC Classification: TA1675 .N68 1994 Dewey Class No.: 621.36/6 20

Novel lasers and devices - basic aspects conference digest. Published/Created: Washington, DC: Optical Society of America, 1999. Description: p.; cm. ISBN: 1557526133 (conference: acid-free paper) Series: Osa technical digest series LC Classification: 9906 BOOK NOT YET IN LC

Novel lasers and devices--basic aspects: 14-16 June 1999, ICM--Internationales Congress Center München, Munich, Germany / sponsored by CLEO/Europe--EQEC ... [et al.]. Edition Information: Postconference ed. Published/Created: Washington, DC: Optical Society of America, c1999. Description: xii, 164 p.: ill.; 28 cm. ISBN: 1557526141 (post-conference: acid-free paper: pbk.) Series: OSA technical digest series

Ophthalmic measurements and optometry: 12-16 May 1997, Kazmierz Dolny, Poland / Maksymilian Pluta, chair/editor, Mariusz Szyjer, co-editor; organized by SPIE Poland Chapter [and] Institute of Applied Optics (Poland); sponsored by SPIE--the International Society for Optical Engineering [and] State Committee for Scientific Research (Poland). Published/Created: Bellingham, Wash., USA: SPIE, c1998. Related Authors: Pluta, Maksymilian. Szyjer, Mariusz. Society of Photo-optical Instrumentation Engineers. Society of Photo-optical Instrumentation Engineers. Poland Chapter. Institute of Applied Optics (Poland) Komitet Bada´n Naukowych (Poland) Description: xvi, 202 p.: ill.; 28 cm. ISBN: 0819430463 Notes: Includes bibliographical references and indexes. Subjects: Optometry--Congresses. Ophthalmology--Congresses. Eye--Examination--Congresses. Lasers in ophthalmology--Congresses. Series: SPIE Poland Chapter proceedings; 42 Proceedings of SPIE--the International Society for Optical Engineering; v. 3579. Variant Series: SPIE proceedings series, 0277-786X; v. 3579 LC Classification: RE76 .O75 1998 Dewey Class No.: 617.7/5 21

Ophthalmic technologies X: 22-23 January 2000, San Jose, USA / Pascal O. Rol, Karen M. Joos, Fabrice Manns, chairs/editors; sponsored by SPIE--the International Society for Optical Engineering [and] IBOS--International Biomedical Optics Society. Published/Created: Bellingham, Wash., USA: SPIE, c2000. Related Authors: Rol, Pascal O. Joos, Karen M. Manns, Fabrice. Description: xv, 280 p.: ill. (some col.); 28 cm. ISBN: 0819435244 Notes: Earlier conference proceedings titled: Proceedings of ophthalmic technologies. Includes bibliographical references and index. Subjects: Ophthalmology--Lasers in ophthalmology--Eye--Surgery--Cornea--Surgery--Imaging systems in medicine--Congresses. Series: Progress in biomedical optics and imaging, 1605-7422; vol. 1, no. 2 Proceedings of SPIE--the International Society for Optical Engineering; v. 3908. Variant Series: Proceedings of SPIE; v. 3908 LC Classification: RE11 .O59 2000 Dewey Class No.: 617.7 21

Ophthalmic technologies XI: 20-21 January 2001, San Jose, USA / Fabrice Manns, Per G. Söderberg, Arthur Ho, chairs/editors; sponsored ... by SPIE--the International Society for Optical Engineering. Published/Created: Bellingham, Wash., USA: SPIE, c2001. Related Authors: Manns, Fabrice. Söderberg, Per G. Ho, Arthur, 1957- Society of Photo-optical Instrumentation Engineers. Description: xviii, 284 p.: ill.; 28 cm. ISBN: 0819439231 Notes: Earlier conference proceedings titled: Proceedings of ophthalmic technologies. Includes bibliographical references and index. Subjects: Lasers in ophthalmology--Eye--Surgery--Cornea--Surgery--Imaging systems in medicine--Congresses. Series: Progress in biomedical optics and imaging, 1605-7422; vol. 2, no. 2 Proceedings of SPIE--the International Society for Optical Engineering; v. 4245. Variant Series: Proceedings of SPIE; v. 4245 LC Classification: RE86 .O63 2001 Dewey Class No.: 617.7/0028 21

Optical amplifiers and their applications: from the topical meeting, July 11-13, 1996, Monterey, California / edited by 1996 Optical Amplifiers and Their Applications Program Committee; sponsored by Optical Society of America in cooperation with IEEE/Lasers and Electro-Optics Society. Published/Created: Washington, DC: Optical Society of America, c1996. Related Authors: Optical Amplifiers and Their Applications Topical Meeting (1996: Monterey, Calif.). Program Committee. Optical Society of America. Lasers and Electro-optics Society (Institute of Electrical and Electronics Engineers) Description: xiii, 414 p.: ill.; 28 cm. ISBN: 155752453X Notes: Includes bibliographical references and indexes. Subjects: Optical communications--Equipment and supplies Congresses. Optical amplifiers--Congresses. Optical fibers--Congresses. Semiconductors--Congresses. Series: OSA trends in optics and photonics; v. 5 LC Classification: TK5103.59 .O654 1996 Dewey Class No.: 621.382/7 21

Optical amplifiers and their applications: from the Topical Meeting Optical Amplifiers and Their Applications, July 21-23, 1997, Victoria, B.C., Canada / edited by Mikhail N. Zervas, Alan E. Willner, Shinya Sasaki; sponsored by Optical Society of America; technical co-sponsor, IEEE/Lasers and Electro-Optics Society. Published/Created: Washington, DC: Optical Society of America, c1997. Related Authors: Zervas, Mikhail N. Willner, Alan E. Sasaki, Shinya. Description: xiv, 526 p.: ill.; 28 cm. ISBN: 1557525056 Notes: Includes bibliographical references (p. 506-520) and index. Subjects: Optical communications--Equipment and supplies--Optical amplifiers--Optical fibers--Congresses. Semiconductors--Congresses. Series: OSA trends in optics and photonics; v. 16. Variant Series: OSA trends in optics and photonics series, 1094-5695; v. 16 LC Classification: TK5103.59 .O6543 1997 Dewey Class No.: 621.382/7 21

Optical amplifiers and their applications: from the topical meeting optical amplifiers and their applications, July 27-29, 1998, Vail, Colorado / [edited by] Douglas M. Baney, Jay Wiesenfeld, Katsumi Emura; sponsored by the Optical Society of America in cooperation with IEEE/Lasers and Electr-Optics Society. Published/Created: Washington, DC: Optical Society of America, 1998. Related Authors: Baney, Douglas M. Wiesenfeld, Jay Martin. Emura, Katsumi. Optical Society of America. Optical Amplifiers and Their Applications Topical Meeting (1998: Vail, Colo.) Description: xii, 318 p.: ill.; 28 cm. ISBN: 1557525595 Notes: Includes bibliographical references (p. 296-314) and indexes. Subjects: Optical communications--Equipment and supplies Congresses. Optical amplifiers--Congresses. Fiber optics--Congresses. Lasers--Congresses. Series: Trends in optics and photonics series; v. 25 LC Classification: TK5103.59 .O6544 1998 Dewey Class No.: 621.382/7 21

Optical amplifiers and their applications: summaries of the papers presented at the topical meeting, 15 June 1995, Davos, Switzerland / sponsored by Optical Society of America; cosponsored by IEEE/Lasers and Electro-optics Society in cooperation with European Physical Society, Quantum Electronics & Optics Division, European Optical Society, Swiss Physical Society. Edition Information: Postconference ed. Published/Created: Washington, DC: Optical Society of America, c1995. Related Authors: Optical Society of America. Description: xi, 284 p.: ill.; 28 cm. ISBN: 1557524068 Notes: Includes bibliographical references and index. Subjects: Optical communications--Equipment and supplies Congresses. Optical amplifiers--Congresses. Lasers--Congresses. Optical fibers--Congresses. Semiconductors--Congresses. Series: Technical digest series (Optical Society of America); 1995, v. 18. Variant Series: Technical digest series; 1995, v. 18 LC Classification: TK5103.59 .O655 1995

Optical biopsy III: 23-24 January 2000, San Jose, California / Robert R. Alfano, chair/editor; sponsored by SPIE--the International Society for Optical Engineering [and] IBOS--International Biomedical Optics Society. Published/Created: Bellingham, Wash., USA: SPIE, c2000. Related Authors: Alfano, R. R. International Biomedical Optics Society. Society of Photo-optical Instrumentation Engineers. Description: ix, 268 p.: ill.; 28 cm. ISBN: 0819435333 Notes: Includes bibliographical references and index. Subjects: Tumors--Spectroscopic imaging--Congresses. Biopsy--Congresses. Fluorescence spectroscopy--Congresses. Spectroscopic imaging--Congresses. Lasers in medicine--Congresses. Tissues--Optical properties--Congresses. Series: Progress in biomedical optics and imaging, 1605-7422; vol. 1, no. 11 Proceedings of SPIE--the International Society for Optical Engineering; v. 3917. Variant Series: Proceedings of SPIE; v. 3917 LC Classification: RC270.3.D53 O68 2000 Dewey Class No.: 616.99/40754 21

Optical data storage 2000: 14-17 May 2000, Whistler, Canada / Douglas G. Stinson, Ryuichi Katayama, chairs/editors; sponsored by IEEE/Lasers and Electro-Optics Society, OSA--Optical Society of America, [and] SPIE--the International Society for Optical Engineering. Published/Created: Bellingham, Wash., USA: SPIE, c2000. Related Authors: Stinson, Douglas G. Katayama, Ryuichi. Lasers and Electro-optics Society (Institute of Electrical and Electronics Engineers) Society of Photo-optical Instrumentation Engineers. Optical Society of America. Topical Meeting on Optical Data Storage (16th: 2000: Whistler, B.C.) Description: xi, 342 p.: ill.; 28 cm. ISBN: 0819437336 Notes: "Sixteenth Topical Meeting on Optical Data Storage (ODS 2000)"--P. xi. Includes bibliographical references and index. Subjects: Optical storage devices--Congresses. Computer storage devices--Congresses. Series: Proceedings of SPIE--the International Society for Optical Engineering; v. 4090. Variant Series: SPIE proceedings series; v. 4090

Optical data storage '91: 25-27 February 1991, Colorado Springs, Colorado / James J.

Burke, Thomas A. Shull, Nobutake Imamura, chairs/editors; sponsored by Optical Society of America, SPIE--the International Society for Optical Engineering, IEEE/Lasers and Electro-Optics Society. Published/Created: Bellingham, Wash.: SPIE, c1991. Related Authors: Burke, J. J. (James Joseph), 1931- Shull, Thomas A. Imamura, Nobutake. Description: ix, 459 p.: ill.; 28 cm. ISBN: 0819406082 Notes: Includes bibliographical references and index. Subjects: Optical storage devices--Congresses. Magnetooptical devices--Congresses. Series: Proceedings of SPIE--the International Society for Optical Engineering; v. 1499. Variant Series: Proceedings / SPIE--the International Society for Optical Engineering; v. 1499 LC Classification: TA1635 .O643 1991 Dewey Class No.: 621.39/767 20

Optical data storage '95: 5-7 July, 1995, San Diego, California / Gordon R. Knight, Hiroshi Ooki, Yuan-Sheng Tyan, chairs/editors; sponsored by SPIE--the International Society for Optical Engineering; cosponsored by IEEE Lasers and Electro-Optics Society, OSA--Optical Society of America. Published/Created: Bellingham, Wash.: SPIE, c1995. Related Authors: Knight, Gordon R. Ooki, Hiroshi. Tyan, Yuan-Sheng. Society of Photo-optical Instrumentation Engineers. Optical Society of America. Lasers and Electro-Optics Society (Institute of Electrical and Electronics Engineers) Description: ix, 404 p.: ill.; 28 cm. ISBN: 0819418730 Notes: Includes bibliographic references and index. Subjects: Computer storage devices--Optical storage devices--Magnetooptical devices--Congresses. Series: Proceedings of SPIE--the International Society for Optical Engineering; v. 2514. Variant Series: Proceedings / SPIE--the International Society for Optical Engineering; v. 2514 LC Classification: TK7895.M4 O675 1995

Optical data storage: 5-7 March 1990, Vancouver, Canada / Maarten de Haan, Yoshito Tsunoda, chairs/editors; sponsored by IEEE Lasers and Electro-optics Society [and] Optical Society of America [and] SPIE--the International Society for Optical Engineering. Published/Created: Bellingham, Wash., USA: SPIE, c1990. Related Authors: DeHaan, Maarten. Tsunoda, Yoshito. Lasers and Electro-optics Society (Institute of Electrical and Electronics Engineers) Optical Society of America. Society of Photo-optical Instrumentation Engineers. Topical Meeting on Optical Data Storage (6th: 1990: Vancouver, B.C.) Description: x, 400 p.: ill.; 28 cm. ISBN: 0819403717 Notes: "Sixth Topical Meeting on Optical Data Storage"--Introd. Includes bibliographical references and index. Subjects: Optical storage devices--Congresses. Magnetooptical devices--Congresses. Series: Proceedings of SPIE--the International Society for Optical Engineering; v. 1316. Variant Series: Proceedings / SPIE--the International Society for Optical Engineering; v. 1316 LC Classification: TA1635 .O64 1990 Dewey Class No.: 621.39/767 20

Optical data storage: 9-14 February 1992, San Jose, California / Donald B. Carlin, David B. Kay, chairs/editors; sponsored by SPIE--the International Society for Optical Engineering, Optical Society of America, IEEE/Lasers and Electro-Optics Society; cooperating organization, IS&T--the Society for Imaging Science and Technology. Published/Created: Bellingham, Wash.: SPIE, c1992. Related Authors: Carlin, Donald B. Kay, David B., 1942- Description: xii, 462 p.: ill.; 28 cm. ISBN: 0819408174 Notes: Includes bibliographical references and index. Subjects: Optical storage devices--Congresses. Series: Proceedings of SPIE--the International Society for Optical Engineering; v. 1663. Variant Series: Proceedings / SPIE--the International Society for Optical Engineering; v. 1663 LC Classification: TA1635 .O642 1992 Dewey Class No.: 621.39/767 20

Optical data storage: May 10-13, 1998, St. Regis Aspen, Aspen, Colorado / sponsored by IEEE/Lasers and Electro-Optics Society, SPIE, and Optical Society of

America. Edition Information: Conference ed. Published/Created: Washington, DC: Optical Society of America, c1998. Related Authors: Lasers and Electro-optics Society (Institute of Electrical and Electronics Engineers) Society of Photo-optical Instrumentation Engineers. Optical Society of America. Description: xii, 187 p.: ill.; 28 cm. ISBN: 1557525439 (Conference ed.) 1557525218 (1998 Technical digest series) Notes: Includes bibliographical references. Subjects: Computer storage devices--Congresses. Optical storage devices--Congresses. Series: Technical digest series (Optical Society of America) (Conference ed.); 1998, v. 8. Variant Series: 1998 technical digest series; v. 8 LC Classification: TK7895.M4 O6784 1998 Dewey Class No.: 621.39/767 21

Optical design and processing technologies and applications: 19 March 1992, Chicago, Illinois / Robert J. Heaston, chair/editor; sponsored by Chicago Regional Chapter of SPIE--the International Society for Optical Engineering ... [et al.]. Published/Created: Bellingham, Wash.: SPIE--the International Society for Optical Engineering, c1992. Related Authors: Heaston, Robert J. Description: x, 275 p.: ill.; 28 cm. ISBN: 0819409510 Notes: Includes bibliographical references and index. Subjects: Optical instruments--Design and construction--Lasers--Congresses. Optical detectors--Holography--Congresses. Series: Proceedings of SPIE--the International Society for Optical Engineering; v. 1779. Variant Series: Proceedings / SPIE--the International Society for Optical Engineering; v. 1779 LC Classification: TS510 .O5813 1992 Dewey Class No.: 621.36 20

Optical diagnostics for industrial applications: 22-24 May 2000, Glasgow, Scotland, United Kingdom / Neil A. Halliwell, chair/editor; sponsored by EOS--European Optical Society ... [et al.]; cooperating organizations, IEE--Institute of Electrical Engineers [and] IMechE--the Institution of Mechanical Engineers (UK). Published/Created: Bellingham, Wash., USA: SPIE, c2000. Related Authors: Halliwell, Neil A. Society of Photo-optical Instrumentation Engineers. European Optical Society. Institution of Electrical Engineers. Institution of Mechanical Engineers (Great Britain) Description: ix, 302 p.: ill. (some col.); 28 cm. ISBN: 0819437131 Cancel/Invalid LCCN: 2001273197 Notes: Includes bibliographical references and index. Subjects: Engineering--Measurement--Congresses. Fluid dynamic measurements--Congresses. Optical measurements--Congresses. Lasers--Industrial applications--Congresses. Series: Proceedings EurOpt series Proceedings of SPIE--the International Society for Optical Engineering; v. 4076. Variant Series: SPIE proceedings series; v. 4076 LC Classification: TA165 .O66 2000 Dewey Class No.: 681/.25 21

Optical diagnostics of living cells III: 24-25 January 2000, San Jose, California / Daniel L. Farkas, Robert C. Leif, chairs/editors; sponsored by SPIE--the International Society for Optical Engineering [and] IBOS--International Biomedical Optics Society Published/Created: Bellingham, Wash., USA: SPIE, c2000. Related Authors: Farkas, Daniel L. Leif, Robert C. Society of Photo-optical Instrumentation Engineers. International Biomedical Optics Society. Description: x, 344 p.: ill. (some col.); 28 cm. ISBN: 0819435376 Notes: Includes bibliographical references and index. Subjects: Cytodiagnosis--Congresses. Lasers in cytology--Congresses. Cytology--Research--Methodology--Congresses. Flow cytometry--Diagnostic use--Congresses. Diagnostic imaging--Congresses. Microscopy--Congresses. Series: Progress in biomedical optics and imaging, 1605-7422; vol. 1, no. 15 Proceedings of SPIE--the International Society for Optical Engineering; v. 3921. Variant Series: Proceedings of SPIE; v. 3921 LC Classification: RB43 .O68 2000 Dewey Class No.: 616.07/582 21

Optical diagnostics of living cells IV: 24-25 January 2001, San Jose, USA / Daniel L. Farkas, Robert C. Leif, chairs/editors; sponsored ... by SPIE--the International Society for Optical Engineering. Published/Created: Bellingham, Wash., USA: SPIE, c2001. Related Authors: Farkas, Daniel L. Leif, Robert C. Society of Photo-optical Instrumentation Engineers. Description: ix, 258 p.: ill.; 28 cm. ISBN: 081943938X Notes: Includes bibliographical references and index. Subjects: Cytodiagnosis--Congresses. Lasers in cytology--Congresses. Cytology--Research--Methodology--Congresses. Flow cytometry--Diagnostic use--Congresses. Diagnostic imaging--Congresses. Microscopy--Congresses. Series: Progress in biomedical optics and imaging, 1605-7422; vol. 21, no. 17 Proceedings of SPIE--the International Society for Optical Engineering; v. 4260. Variant Series: Proceedings of SPIE; v. 4260 LC Classification: RB43 .O682 2001 Dewey Class No.: 616.07/582 21

Optical fibers and sensors for medical applications: 20-21 January 2001, San Jose, USA / Israel Gannot, chair/editor; sponsored ... by SPIE--the International Society for Optical Engineering. Published/Created: Bellingham, Wash., USA: SPIE, c2001. Related Authors: Gannot, Israel. Society of Photo-optical Instrumentation Engineers. Description: vii, 190 p.: ill.; 28 cm. ISBN: 0819439312 Notes: Includes bibliographical references and index. Subjects: Optical fibers in medicine--Optical wave guides--Biosensors--Lasers in medicine--Congresses. Series: Progress in biomedical optics and imaging, 1605-7422; vol. 2, no. 10 Proceedings of SPIE--the International Society for Optical Engineering; v. 4253. Variant Series: SPIE proceedings series; v. 4253 LC Classification: R857.O59 O68 2001 Dewey Class No.: 610/.28 21

Optical fibre lasers and amplifiers / edited by P.W. France. Published/Created: Glasgow: Blackie; Boca Raton, Fla.: CRC Press, 1991. Related Authors: France, P. W. Description: xii, 259 p.: ill.; 24 cm. ISBN: 0216931576 0849377161 Notes: Spine Title - Optical fibre lasers & amplifiers. Includes bibliographical references and index. Subjects: Rare earth lasers. Fiber optics. Optical communications. LC Classification: TA1677 .F53 1991 Dewey Class No.: 621.36/6 20

Optical laser microlithography III: 7-9 March 1990, San Jose, California / Victor Pol, chair/editor; sponsored by SPIE--the International Society for Optical Engineering. Published/Created: Bellingham, Wash., USA: SPIE, c1990. Related Authors: Pol, Victor. Society of Photo-optical Instrumentation Engineers. Description: x, 586 p.: ill.; 28 cm. ISBN: 0819403113 Notes: Includes bibliographical references and index. Subjects: Lasers--Industrial applications--Congresses. Optical instruments--Congresses. Microlithography--Congresses. Series: Proceedings of SPIE--the International Society for Optical Engineering; v. 1264. Variant Series: Proceedings / SPIE--the International Society for Optical Engineering; v. 1264 LC Classification: TA1677 .O68 1990 Dewey Class No.: 621.36/6 20

Optical materials / editor, Marvin J. Weber. Published/Created: Boca Raton: CRC Press, c1995. Related Authors: Weber, Marvin J., 1932- Description: 833 p.: ill.; 26 cm. ISBN: 0849335078 (acid-free paper) Notes: Includes bibliographical references and index. Subjects: Optical materials--Handbooks, manuals, etc. Lasers--Handbooks, manuals, etc. Series: CRC handbook of laser science and technology. Supplement; 2 The CRC Press laser and optical science and technology series LC Classification: QC374 .O66 1995 Dewey Class No.: 621.36/6 20

Optical methods for tumor treatment and detection: mechanisms and techniques in photodynamic therapy IX: 22-23 January 2000, San Jose, California / Thomas J. Dougherty, chair/editor; sponsored by SPIE--the International Society for Optical Engineering [and] IBOS--the International Biomedical Optics Society.

Published/Created: Bellingham, Wash., USA: SPIE, c2000. Related Authors: Dougherty, Thomas J. (Thomas John), 1933- Society of Photo-optical Instrumentation Engineers. International Biomedical Optics Society. Description: vii, 148 p.: ill.; 28 cm. ISBN: 0819435252 Notes: Earlier conferences titled: Proceedings of optical methods for tumor treatment and detection. Includes bibliographical references and index. Subjects: Cancer--Photochemotherapy--Photochemotherapy--Lasers in medicine--Congresses. Series: Progress in biomedical optics, 1017-2661; vol. 1, no. 3 Proceedings of SPIE--the International Society for Optical Engineering; v. 3909. Variant Series: Proceedings of SPIE, 0277-786X; v. 3909

Optical methods for tumor treatment and detection: mechanisms and techniques in photodynamic therapy X: 20-21 January 2001, San Jose, USA / Thomas J. Dougherty, chair/editor; sponsored ... by SPIE--the International Society for Optical Engineering. Published/Created: Bellingham, Wash., USA: SPIE, c2001. Related Authors: Dougherty, Thomas J. (Thomas John), 1933- Society of Photo-optical Instrumentation Engineers. Description: vii, 192 p.: ill.; 28 cm. ISBN: 0819439266 Notes: Earlier conferences titled: Proceedings of optical methods for tumor treatment and detection. Includes bibliographical references and index. Subjects: Cancer--Photochemotherapy--Congresses. Photochemotherapy--Congresses. Lasers in medicine--Congresses. Series: Progress in biomedical optics and imaging, 1605-7422; vol. 2, no. 5 Proceedings of SPIE--the International Society for Optical Engineering; v. 4248. Variant Series: Proceedings of SPIE; v. 4248 LC Classification: RC271.P43 O68 2001 Dewey Class No.: 616.99/40631 21

Optical methods for ultrasensitive detection and analysis: techniques and applications: 21-23 January 1991, Los Angeles, California / Bryan L. Fearey, chair/editor; sponsored and published by SPIE--the International Society for Optical Engineering. Published/Created: Bellingham, Wash., USA: SPIE, c1991. Related Authors: Fearey, Bryan L. Society of Photo-optical Instrumentation Engineers. Description: x, 369 p.: ill.; 28 cm. ISBN: 0819405256 Notes: "Part of a three-conference program ... held at SPIE's Symposium on Laser Spectroscopy, a part of OE/LASE '91, 20-25 January 1991"--P. vii. Includes bibliographical references and index. Subjects: Laser spectroscopy--Congresses. Atomic absorption spectroscopy--Congresses. Lasers--Industrial applications--Congresses. Resonance ionization spectroscopy--Congresses. Surface chemistry--Technique--Congresses. Series: Proceedings of SPIE--the International Society for Optical Engineering; v. 1435. Variant Series: Proceedings / SPIE--the International Society for Optical Engineering; v. 1435 LC Classification: QC454.L3 O68 1991 Dewey Class No.: 621.36/1 20

Optical methods in engineering metrology / edited by D.C. Williams. Edition Information: 1st ed. Published/Created: London; New York: Chapman & Hall, 1993. Related Authors: Williams, D. C. (David C.) Description: xvi, 477 p.: ill.; 24 cm. ISBN: 0412396408 Notes: Includes bibliographical references and index. Subjects: Mensuration. Optical measurements. Series: Engineering aspects of lasers series LC Classification: T50 .O667 1993 Dewey Class No.: 620/.0044 20

Optical methods of biomedical diagnostics and therapy: 1-3 July 1992, Saratov, Russia / Valery V. Tuchin, chair/editor; organized by Saratov State University, Saratov Medical Institute, Saratov Institute of Rural Hygiene; cosponsored by SPIE/Russia--the International Society for Optical Engineering/Russia Chapter, Saratov Scientific Research Institute "Volga," [and] Saratov Center for Control and Exploration of Physical Fields and Radiations, Russian Academy of Sciences. Published/Created: Bellingham, Wash., USA: SPIE, c1993. Related Authors: Tuchin, V. V. (Valerii Viktorovich) Saratovskii gosudarstvennyi universitet im. N.G. Chernyshevskogo. Saratov Medical Institute. Saratov Institute of Rural Hygiene. Society of Photo-optical Instrumentation Engineers. Society of Photo-optical Instrumentation Engineers. Russian Chapter. Saratov Scientific Research Institute "Volga." Saratov Center for Control and Exploration of Physical Fields and Radiations. SPIE International Symposium on Physical Methods in Biomedical Diagnostics and Therapy (1992: Saratov, Russia) Description: x, 309 p.: ill.; 28 cm. ISBN: 0819412287 Notes: Proceedings of the SPIE International Symposium on Physical Methods in Biomedical Diagnostics and Therapy. Includes bibliographical references and index. Subjects: Lasers in medicine--Lasers--Diagnostic use--Therapeutic use--Congresses. Series: Proceedings of SPIE--the International Society for Optical Engineering; v. 1981. Variant Series: SPIE proceedings series; v. 1981 LC Classification: R857.L37 O667 1993 Dewey Class No.: 616.07/54 20

Optical organic and inorganic materials: 16-19 August, 2000, Vilnius, Lithuania / Steponas P. Asmontas, Jonas Gradauskas, chairs/editors; organized by, Semiconductor Physics Institute (Lithuania), SPIE Baltic Chapter; sponsored by, Lithuanian Ministry of Education and Research ... [et al.]; published by SPIE--the International Society for Optical Engineering. Published/Created: Bellingham, Washington: SPIE, c2001. Related Authors: Asmontas, Steponas P. Gradauskas, Jonas. Puslaidininkiu fizikos institutas (Lietuvos Mokslu akademija) Society of Photo-optical Instrumentation Engineers. Baltic Chapter. Lithuania. Ministry of Education and Research. Society of Photo-optical Instrumentation Engineers. Description: xi, 298 p.: ill.; 28 cm. ISBN: 0819441201 Notes: Includes bibliographic references and author index. Subjects: Optical materials--Congresses. Nonlinear optics--Congresses. Semiconductors--Materials--Congresses. Lasers--Materials--Congresses. Chalcogenides--Congresses. Series: Proceedings of SPIE--the International Society for Optical Engineering; v. 4415. Variant Series: Proceedings / SPIE--the International Society for optical Engineering; v. 4415

Optical organic and semiconductor inorganic materials: 26-29 August, 1996, Riga, Latvia / Edgar A. Silinsh ... [et al.], chairs/editors; organized by, Institute of Solid State Physics/University of Latvia ... [et al.]; sponsored by, Latvian Council of Science ... [et al.]; published by SPIE--the International Society for Optical Engineering. Published/Created: Bellingham, Washington: SPIE, c1997. Related Authors: Silins, E. Latvijas universit¯ate. Cietvielu fizikas instit¯uts. Latvijas Zin¯atnes padome. Society of Photo-optical Instrumentation Engineers. Description: xi, 324 p.: ill.; 28 cm. ISBN: 0819423742 Notes: Includes bibliographical references and index. Subjects: Optical materials--Congresses. Nonlinear optics--Congresses. Semiconductors--Materials--Congresses. Lasers--Materials--Congresses. Chalcogenides--Congresses. Series: Proceedings of SPIE--the International Society for Optical Engineering; v. 2968. Variant Series: Proceedings / SPIE--the International Society for optical Engineering; v. 2968 LC Classification: QC374 .O72 1997

Optical processes in microcavities / editors Richard K. Chang, Anthony J. Campillo. Published/Created: Singapore; New Jersey: World Scientific, c1996. Related Authors: Chang, Richard K. (Richard Kounai), 1940- Campillo, Anthony J. Description: x, 434 p.: ill.; 23 cm. ISBN: 9810223447 Notes: Includes bibliographical references and index. Subjects: Lasers. Quantum electrodynamics. Electromagnetic interactions. Semiconductors. Hybrid integrated circuits. Series: Advanced series in applied physics; v. 3 Variant Series: Advanced series in applied physics; vol. 3 LC Classification: TA1677 .O78 1996 Dewey Class No.: 537.6/7 20

Optical resonators: 16-18 January 1990, Los Angeles, California / Dale A. Holmes, chair/editor; sponsored by SPIE--the International Society for Optical Engingeering. Published/Created: Bellingham, Wash., USA: SPIE, c1990. Related Authors: Holmes, Dale A. Society of Photo-optical Instrumentation Engineers. Symposium on High-Power Lasers and Optical Computing (1990: Los Angeles, Calif.) Description: viii, 518 p.: ill.; 28 cm. ISBN: 0819402656 Notes: Papers presented at a technical conference held at the Symposium on High-Power Lasers and Optical Computing, held 14-19 Jan. 1990, in Los Angeles, Calif. Includes bibliographical references and index. Subjects: Lasers--Resonators--Congresses. Series: Proceedings of SPIE--the International Society for Optical Engineering; v. 1224. Variant Series: Proceedings / SPIE--the International Society for Optical Engineering; v. 1224 LC Classification: TA1673 .O693 1990 Dewey Class No.: 621.36/6 20

Optical resonators: science and engineering / edited by Ram Kossowsky, Miroslav Jelínek, and Josef Novák. Published/Created: Dordrecht; Boston: Kluwer Academic Publishers, c1998. Related Authors: Kossowsky, Ram. Jelínek, Miroslav. Novák, Josef, Ing. North Atlantic Treaty Organization. Scientific Affairs Division. NATO Advanced Research Workshop on Optical Resonators: Theory and Design (1997: Smolenice, Slovakia) Description: xi, 504 p.: ill.; 25 cm. ISBN: 0792349628 (alk. paper) Notes: Published in cooperation with NATO Scientific Affairs Division." "Proceedings of the NATO Advanced Research Workshop on Optical Resonators: Theory and Design, Smolenice, Slovak Republic, July 1-5, 1997"--T.p. verso. Includes bibliographical references and index. Subjects: Lasers--Resonators. Optical resonance. Laser beams. Series: NATO ASI series. Partnership sub-series 3, High technology; vol. 45 LC Classification: TA1677 .O79 1998 Dewey Class No.: 621.36/6 21

Optical scanning systems: design and applications: 30-31 July, 1997, San Diego, California / Leo Beiser, Stephen F. Sagan, chairs/editors; sponsored and published by, SPIE--the International Society for Optical Engineering. Published/Created: Bellingham, Washington: SPIE, c1997. Related Authors: Beiser, Leo. Sagan, Stephen F. Society of Photo-optical Instrumentation Engineers. Description: ix, 308 p.: ill.; 28 cm. ISBN: 0819425532 Notes: Includes bibliographic references and author index. Subjects: Optical scanners--Design and construction--Congresses Lasers--Congresses. Series: Proceedings of SPIE--the International Society for Optical Engineering; v. 3131. Variant Series: Proceedings / SPIE--The International Society for Optical Engineering; v. 3131 LC Classification: TK7882.S3 O66 1997 Dewey Class No.: 621.39/9 21

Optical security and anticounterfeiting systems: 15-16 January 1990, Los Angeles, California / William F. Fagan, chair/editor; sponsored by SPIE--the International Society for Optical Engineering. Published/Created: Bellingham, Wash., USA: SPIE, c1990. Related Authors: Fagan, William F. Society of Photo-optical Instrumentation Engineers. Symposium on High-Power Lasers and Optical Computing (1990: Los Angeles, Calif.) Description: vii, 133 p.: ill.; 28 cm. ISBN: 0819402516 Notes: "Part of SPIE's Symposium on High-Power Lasers and Optical Computing held at OE LASE '90, 14-19-January 1990, Los Angeles, California"--P. vi. Includes bibliographical references and index. Subjects: Holography--Congresses. Security systems--Congresses. Counterfeits and counterfeiting--Congresses. Series: Proceedings of SPIE--the International Society for Optical Engineering: v. 1210. Variant Series: Proceedings / SPIE--the International Society for Optical Engineering; v. 1210 LC Classification: TA1542 .O66 1990 Dewey Class No.: 621.36/75 20

Optical sensing, imaging, and manipulation for biological and biomedical applications: 26-

28 July 2000, Taipei, Taiwan / Robert R. Alfano, Ping-Pei Ho, Arthur E.T. Chiou, chairs/editors; sponsored by SPIE--the International Society for Optical Engineering, National Science Council (Taiwan), [and] PIDA--Photonics Industry Development Association. Published/Created: Bellingham, Wash., USA: SPIE, c2000. Related Authors: Alfano, R. R. Ho, Ping-Pei. Chiou, Arthur E. T. Society of Photo-optical Instrumentation Engineers. Kuo chia k`o hsüeh wei yüan hui. Photonics Industry Development Association. Description: xii, 330 p.: ill.; 28 cm. ISBN: 0819437212 Notes: Includes bibliographical references and index. Subjects: Diagnostic imaging--Congresses. Biosensors--Congresses. Optical detectors--Congresses. Lasers in medicine--Congresses. Series: Proceedings of SPIE--the International Society for Optical Engineering; v. 4082. Variant Series: SPIE proceedings series; v. 4082 LC Classification: RC78.7.D53 O65 2000 Dewey Class No.: 616.07/54 21

Optical systems in adverse environments: proceedings: 22-27 October 1990, Singapore / Siu-Chung Tam, Donald E. Silva, M.H. Kuok, chairs/editors; organizers, Institute of Physics, Singapore (IPS), IEEE Singapore Section, SPIE--the International Society for Optical Engineering; sponsors, International Commission for Optics (ICO), Optical Society of America (OSA); cosponsors, Schott Glass Singapore Pte. Ltd. ... [et al.]. Published/Created: Bellingham, Wash., USA: SPIE, c1991. Related Authors: Tam, Siu-Chung. Silva, Donald E. Kuok, M. H. Institute of Physics, Singapore. IEEE Singapore Section. Society of Photo-optical Instrumentation Engineers. International Commission on Optics. Optical Society of America. Schott Glass Singapore Pte. Ltd. Asia Pacific Conference on Optical Technology (1990: Singapore) Description: viii, 214 p.: ill.; 28 cm. ISBN: 0819404829 Notes: "One of three parallel conferences held under the auspices of APCOT '90--the Asia Pacific Conference on Optical Technology 1990"--P. vii. Includes bibliographical references and index. Subjects: Optical instruments--Congresses. Lasers--Congresses. Optoelectronic devices--Effect of radiation on Congresses. Series: Proceedings of SPIE--the International Society for Optical Engineering; v. 1399. Variant Series: SPIE proceedings series; v. 1399 LC Classification: TS510 .O63 1991 Dewey Class No.: 621.36 20

Optical/laser microlithography / Burn J. Lin, chair/editor; sponsored by SPIE--the International Society for Optical Engineering. Published/Created: Bellingham, Wash., USA: SPIE, c1988-c1989. Related Authors: Lin, Burn Jeng, 1942- Society of Photo-optical Instrumentation Engineers. Description: 2 v.: ill.; 28 cm. ISBN: 0892529571 (v. 1) 0819401234 (v. 2) Contents: [1]. 2-4 March 1988 -- 2. 1-3 March 1989, San Jose, Calif. Notes: Includes bibliographies and index. Subjects: Lasers--Industrial applications--Congresses. Optical instruments--Congresses. Microlithography--Congresses. Series: Proceedings of SPIE--the International Society for Optical Engineering; v. 922, 1088 LC Classification: TA1677 .O67 1988 Dewey Class No.: 621.36/6 20

Optical/laser microlithography IV: 6-8 March 1991, San Jose, California / Victor Pol, chair/editor; sponsored and published by SPIE--the International Society for Optical Engineering. Published/Created: Bellingham, Wash., USA: SPIE, c1991. Related Authors: Pol, Victor. Society of Photo-optical Instrumentation Engineers. Description: xii, 754 p.: ill.; 28 cm. ISBN: 0819405620 Notes: Includes bibliographical references and index. Subjects: Lasers--Industrial applications--Congresses. Optical instruments--Congresses. Microlithography--Congresses. Series: Proceedings of SPIE--the International Society for Optical Engineering; v. 1463. Variant Series: Proceedings / SPIE--the International Society for Optical Engineering; v. 1463 LC Classification: TA1677 .O67 1991 Dewey Class No.: 621.36/6 20

Optical/laser microlithography. Published/Created: Bellingham, Wash.: SPIE-the International Society for Optical Engineering, c1988- Related Authors: Society of Photo-optical Instrumentation Engineers. Description: v.: ill.; 28 cm. Issued 1992- in pts. Issue for 1988 lacks numerical designation but constitutes 1. 2-4 Mar. 1988- Current Frequency: Annual Cancel/Invalid LCCN: sn 93042097 Notes: SERBIB/SERLOC merged record Subjects: Lasers--Industrial applications--Congresses. Optical instruments--Congresses. Microlithography--Congresses. Series: Proceedings of SPIE--the International Society for Optical Engineering. LC Classification: TA1671 .O69 Dewey Class No.: 621.3815/31 20

Optical-thermal response of laser-irradiated tissue / edited by Ashley J. Welch and Martin J.C. van Gemert. Published/Created: New York: Plenum Press, c1995. Related Authors: Welch, Ashley J., 1933- Gemert, Martin J. C. van Description: xxvi, 925 p.: ill.; 24 cm. ISBN: 0306449269 Notes: Includes bibliographical references and index. Subjects: Tissues--Optical properties. Tissues--Thermal properties. Lasers--Physiological effect. Lasers. Thermal Conductivity. Radiation Effects. Biomedical Engineering. Series: Lasers, photonics, and electro-optics LC Classification: QH642 .O65 1995 Dewey Class No.: 574.19/15 20

Optics for fourth-generation x-ray sources: 1-2 August 2001, San Diego, USA / Roman O. Tatchyn, Andreas K. Freund, Tadashi Matsushita, chairs/editors; sponsored ... by SPIE--the International Society for Optical Engineering. Published/Created: Bellingham, Wash., USA: SPIE, c2001. Related Authors: Tatchyn, Roman Orest. Freund, Andreas K. Matsushita, Tadashi. Society of Photo-optical Instrumentation Engineers. Description: vii, 196 p.: ill.; 28 cm. ISBN: 0819442143 Notes: Includes bibliographical references and index. Subjects: X-ray optics--Congresses. X-ray lasers--Congresses. Free electron lasers--Congresses. Series: Proceedings of SPIE--the International Society for Optical Engineering; v. 4500. Variant Series: SPIE proceedings series; v. 4500

Optics in computing: March 18-21, 1997, Hyatt Regency Lake Tahoe, Incline Village, Nevada / technical cosponsor, IEEE/Lasers and Electro-Optics Society, SPIE; in cooperation with ICO; sponsored and managed by Optical Society of America. Edition Information: Conference ed. Published/Created: Washington, DC: Optical Society of America, c1997. Related Authors: IEEE Communications Society. Lasers and Electro-optics Society (Institute of Electrical and Electronics Engineers) Optical Society of America. Description: xiii, 272 p.: ill.; 28 cm. ISBN: 1557524904 (Conference ed.) 1557524858 (1997 Technical Digest Series) Notes: Includes bibliographical references. Subjects: Computers--Optical equipment--Congresses. Integrated optics--Congresses. Optical data processing--Congresses. Series: Technical digest series (Optical Society of America) (Conference ed.); 1997, v. 8. Variant Series: 1997 technical digest series; v. 8 LC Classification: TK7895.O6 O68 1997 Dewey Class No.: 621.39 21

Optics of nanostructured materials / edited by Vadim Markel, Thomas George. Published/Created: New York: Wiley, c2001. Related Authors: Markel′, V. A. (Vadim Arkad′evich) George, Thomas F., 1947- Description: x, 553 p.: ill.; 24 cm. ISBN: 0471349682 (cloth) Notes: "A Wiley-Interscience publication." Includes bibliographical references and index. Subjects: Optoelectronics--Materials. Nanowires. Nanostructure materials--Optical properties. Series: Wiley series in lasers and applications LC Classification: TA418.9.N35 O68 2001 Dewey Class No.: 621.36 21

Optics, optical systems and applications / edited by E. Jakeman. Published/Created: Bristol [England]; Philadelphia: A. Hilger, c1988. Related Authors: Jakeman, E. European Conference on Optics, Optical Systems and Applications (1988: Birmingham, England)

Description: 190 p.: ill.; 30 cm. ISBN: 0852742460: Notes: Selected papers presented at the European Conference on Optics, Optical Systems and Applications held in Birmingham in March 1988. Includes bibliographical references. Subjects: Optics--Congresses. Lasers--Congresses. LC Classification: TA1505 .O685 1988 Dewey Class No.: 535 19

Optoelectronic component technologies: 16-18 December 1992, National Chiao Tung University, Hsinchu, Taiwan, China / Guo-Chung Chi, C.S. Hong, chairs/editors; co-organized by National Chiao Tung University, SPIE--the International Society for Optical Engineering; cooperating organizations, Asia-Pacific Optics Federation ... [et al.]. Published/Created: Bellingham, Wash.: SPIE, c1992. Related Authors: Chi, Guo-Chung. Hong, C.-S. (Chi-Shain) Shang-hai chiao t`ung ta hsüeh. Society of Photo-optical Instrumentation Engineers. Description: ix, 326 p.: ill.; 28 cm. ISBN: 0819410136 Notes: Includes bibliographical references and index. Subjects: Optoelectronic devices--Congresses. Lasers--Congresses. Series: Proceedings of SPIE--the International Society for Optical Engineering; v. 1813. Variant Series: Proceedings / SPIE--the International Society for Optical Engineering; v. 1813 LC Classification: TA1750 .O6733 1992 Dewey Class No.: 621.381/045 20

Optoelectronic devices and applications: 10-11 July 1990, San Diego, California / Sriram Sriram, chair/editor; sponsored by SPIE--the International Society for Optical Engineering. Published/Created: Bellingham, Wash., USA: The Society, c1990. Related Authors: Sriram, S. Society of Photo-optical Instrumentation Engineers. International Symposium on Optical and Optoelectronic Applied Sciences and Engineering (34th: 1990: San Diego, Calif.) Description: vii, 275 p.: ill.; 28 cm. ISBN: 0819403997 Notes: "Part of a three-conference program on optoelectronic materials and applications held at SPIE's International Symposium on Optical and Optoelectronic Applied Science and Engineering, 8-13 July 1990, San Diego, California"--p. v. Includes bibliographical references and index. Subjects: Optoelectronic devices--Congresses. Integrated optics--Congresses. Lasers--Congresses. Series: Proceedings of SPIE--the International Society for Optical Engineering; v. 1338. Variant Series: Proceedings / SPIE--the International Society for Optical Engineering; v. 1338 LC Classification: TA1750 .O6734 1990 Dewey Class No.: 621.381/045 20

Optomechanical design of laser transmitters and receivers: 16-17 January 1989, Los Angeles, California / Bernard D. Seery, chair/editor; sponsored by SPIE--the International Society for Optical Engineering; cooperating organizations, Applied Optics Laboratory/New Mexico State University ... [et al.]. Published/Created: Bellingham, Wash., USA: SPIE, c1989. Related Authors: Seery, Bernard D. (Bernard David) Society of Photo-optical Instrumentation Engineers. Symposium on Lasers and Optics (1989: Los Angeles, Calif.) Description: viii, 278 p.: ill.; 28 cm. ISBN: 0819400793 Notes: Papers of the Symposium on Lasers and Optics. Includes bibliographical references and index. Subjects: Semiconductor lasers--Congresses. Laser communication systems--Congresses. Optical detectors--Congresses. Series: Proceedings of SPIE--the International Society for Optical Engineering; v. 1044. Variant Series: Proceedings / SPIE--the International Society for Optical Engineering; v. 1044 LC Classification: TA1700 .O68 1989 Dewey Class No.: 621.382/7 20

OSA proceedings on advanced solid-state lasers: proceedings of the topical meeting. Published/Created: Washington, DC: Optical Society of America, c1991- Description: v.: ill.; 29 cm. Vols. for 1990-<1994 lack series statement, OSA proceeding series, but carry its numbering, e.g., 1990 called also v. 6, 1993 called also v. 15, etc. 1990- Current Frequency: Annual Continues: OSA proceedings on tunable solid state lasers (DLC) 96659124

(OCoLC)34737957 Notes: SERBIB/SERLOC merged record Subjects: Solid-state lasers--Tunable lasers--Congresses. LC Classification: TA1705 .O817 Dewey Class No.: 621.36/61 20

OSA proceedings on extreme ultraviolet lithography: proceedings of the topical meeting, September 19-21, 1994, Monterey, California / edited by Frits Zernike and David T. Attwood; sponsored by Optical Society of America. Published/Created: Washington, DC: The Society, c1995. Related Authors: Zernike, Frits, 1930- Attwood, David T. Optical Society of America. Description: xi, 283 p.: ill.; 24 cm. ISBN: 1557523630 Notes: "Volume 23." Includes bibliographical references and index. Subjects: Optical coatings--Photolithography--Ultraviolet radiation--Industrial applications--Interferometry--Lasers--Industrial applications--Congresses. LC Classification: TS517.2 .O83 1995

OSA proceedings on nonlinear dynamics in optical systems: proceedings of the international topical meeting, June 4-8, 1990, Afton, Oklahoma / edited by Neal B. Abraham, Elsa M. Garmire, and Paul Mandel; sponsored by the Optical Society of America; supported by Air Force Office of Scientific Research ... [et al.]; in cooperation with International Commission for Optics. Published/Created: Washington, D.C.: The Society, c1991. Related Authors: Abraham, Neal B. Garmire, E. Mandel, P. (Paul), 1942- Description: xxi, 605 p.: ill.; 29 cm. ISBN: 1557521271 Notes: "Contributions to the International Topical Meeting on Nonlinear Dynamics in Optical Systems"--P. xxi. "Volume 7." Includes bibliographical references and index. Subjects: Semiconductors--Dynamics--Nonlinear theories--Optical bistability--Lasers--Congresses. LC Classification: QC610.9 .O82 1991 Dewey Class No.: 621.36/6 20

OSA proceedings on photonic switching: proceedings of the international topical meeting, March 6-8, 1991, Salt Lake City, Utah / edited by H. Scott Hinton and Joseph W. Goodman; sponsored by the Optical Society of America, IEEE/Lasers and Electro-optics Society. Published/Created: Washington, DC: Optical Society of America, c1991. Related Authors: Hinton, H. Scott. Goodman, Joseph W. Optical Society of America. Lasers and Electro-optics Society (Institute of Electrical and Electronics Engineers) Description: xv, 276 p.: ill.; 29 cm. ISBN: 1557521735 Notes: Spine Title - Photonic switching. "Volume 8." Includes bibliographical references and index. Subjects: Photonics--Switching circuits--Telecommunication--Switching systems--Congresses. LC Classification: TA1505 .O728 1991 Dewey Class No.: 621.382/7 20

OSA proceedings on photonic switching: proceedings of the OSA topical meeting, March 1-3, 1989, Salt Lake City, Utah / edited by John E. Midwinter and H. Scott Hinton; sponsored by the Optical Society of America in cooperation with the Lasers and Electro-optics Society of the Institute of Electrical and Electronics Engineers. Published/Created: Washington, DC: Optical Society of America, c1989. Related Authors: Midwinter, John E. Hinton, H. Scott. Description: xii, 292 p.: ill.; 29 cm. ISBN: 1557521093 Notes: Spine Title - Photonic switching. "Volume 3." Includes bibliographical references and index. Subjects: Photonics--Congresses. Switching circuits--Congresses. Telecommunication--Switching systems--Congresses. LC Classification: TA1505 .O73 1989 Dewey Class No.: 621.36 20

OSA proceedings on photonics in switching: proceedings of the topical meeting, March 15-17, 1993, Palm Springs, California / edited by Joseph W. Goodman and Rod C. Alferness; sponsored by the Optical Society of America, IEEE/Lasers and Electro-optics Society. Published/Created: Washington, DC: Optical Society of America, c1993. Related Authors: Goodman, Joseph W. Alferness, R. C. Optical Society of America. Lasers and

Electro-optics Society (Institute of Electrical and Electronics Engineers) Description: xi, 216 p.: ill.; 29 cm. ISBN: 1557522863 Notes: Spine Title - Photonics in switching. "Volume 16." Includes bibliographical references and index. Subjects: Photonics--Switching circuits--Congresses. Telecommunication--Switching systems--Congresses. LC Classification: TA1505 .O733 1993 Dewey Class No.: 621.382/7 20

OSA proceedings on picosecond electronics and optoelectronics: proceedings of the OSA topical meeting, March 8-10, 1989, Salt Lake City, Utah / edited by T.C.L. Gerhard Sollner and David M. Bloom.; cosponsored by the Optical Society of America and by the Lasers and Electro-Optics Society of the Institute of Electrical and Electronics Engineers. Published/Created: Washington, DC: OSA, c1989. Related Authors: Sollner, T. C. L. Gerhard. Bloom, D. M. (David M.), 1948- Optical Society of America. Lasers and Electro-optics Society (Institute of Electrical and Electronics Engineers) Picosecond Electronics and Optoelectronics Topical Meeting (1989: Salt Lake City, Utah) Description: xii, 272 p.: ill.; 29 cm. ISBN: 1557521107 Notes: Spine Title - Picosecond electronics and optoelectronics. "Papers ... presented at the 1989 Picosecond Electronics and Optoelectronics Topical Meeting"--P. xi. Includes bibliographical references and indexes. Subjects: Optoelectronics--Congresses. Laser pulses, Ultrashort--Congresses. Quantum electronics--Congresses. Series: OSA proceeding series; v. 4 LC Classification: TA1673 .O73 1989 Dewey Class No.: 621.381/045 20

OSA proceedings on ultrafast electronics and optoelectronics: proceedings of the topical meeting, January 25-27, 1993, San Francisco, California / edited by Jagdeep Shah and Umesh Mishra; cosponsored by Optical Society of America, IEEE/Lasers and Electro-optics Society; in cooperation with IEEE/Electron Devices. Published/Created: Washington, DC: Optical Society of America, c1993. Related Authors: Shah, J. (Jagdeep) Mishra, Umesh Kumar, 1958- Description: xiv, 248 p.: ill.; 29 cm. ISBN: 1557522758 Notes: "Fifth Topical Meeting on Ultrafast Electronics and Optoelectronics ... held in San Francisco, January 23-25, 1993"--Pref. Includes bibliographical references and index. Subjects: Optoelectronics--Laser pulses, Ultrashort--Quantum electronics--Semiconductors--Congresses. Series: OSA proceedings on; v. 14 LC Classification: TA1673 .O76 1993 Dewey Class No.: 621.381/045 20

Phase conjugation of laser emission / edited by N.G. Basov; translated by Kevin S. Hendzel. Edition Information: 50th anniversary ed. Published/Created: Commack, N.Y.: Nova Science Publishers, c1988. Related Authors: Basov, N. G. (Nikolai Gennadievich), 1922- Description: vii, 240 p.: ill.; 25 cm. ISBN: 0941743071: Contents: The Formation of the space-time structure of lightwaves by stimulated scattering in hypersound / N.G. Basov ... [et al] -- Phase conjugation of pulsed CO2 laser emission / N.G. Basov ... [et al]. Notes: Translation of: Obrashchenie volnovogo fronta lazernogo izlucheniia. Includes bibliographies and index. Subjects: Quantum electronics. Optical phase conjugation. Carbon dioxide lasers. Series: Trudy Fizicheskogo instituta. English; v. 172. Variant Series: Proceedings of the Lebedev Physics Institute of the Academy of Sciences of the USSR; v. 172 LC Classification: QC1 .A4114 vol. 172 QC688 Dewey Class No.: 530 s 537.5 19

Photoacoustic, photothermal, and photochemical processes at surfaces and in thin films / edited by P. Hess; with contributions by A.C. Boccara ... [et al.]. Published/Created: Berlin; New York: Springer-Verlag, c1989. Related Authors: Hess, P. (Peter) Boccara, A. C. Physikzentrum (Bad Honnef, Germany) Description: xiv, 376 p.: ill.; 25 cm. ISBN: 0387517030 (U.S.: alk. paper) Notes: "Comprises review articles based on talks presented at the 49th We-Heraeus seminar, which was held at the Physikzentrum, Bad Honnef, November 21-23, 1988"--Pref. Includes bibliographical references and index. Subjects: Thin films--Surfaces--Photochemistry--Congresses. Lasers in physics--Congresses. Series: Topics in current physics; 47 LC Classification: QC176.84.S93 P46 1989 Dewey Class No.: 530.4/175 20

Photochemistry in thin films: 17-18 January 1989 / Thomas F. George, chair/editor; sponsored by SPIE--the International Society for Optical Engineering; cooperating organizations, Applied Optics Laboratory/New Mexico State University ... [et al.]. Published/Created: Bellingham, Wash., USA: SPIE, c1989. Related Authors: George, Thomas F., 1947- Society of Photo-optical Instrumentation Engineers. Symposium on Lasers and Optics (1989: Los Angeles, Calif.) Description: viii, 270 p.: ill.; 28 cm. ISBN: 0819400912 Notes: Papers of one of a nineteen part program held at the Symposium on Lasers and Optics. Includes bibliographical references. Subjects: Thin films--Surfaces--Congresses. Photochemistry--Congresses. Lasers in physics--Congresses. Series: Proceedings of SPIE--the International Society for Optical Engineering; v. 1056. Variant Series: Proceedings / SPIE--the International Society for Optical Engineering; 1056 LC Classification: QC176.84.S93 P47 1989 Dewey Class No.: 530.4/175 20

Photodynamic therapy: mechanisms, 19-20 January 1989, Los Angeles, California / Thomas J. Dougherty, chair/editor; sponsored by SPIE--the International Society for Optical Engineering; cooperating organizations, American Academy of Dermatology ... [et al.]. Published/Created: Bellingham, Wash., USA: SPIE, c1989. Related Authors: Dougherty, Thomas J. (Thomas John), 1933- Description: viii, 206 p.: ill.; 28 cm. ISBN: 0819401005 Notes: "Symposium on Medical Applications of Lasers and Optics; this conference was part of a six-conference program ... held at SPIE's OE/LASE '89 Symposium on Optics, Electro-Optics & Laser Applications in Science & Engineering"--P. vi. Errata slip inserted. Includes bibliographical references. Subjects: Cancer--Photochemotherapy--Congresses. Series: Proceedings of SPIE--the International Society for Optical Engineering; v. 1065. Variant Series: Proceedings / SPIE--the International Society for Optical Engineering; v. 1065 LC Classification: RC271.P43 P46 1989 Dewey Class No.: 616.99/40631 20

Photon migration in tissues / edited by Britton Chance. Published/Created: New York: Plenum Press, c1989. Related Authors: Chance, Britton. Description: x, 195 p.: ill.; 26 cm. ISBN: 0306435225 Notes: Proceedings of a workshop held April 17, 1988, in Philadelphia, Pa. Includes bibliographical references and index. Subjects: Lasers--Physiological effect--Congresses. Laser spectroscopy--Congresses. Radiation--congresses. Spectrophotometry--congresses. LC Classification: QP82.2.L3 P48 1990 Dewey Class No.: 599/.08/2028 20

Photonic component engineering and applications: 8-9 April 1996, Orlando, Florida / Andrew R. Pirich, chair/editor; sponsored and published by SPIE--the International Society of Optical Engineering. Published/Created: Bellingham, Wash.: SPIE, c1996. Related Authors: Pirich, Andrew R. Society of Photo-optical Instrumentation Engineers. Description: ix, 230 p.: ill.; 28 cm. ISBN: 0819421308 Notes: Includes bibliographical references and index. Subjects: Photonics--Congresses. Optoelectronics--Congresses. Lasers--Congresses. Signal processing--Congresses.. Neural networks (Computer science)--Congresses. Series: Proceedings of SPIE--the International Society of Optical Engineering; v. 2749. Variant Series: Proceedings / SPIE--the International Society of Optical Engineering; v. 2749 LC Classification: TA1505 .P486 1996

Photonic switching / edited by H. Scott Hinton, John E. Midwinter. Published/Created: New York: IEEE Press, c1990. Related Authors: Hinton, H. Scott. Midwinter, John E. IEEE Communications Society. Description: ix, 447 p.: ill.; 29 cm. ISBN: 0879422602 Notes: A collection of reprints of articles orginally published from 1975 to 1989. "Published in cooperation with the IEEE Communications Society." "IEEE order number: PC0253-5"--T.p. verso. Includes bibliographical references and indexes. Subjects: Telecommunication--Switching systems--Equipment and supplies. Optical communications. Optical data processing. Series: Progress in lasers and electro-optics LC Classification: TK5103.8 .P49 1989 Dewey Class No.: 621.381/045 20

Photonic switching: proceedings of the first topical meeting, Incline Village, Nevada, March 18-20, 1987 / editors, T.K. Gustafson and P.W. Smith. Published/Created: Berlin; New York: Springer-Verlag, c1988. Related Authors: Gustafson, T. K. (Ture Kenneth), 1940- Smith, P. W. (Peter W.), 1937- Lasers and Electro-optics Society (Institute of Electrical and Electronics Engineers) Optical Society of America. IEEE Communications Society. Description: x, 218 p.: ill.; 24 cm. ISBN: 0387188665 (U.S.) Notes: "Sponsored by the IEEE Lasers and Electro-Optics Society and the Optical Society of America with the cooperation of the IEEE Communications Society"--Pref. Includes bibliographies and index. Subjects: Photonics--Congresses. Switching circuits--Congresses. Series: Springer series in electronics and photonics; v. 25 LC Classification: TA1505 .P49 1988 Dewey Class No.: 621.36 19

Photonic systems and applications in defense and manufacturing: 1-2 December 1999, Singapore / Yee-Loy Lam, Koji Ikuta, Metin S. Mangir, chairs/editors; sponsored by SPIE--the International Society for Optical Engineering [and] Nanyang Technological University, Singapore; cosponsored by SPIE Singapore Chapter ... [et al.]; cooperating organizations, National University of Singapore ... [et al.]. Published/Created: Bellingham, Wash., USA: SPIE, c1999. Related Authors: Lam, Yee-Loy. Ikuta, Koji, 1953- Mangir, Metin S. Society of Photo-optical Instrumentation Engineers. Nanyang Technological University. Society of Photo-optical Instrumentation Engineers. Singapore Chapter. National University of Singapore. Description: x, 438 p.: ill.; 28 cm. ISBN: 0819435007 Notes: Includes bibliographical references and index. Subjects: Electrooptics--Military applications--Congresses. Lasers--Military applications--Congresses. Photonics--Industrial applications--Congresses. Lasers--Industrial applications--Congresses. Series: Proceedings of SPIE--the International Society for Optical Engineering; v. 3898. Variant Series: SPIE proceedings series; v. 3898

Photonic systems and applications: 27-30 November 2001, Singapore / Yakov S. Sidorin, Dingyuan Tang, chairs/editors; sponsored by SPIE--the International Society for Optical Engineering [and] Nanyang Technological University (Singapore). Published/Created: Bellingham, Wash., USA: SPIE, c2001. Related Authors: Sidorin, Yakov S. Tang, Dingyuan. Society of Photo-optical Instrumentation Engineers. Nanyang Technological University. Description: xi, 336 p.: ill.; 28 cm. ISBN: 0819443255 Notes: Includes bibliographical references and index. Subjects: Photonics--Industrial applications--Congresses. Lasers--Industrial applications--Congresses. Series: Proceedings of SPIE--the International Society for Optical Engineering; v. 4595. Variant Series: SPIE proceedings series; v. 4595

Photonics in switching: April 2-4, 1997, Royal Institute of Technology, Stockholm, Sweden / organized by Optical Society of America, Royal Institute of Technology; technical cosponsor, IEEE/Lasers and Electro-Optics Society. Published/Created: Washington, DC: The Society, c1997. Related Authors: Optical Society of

America. Kungl. Tekniska högskolan. Lasers and Electro-optics Society (Institute of Electrical and Electronics Engineers) Description: 206 p.: ill.; 28 cm. + 1 addendum and postdeadline papers ISBN: 1557524971 Notes: Includes bibliographical references and index. Subjects: Telecommunication--Switching systems--Congresses. Photonics--Congresses. Switching circuits--Congresses. Series: Technical digest series (Optical Society of America); 1995, v. 10. Variant Series: Technical digest; v. 10 LC Classification: TK5103.8 .P547 1997

Photons and low energy particles in surface processing: symposium held December 3-6, 1991, Boston, Massachusetts, U.S.A. / editors, Carol I.H. Ashby, James H. Brannon, Stella W. Pang. Published/Created: Pittsburgh, Pa.: Materials Research Society, c1992. Related Authors: Ashby, Carol Iris Hill, 1953- Brannon, James H. Pang, Stella W. Description: xv, 552 p.: ill.; 24 cm. ISBN: 1558991301 Notes: Includes bibliographical references and indexes. Subjects: Surfaces (Technology)--Congresses. Plasma etching--Congresses. Lasers--Industrial applications--Congresses. Photon beams--Industrial applications--Congresses. Plasma-enhanced chemical vapor deposition--Congresses. Series: Materials Research Society symposia proceedings; v. 236. Variant Series: Materials Research Society symposium proceedings, 0272-9172; v. 236 LC Classification: TA418.7 .P46 1992 Dewey Class No.: 620/.44 20

Photopolymer device physics, chemistry, and applications: 17-19 January 1990, Los Angeles, California / Roger A. Lessard, chair/editor; sponsored by SPIE--the International Society for Optical Engineering. Published/Created: Bellingham, Wash., USA: SPIE, c1990. Related Authors: Lessard, Roger A. Society of Photo-optical Instrumentation Engineers. Symposium on High-Power Lasers and Optical Computing (1990: Los Angeles, Calif.) Description: vii, 223 p.: ill.; 28 cm. ISBN: 0819402540 Notes: "Part of SPIE's Symposium on High-Power Lasers and Optical Computing held at OE LASE '90, 14-19 January 1990, Los Angeles, California"--P. vi. Includes bibliographical references and index. Subjects: Holography--Equipment and supplies--Congresses. Photopolymers--Congresses. Optical wave guides--Materials--Congresses. Photochemistry--Congresses. Series: Proceedings of SPIE--the International Society for Optical Engineering; v. 1213. Variant Series: Proceedings / SPIE--the International Society for Optical Engineering; v. 1213 LC Classification: TA1542 .P49 1990 Dewey Class No.: 621.381/045 20

Physical science. III, Learning all about lights and lasers [computer file]. Edition Information: MS-DOS version. Published/Created: Fairfield, CT: Queue, c1994. Related Authors: Queue, Inc. Description: 1 computer laser optical disc; 4 3/4 in. + setup instructions (1 folded sheet). Computer File Info.: Computer data and programs. IBM PC MS-DOS CD-ROM player Summary: A collection of Queue's educational software programs for physical science instruction concerning lights and lasers. The programs provide an interactive learning format featuring immediate feedback, help screens, and scoring. Notes: Title from disc label. Issued also in Macintosh version. System requirements: IBM-compatible PC; 640K RAM minimum; MS-DOS; VGA or MCGA monitor; 500K additional hard disk space to install; Sound Blaster card or compatible optional. Subjects: Light--Study and teaching--Software. Lasers--Study and teaching--Software. LC Classification: QC363 Dewey Class No.: 535 12

Physical science. III, Learning all about lights and lasers [computer file]. Edition Information: Macintosh version. Published/Created: Fairfield, CT: Queue, c1994. Related Authors: Queue, Inc. Description: 1 computer laser optical disc; 4 3/4 in. + setup instructions (1 folded sheet). Computer File Info.: Computer data and programs. Macintosh CD-ROM player

Summary: A collection of Queue's educational software programs for physical science instruction concerning lights and lasers. The programs provide an interactive learning format featuring immediate feedback, help screens, and scoring. Notes: Title from disc label. Issued also in MS-DOS version. System requirements: Macintosh; 2MB RAM; color monitor; CD-ROM drive. Subjects: Light--Study and teaching--Software. Lasers--Study and teaching--Software. LC Classification: QC363 Dewey Class No.: 535 12

Plasma and laser processing of materials / edited by Kamleshwar Upadhya. Published/Created: Warrendale, Pa.: Minerals, Metals & Materials Society, c1991. Related Authors: Upadhya, Kamleshwar. Description: viii, 381 p.: ill.; 24 cm. ISBN: 0873391624 Notes: "Papers presented in the conference ... held in New Orleans, Louisiana, February 18-21, 1991 ... jointly sponsored by the Structural Materials Divison and Electronic and Photonic divisions of TMS"--Pref. Includes bibliographical references and index. Subjects: Vapor-plating--Finishes and finishing--Thin films--Plasma-enhanced chemical vapor deposition--Lasers in engineering--Congresses. LC Classification: TS695 .P527 1991 Dewey Class No.: 620/.44/028 20

Plasma kinetics in atmospheric gases / M. Capitelli ... [et al.], (eds.). Published/Created: Berlin; New York: Springer, c2000. Related Authors: Capitelli, M. Description: ix, 300 p.: ill.; 25 cm. ISBN: 3540674160 (alk. paper) Notes: Includes bibliographical references and index. Subjects: Nonequilibrium plasmas. Molecular gas lasers. Kinetic theory of gases. Nitrogen. Oxygen. Series: Springer series on atomic, optical, and plasma physics, 1615-5653; 31 LC Classification: QC718.5.E66 P53 2000 Dewey Class No.: 530.4/46 21

Primer on laser angioplasty / edited by Robert Ginsburg, Herbert J. Geschwind. Edition Information: 2nd ed. Published/Created: Mt. Kisco, NY: Futura Pub. Co., c1992. Related Authors: Ginsburg, Robert, M.D. Geschwind, Herbert J. Description: xvii, 520 p.: ill.; 24 cm. ISBN: 0879935286 (acid-free paper) Notes: Includes bibliographical references (p. 489-512) and index. Subjects: Laser angioplasty. Angioplasty, Transluminal. Coronary Disease--therapy. Lasers--therapeutic use. Vascular Diseases--therapy. LC Classification: RD598.5 .P75 1992 Dewey Class No.: 617.4/13059 20

Primer on laser angioplasty / editor, Robert Ginsburg; assistant editor, Jonathan C. White. Published/Created: Mount Kisco, N.Y.: Futura Pub. Co., 1989. Related Authors: Ginsburg, Robert, M.D. White, J. C. (Jonathan Curtis), 1952- Description: x, 303 p.: ill.; 24 cm. ISBN: 0879933291 Notes: Includes index. Bibliography: p. 281-297. Subjects: Laser angioplasty. Angioplasty, Transluminal. Coronary Disease--therapy. Lasers--therapeutic use. Vascular Diseases--therapy. LC Classification: RD598.5 .P75 1989 Dewey Class No.: 617/.4130592 19

Principles of laser dynamics / edited by Y.I. Khanin. Published/Created: Amsterdam; New York: Elsevier, 1995. Related Authors: Khanin, IAkov Izrailevich. Description: xii, 407 p.: ill.; 25 cm. ISBN: 0444896961 (acid-free paper) Notes: Includes bibliographical references (p. 359-374) and indexes. Subjects: Lasers. LC Classification: QC688 .P75 1995 Dewey Class No.: 621.36/6 20

Problems in laser physics / G. Cerullo ... [et al.]. Published/Created: New York: Kluwer Academic/Plenum Publishers, c2001. Related Authors: Cerullo, G. Description: xiv, 308 p.: ill.; 25 cm. ISBN: 030646649X Subjects: Lasers--Problems, exercises, etc. LC Classification: QC688 .P77 2001 Dewey Class No.: 621.36/6 21

Proceedings of advances in laser and light spectroscopy to diagnose cancer and other diseases III: optical biopsy, 29-30 January 1996, San Jose, California / Robert R. Alfano, chair/editor; sponsored by SPIE--the International Society for Optical

Engineering, New York State Center for Advanced Technology in Ultrafast Photonic Materials and Applications at CUNY, Mediscience Technology Corporation. Published/Created: Bellingham, Wash.: SPIE, c1996. Related Authors: Alfano, R. R. Society of Photo-optical Instrumentation Engineers. Description: x, 246 p.: ill. (some col.); 28 cm. ISBN: 0819420530 Notes: Includes bibliographical references and author index. Subjects: Lasers in medicine--Lasers--Diagnostic use--Fluorescence spectroscopy--Cancer--Diagnosis--Congresses. Series: Progress in biomedical optics Proceedings of SPIE--the International Society for Optical Engineering; v. 2387. Variant Series: SPIE proceedings series; v. 2679 LC Classification: R857.L37 P733 1996 Dewey Class No.: 616.07/545 21

Proceedings of advances in optical biophysics: 25-26 January 1998, San Jose, California / Joseph R. Lakowicz, J.B. Alexander Ross, chairs/editors; sponsored by SPIE--the International Society for Optical Engineering ... [et al.]. Published/Created: Bellingham, Wash., USA: SPIE, c1998. Related Authors: Lakowicz, Joseph R. Ross, J. B. Alexander. Society of Photo-optical Instrumentation Engineers. Description: ix, 280 p.: ill.; 28 cm. ISBN: 0819426954 Notes: Includes bibliographical references and index. Subjects: Lasers in biophysics--Congresses. Lasers--Diagnostic use--Congresses. Series: Progress in biomedical optics Proceedings of SPIE--the International Society for Optical Engineering; v. 3256. Variant Series: SPIE proceedings series; v. 3256 LC Classification: QH505 .P675 1998 Dewey Class No.: 571.4/028 21

Proceedings of biomedical fiber optic instrumentation: 24-27 January 1994, Los Angeles, California / James A. Harrington ... [et al.], chairs/editors; sponsored and published by SPIE--the International Society for Optical Engineering. Published/Created: Bellingham, Wash., USA: SPIE, c1994. Related Authors: Harrington, James A., 1942- Society of Photo-optical Instrumentation Engineers. Description: x1, 622 p.: ill.; 28 cm. ISBN: 0819414247 (pbk.) Notes: Spine Title - Biomedical fiber optic instrumentation. Includes bibliographical references and author index. Subjects: Optical fibers in medicine--Congresses. Infrared technology--Congresses. Lasers in medicine--Congresses. Optical detectors--Congresses. Series: Progress in biomedical optics Proceedings of SPIE--the International Society for Optical Engineering; v. 2131. Variant Series: SPIE proceedings series; v. 2131 LC Classification: R857.O59 P75 1994 Dewey Class No.: 610/.28 20

Proceedings of biomedical fiber optics: 31 January 1996, San Jose, California / Abraham Katzir, James A. Harrington, chairs/editors; sponsored and published by SPIE--the International Society for Optical Engineering. Published/Created: Bellingham, Wash.: SPIE, c1996. Related Authors: Katzir, Abraham. Harrington, James A., 1942- Society of Photo-optical Instrumentation Engineers. Description: v, 156 p.: ill.; 28 cm. ISBN: 0819420514 Notes: Includes bibliographical references and index. Subjects: Optical fibers in medicine--Congresses. Infrared technology--Congresses. Lasers in medicine--Congresses. Series: Progress in biomedical optics Proceedings of SPIE--the International Society for Optical Engineering; v. 2677. Variant Series: SPIE proceedings series; v. 2677 LC Classification: R857.O59 P754 1996 Dewey Class No.: 610/.28 21

Proceedings of biomedical optoelectronic instrumentation: 7-9 February 1995, San Jose, California / James A. Harrington, David M. Harris, Abraham Katzir, chairs/editors; sponsored and published by SPIE--the International Society for Optical Engineering. Published/Created: Bellingham, Wash., USA: SPIE, c1995. Related Authors: Harrington, James A., 1942- Harris, David M. Katzir, Abraham. Description: viii, 354 p.: ill.; 28 cm. ISBN: 0819417432 (pbk.) Notes: Includes bibliographical references and author index. Subjects: Optical fibers in medicine--Optoelectronic devices--Lasers in medicine--Optical detectors--Congresses. Series: Progress in biomedical optics Proceedings of SPIE--the International Society for Optical Engineering; v. 2396. Variant Series: SPIE proceedings series; v. 2396 LC Classification: R857.O59 P756 1995 Dewey Class No.: 610/.28 20

Proceedings of biomedical optoelectronics in clinical chemistry and biotechnology: 14-15 September 1995, Barcelona, Spain / Stefan Andersson-Engels ... [et al.], chairs/editors; sponsored by ELA--the European Laser Association ... [et al.]. Published/Created: Bellingham, Wash.: SPIE--the International Society for Optical Engineering, c1996. Related Authors: Andersson-Engels, Stefan. Description: xvii, 336 p.: ill.; 28 cm. ISBN: 0819419931 Notes: Includes bibliographical references and index. Subjects: Optoelectronic devices--Lasers in medicine--Clinical chemistry--Technique--Congresses. Series: Progress in biomedical optics Proceedings EurOpt series. Proceedings of SPIE--the International Society for Optical Engineering, v. 2629. Variant Series: EurOpt series SPIE proceedings series; v. 2629 LC Classification: R857.O59 P7565 1996 Dewey Class No.: 610/.28 21

Proceedings of biomedical sensing, imaging, and tracking technologies II: 11-13 February 1997, San Jose, California / Tuan Vo-Dinh, Robert A. Lieberman, Gerald G. Vurek, chairs/editors; sponsored by IBOS--the International Biomedical Optics Society, SPIE--the International Society for Optical Engineering; cooperating organization, American Society for Laser Medicine and Surgery, Inc. Published/Created: Bellingham, Wash., USA: SPIE, c1997. Related Authors: Vo-Dinh, Tuan. Lieberman, Robert A. Vurek, Gerald G. International Biomedical Optics Society. Society of Photo-optical Instrumentation Engineers. American Society for Laser Medicine and Surgery. Description: viii, 382 p.: ill.; 28 cm. ISBN: 0819423874 Notes: Includes bibliographical references and index. Subjects: Biosensors--Lasers in medicine--Optical fibers in medicine--Diagnostic imaging--Congresses. Series: Progress in biomedical optics Proceedings of SPIE--the International Society for Optical Engineering; v. 2976. Variant Series: SPIE proceedings series, 0277-786X; v. 2976 LC Classification: R857.B54 P765 1997 Dewey Class No.: 610/.28 21

Proceedings of biomedical systems and technologies II: 4-6 September 1997, San Remo, Italy / Francesco Baldini ... [et al.], chairs/editors; sponsored by SILCM--Società Italiana di Laser Chirurgia e Medicina ... [et al.]. Published/Created: Bellingham, Wash., USA: SPIE, c1998. Related Authors: Baldini, Francesco. Description: vii, 308 p.: ill.; 28 cm. ISBN: 0819426318 Notes: Includes bibliographical references and index. Subjects: Optical fibers in medicine--Imaging systems in medicine--Lasers in medicine--Diagnostic imaging--Congresses. Series: Progress in biomedical optics Proceedings of SPIE--the International Society for Optical Engineering; v. 3199. Proceedings EurOpt series. Variant Series: SPIE proceedings series; v. 3199 EurOpt series LC Classification: R857.O6 P725 1998 Dewey Class No.: 610/.28 21

Proceedings of biomedical systems and technologies: 8-10 September 1996, Vienna, Austria / Nathan I. Croitoru ... [et al.], chairs/editors; sponsored by ... ELA--European Laser Association ... [et al.]. Published/Created: Bellingham, Wash., USA: SPIE--the International Society for Optical Engineering, c1996. Related Authors: Croitoru, Nathan I. Society of Photo-optical Instrumentation Engineers. European Laser Association. Description: vii, 284 p.: ill.; 28 cm. ISBN: 0819423300 Notes: Includes bibliographical references and index. Subjects: Optical fibers in medicine--Imaging systems in medicine--Lasers in medicine--Diagnostic imaging--Congresses. Series: Progress in biomedical optics Proceedings of SPIE--the International Society for Optical Engineering; v. 2928. Proceedings EurOpt series. Variant Series: SPIE proceedings series; v. 2928 EurOpt series LC Classification: R857.O6 P724 1996 Dewey Class No.: 610/.28 21

Proceedings of clinical applications of modern imaging technology: 17-19 January 1993, Los Angeles, California / Abund O. Wist, general editor; sponsored by SPIE--the International Society for Optical Engineering, BiOS--Biomedical Optics Society. Published/Created: Bellingham, Wash., USA: SPIE, c1993. Related Authors: Wist, Abund Ottokar. Description: x, 338 p.: ill.; 28 cm. ISBN: 0819411213 (pbk.) Notes: Includes bibliographical references and author index. Subjects: Imaging systems in medicine--Diagnostic imaging--Neurology--Equipment and supplies--Lasers in medicine--Congresses. Series: Progress in biomedical optics Proceedings of SPIE--the International Society for Optical Engineering; v. 1894. Variant Series: SPIE proceedings series; v. 1894 LC Classification: R857.O6 P73 1993 Dewey Class No.: 616.07/54 20

Proceedings of clinical applications of modern imaging technology II: 23-26 January 1994, Los Angeles, California / Leonard J. Cerullo ... [et al.], chairs/editors; sponsored and published by SPIE--the International Society for Optical Engineering. Published/Created: Bellingham, Wash., USA: SPIE, c1994. Related Authors: Cerullo, L. J. (Leonard J.) Description: x, 494 p.: ill.; 28 cm. ISBN: 0819414271 Notes: Includes bibliographical references and author index. Subjects: Imaging systems in medicine--Lasers in medicine--Diagnostic imaging--Radiology, Medical--Congresses. Series: Progress in biomedical optics Proceedings of SPIE--the International Society for Optical Engineering; v. 2132. Variant Series: SPIE proceedings series; v. 2132 LC Classification: R857.O6 P74 1994 Dewey Class No.: 616.07/54 20

Proceedings of dental applications of lasers: 1-2 September 1993, Budapest, Hungary / Grigori B. Altshuler, Raimund Hibst, chairs/editors; sponsored by BiOS--Biomedical Optics Society, European Optical Society, SPIE--the International Society for Optical Engineering; under the patronage of Domokos Kosáry, Miklos Réthelyi; hosted by Hungarian Medical Laser and Medical Optics Society, HUNGOPTIKA--SPIE Hungary Chapter, Semmelweis University Laser Center. Published/Created: Bellingham, Wash., USA: SPIE, c1993. Related Authors: Altshuler, Grigori B. Hibst, Raimund. Biomedical Optics Society. European Optical Society. Society of Photo-optical Instrumentation Engineers. Description: iv, 200 p.: ill.; 28 cm. ISBN: 081941347X (pbk.) Notes: Spine Title - Dental applications of lasers. Includes bibliographical references and author index. Subjects: Lasers in dentistry--Congresses. Series: Progress in biomedical optics Proceedings of SPIE--the International Society for Optical Engineering; v. 2080. Proceedings EurOpt series Variant Series: EurOpt series SPIE proceedings series; v. 2080 LC Classification: RK685.L37 .P76 1993 Dewey Class No.: 617.6/0028 20

Proceedings of effects of low-power light on biological systems II: 9 September 1996, Vienna, Austria / Giulio Jori, Tina I. Karu, chairs/editors; sponsored by Laser Vision ... [et al.]. Published/Created: Bellingham, Wash., USA: SPIE, c1996. Related Authors: Jori, Giulio. Karu, T. I. (Tiina I.) Laser Vision (Firm) Description: vii, 206 p.: ill.; 28 cm. ISBN: 0819423319 (pbk.) Notes: Includes bibliographical references and index. Subjects: Lasers--Therapeutic use--Congresses. Lasers--Physiological effect--Congresses. Series: Progress in biomedical optics (Unnumbered) Proceedings EurOpt series. Proceedings of SPIE--the International Society for Optical Engineering; v. 2929. Variant Series: Progress in biomedical optics EurOpto series SPIE proceedings series; v. 2929 LC Classification: R857.L37 P7335 1996

Proceedings of effects of low-power light on biological systems III: 8 September 1997, San Remo, Italy / Giovanni F. Bottiroli, Tina I. Karu, Rachel Lubart, chairs/editors; sponsored by SILCM--Società italiana di laser chirurgia e medicina ... [et al.]. Published/Created: Bellingham, Wash., USA: SPIE, c1997. Related Authors: Bottiroli, Giovanni F. Karu, T. I. (Tiina I.) Lubart, Rachel. Società italiana di laser chirurgia e medicina. Description: iv, 128 p.: ill.; 28 cm. ISBN: 081942630X Notes: Includes bibliographical references and index. Subjects: Lasers--Physiological effect--Congresses. Lasers in medicine--Congresses. Lasers in biology--Congresses. Infrared radiation in medicine--Congresses. Series: Progress in biomedical optics (Unnumbered) Proceedings EurOpt series. Proceedings of SPIE--the International Society for Optical Engineering; v. 3198. Variant Series: Progress in biomedical optics EurOpt series SPIE proceedings series; v. 3198 LC Classification: QP82.2.L3 P755 1997

Proceedings of effects of low-power light on biological systems IV: 8-9 September 1998, Stockholm, Sweden / Giovanni F. Bottiroli, Tina I. Karu, Rachel Lubart, chairs/editors; sponsored by EOS--The European Optical Society, SPIE--The International Society for Optical Engineering, [and] ELA--The European Laser Association; cosponsored by SSL--The Scandinavian Society for Laser Therapy ... [et al.]. Published/Created: Bellingham, Wash., USA: SPIE, c1998. Related Authors: Bottiroli, Giovanni F. Karu, T. I. (Tiina I.) Lubart, Rachel. European Optical Society. Society of Photo-optical Instrumentation Engineers. European Laser Association. Scandinavian Society for Laser Therapy. Description: v, 112 p.: ill.; 28 cm. ISBN: 0819430315 Notes: Includes bibliographical references and index. Subjects: Lasers--Therapeutic use--Congresses. Lasers--Physiological effect--Congresses. Lasers in biology--Congresses. Infrared radiation in medicine--Congresses. Series: Progress in biomedical optics Proceedings EurOpt series. Proceedings of SPIE--the International Society for Optical Engineering; v. 3569. Variant Series: EurOpt series SPIE proceedings series; v. 3569

Proceedings of effects of low-power light on biological systems: 14-15 September, Barcelona, Spain / Tiina I. Karu, Anthony [sic] R. Young, chairs/editors; sponsored by ELA--the European Laser Association ... [et al.]. Published/Created: Bellingham, Wash., USA: SPIE--the International Society for Optical Engineering, c1996. Related Authors: Karu, T. I. (Tiina I.) Young, Antony R. Description: xv, 162 p.: ill.; 28 cm. ISBN: 081941994X (pbk.) Notes: Includes bibliographical references and index. Subjects: Lasers--Therapeutic use--Congresses. Infrared radiation in medicine--Congresses. Series: Progress in biomedical optics Proceedings EurOpt series. Proceedings of SPIE--the International Society for Optical Engineering; v. 2630. Variant Series: EurOpt series SPIE proceedings series; v. 2630 LC Classification: TR692.5 .P7627 19960 Dewey Class No.: 610/.28 21

Proceedings of functional imaging and optical manipulation of living cells: 10-11 February 1997, San Jose, California / Daniel L. Farkas, Bruce J. Tromberg, chairs/editors; sponsored by SPIE--the International Society for Optical Engineering [and] IBOS--the International Biomedical Optics Society; cooperating organization, American Society for Laser Medicine and Surgery, Inc. Published/Created: Bellingham, Wash., USA: SPIE, c1997. Related Authors: Farkas, Daniel L. Tromberg, Bruce J. Description: v, 138 p.: ill. (some col.); 28 cm. ISBN: 0819423947 Notes: Includes bibliographical references and index. Subjects: Lasers in cytology--Imaging systems in biology--Congresses. Series: Progress in biomedical optics Proceedings of SPIE--the International Society for Optical Engineering; v. 2983. Variant Series: SPIE proceedings series; v. 2983 LC Classification: QH585.5.L37 P76 1997

Proceedings of laser and noncoherent ocular effects: epidemiology, prevention, and treatment: 10-11 February 1997, San Jose, California / Bruce E. Stuck, Michael Belkin, chairs/editors; sponsored by Air Force Office of Scientific Research, IBOS--the International Biomedical Optics Society [and] SPIE--the International Society for Optical Engineering; cooperating organization, American Society for Laser Medicine and Surgery, Inc. Published/Created: Bellingham, Wash., USA: SPIE, c1997. Related Authors: Stuck, Bruce E. Belkin, Michael. Description: ix, 232 p.: ill.; 28 cm. ISBN: 0819423858 Notes: Includes bibliographical references and index. Subjects: Eye--Wounds and injuries--Eye--Effect of radiation on--Lasers in ophthalmology--Lasers--Physiological effects--Eye--Radiation injuries--Congresses. Series: Progress in biomedical optics Proceedings of SPIE--the International Society for Optical Engineering; v. 2974. Variant Series: SPIE proceedings series; v. 2974 LC Classification: RE831 .P755 1997 Dewey Class No.: 617.7/13 21

Proceedings of laser applications in medicine and dentistry: 7-10 September 1996, Vienna, Austria / Gregory B. Altshuler ... [et al.], chairs/editors. Published/Created: Bellingham, Wash., USA: SPIE-The International Society for Optical Engineering, c1996. Related Authors: Altshuler, Grigori B. Description: x, 462 p.: ill.; 28 cm. ISBN: 0819423246 Notes: "Sponsored by Laser Vision" ... [et al.]. Includes bibliographical references and index. Subjects: Lasers in medicine--Congresses. Lasers in dentistry--Congresses. Series: Progress in biomedical optics Proceedings EurOpt series. Proceedings of SPIE--the International Society for Optical Engineering; v. 2922. Variant Series: EurOpt series SPIE proceedings series; v. 2922 LC Classification: R857.L37 P734 1996 Dewey Class No.: 610/.28 21

Proceedings of laser applications in ophthalmology: 2-3 September 1993, Budapest, Hungary / Shlomo T. Melamed, chair/editor; sponsored by BiOS--Biomedical Optics Society, European Optical Society (EOS), SPIE--the International Society for Optical Engineering; under the patronage of Domokos Kosáry, Miklos Réthelyi; hosted by Hungarian Medical Laser and Medical Optics Society, HUNGOPTIKA--SPIE Hungary Chapter, Semmelweis University Laser Center. Published/Created: Bellingham, Wash., USA: SPIE, c1994. Related Authors: Melamed, Shlomo T. Biomedical Optics Society. European Optical Society. Society of Photo-optical Instrumentation Engineers. Description: vii, 200 p.: ill.; 28 cm. ISBN: 0819413461 (pbk.) Notes: Includes bibliographical references and index. Subjects: Lasers in ophthalmology--Congresses. Series: Progress in biomedical optics Proceedings EurOpt series. Proceedings of SPIE--the International Society for Optical Engineering; v. 2079. Variant Series: EurOpt series SPIE proceedings series; v. 2079 LC Classification: RE86 .P75 1994 Dewey Class No.: 617.7/1 20

Proceedings of laser interaction with hard and soft tissue II: 6-9 September 1994, Lille, France / Hans Jörg Albrecht ... [et al.], chairs/editors; sponsored by the Commission of the European Communities, Directorate General for Science, Research, and Development ... [et al.]. Published/Created: Bellingham, Wash., USA: SPIE--the International Society for Optical Engineering, c1995. Related Authors: Albrecht, Hans Jörg. Description: ix, 552 p.: ill.; 28 cm. ISBN: 0819416568 (pbk.) Notes: Includes bibliographical references and index. Subjects: Lasers in medicine--Lasers in biology--Lasers--Therapeutic use--Congresses. Series: Progress in biomedical optics Proceedings EurOpt series. Proceedings of SPIE--the International Society for Optical Engineering; v. 2323. Variant Series: EurOpt series SPIE proceedings series; v. 2323 LC Classification: R857.L37 P736 1994 Dewey Class No.: 610/.28 20

Proceedings of laser surgery: advanced characterization, therapeutics, and systems. Published/Created: Bellingham, Wash.: SPIE, c1990- Related Authors: Society of Photo-optical Instrumentation Engineers. Description: 8 v.: ill.; 28 cm. 2 (Jan. 14, 16-19, 1990)- Ceased with: 9 (Jan. 23-24, 1999). Current Frequency: Annual, 1994- Former Frequency: Annual, 1990 Biennial, 1992 Continues: Laser surgery--advanced characterization, therapeutics, and systems (OCoLC)35518485 Notes: Beginning with the 2000 conference, issues are cataloged separately. SERBIB/SERLOC merged record Subjects: Lasers in surgery--Congresses. Series: Progress in biomedical optics Proceedings of SPIE--the International Society for Optical Engineering. Variant Series: SPIE proceedings series LC Classification: RD73.L3 P765 Dewey Class No.: 617/.05 21

Proceedings of laser-inflicted eye injuries: epidemiology, prevention, and treatment: 29-30 January 1996, San Jose, California / Bruce E. Stuck, Michael Belkin, chairs/editors; sponsored and published by SPIE--the International Society for Optical Engineering. Published/Created: Bellingham, Wash., USA: SPIE, c1996. Related Authors: Stuck, Bruce E. Belkin, Michael. Society of Photo-optical Instrumentation Engineers. Description: x, 220 p.: ill.; 28 cm. ISBN: 0819420484 Notes: Includes bibliographical references and index. Subjects: Eye--Wounds and injuries--Congresses. Eye--Effect of radiation on--Congresses. Lasers--Therapeutic use--Congresses. Lasers in medicine--Congresses. Series: Progress in biomedical optics Proceedings of SPIE--the International Society for Optical Engineering, v. 2674. Variant Series: SPIE proceedings series; v. 2674 LC Classification: RE831 .P76 1996 Dewey Class No.: 617.7/13 21

Proceedings of lasers in urology, gynecology, and general surgery: 16-18 January 1993, Los Angeles, California / Christopher J. Daly ... [et al.]; sponsored and published by SPIE--the Inernational Society for Optical Engineering; cosponsored by BIOS--Biomedical Optics Society. Published/Created: Bellingham, Wash., USA: SPIE, c1993. Related Authors: Daly, Christopher J. Society of Photo-optical Instrumentation Engineers. Biomedical Optics Society. Description: vii, 248 p.: ill.; 28 cm. ISBN: 081941106X Notes: Includes bibliographical references and index. Subjects: Urinary organs--Laser surgery--Generative organs, Female--Laser surgery--Lasers in surgery--Congresses. Series: Progress in biomedical optics Proceedings of SPIE--the International Society for Optical Engineering; v. 1879. Variant Series: SPIE proceedings series; v. 1879 LC Classification: RD571 .P76 1993 Dewey Class No.: 610/.28 20

Proceedings of lasers in urology, laparoscopy, and general surgery: 21-23-January 1991, Los Angeles, California / Grah[a]m M. Watson, Rudolf W. Steiner, Joseph J. Pietrafitta, chairs/editors; sponsored and published by SPIE--the International Society for Optical Engineering. Published/Created: Bellingham, Wash., USA: SPIE, c1991. Related Authors: Watson, Graham M. Steiner, R. (Rudolf), 1941- Pietrafitta, Joseph J. Society of Photo-optical Instrumentation Engineers. Description: ix, 212 p.: ill.; 28 cm. ISBN: 0819405116 Notes: One of four conferences held as part of the Program on Laser Surgery of Biomedical Optics '91. Includes bibliographical references and index. Subjects: Lasers in surgery--Congresses. Prostate--Laser surgery--Congresses. Laser lithotripsy--Congresses. Endoscopic surgery--Congresses. Series: Progress in biomedical optics Proceedings of SPIE--the International Society for Optical Engineering; v. 1421. Variant Series: SPIE proceedings series; v. 1421 LC Classification: RD73.L3 P77 1991 Dewey Class No.: 617/.05 20

Proceedings of laser-tissue interaction / sponsored by SPIE--the International Society for Optical Engineers. Published/Created: Bellingham, Wash.: SPIE, c1990- Related Authors: Society of Photo-optical Instrumentation Engineers.

Description: v.: ill.; 28 cm. Issue for Jan. 15-17, 1990 lacks numerical designation but constitutes 1. Jan. 15-17, 1990- Ceased with: 10 (1999). Current Frequency: Annual Notes: Beginning with the 2000 conference, issues are cataloged separately. SERBIB/SERLOC merged record Subjects: Lasers in medicine--Congresses. Lasers in biology--Congresses. Series: Progress in biomedical optics Proceedings of SPIE--the International Society for Optical Engineering Variant Series: SPIE proceedings series LC Classification: R857.L37 P74 Dewey Class No.: 610/.28 20

Proceedings of laser-tissue interaction and tissue optics: 12-13,16 September, 1995, Barcelona, Spain / Hans J. Albrecht ... [et al.], chairs/editors; sponsored by ELA--the European Laser Association ... [et al.]. Published/Created: Bellingham, Wash., USA: SPIE--the International Society for Optical Engineering, c1996. Related Authors: Albrecht, Hans Jörg. European Laser Association. Society of Photo-optical Instrumentation Engineers. Description: xvii, 284 p.: ill.; 28 cm. ISBN: 0819419885 (pbk.) Notes: Includes bibliographical references and index. Subjects: Lasers in medicine--Lasers in biology--Lasers--Therapeutic use--Congresses. Series: Progress in biomedical optics Proceedings EurOpt series. Proceedings of SPIE--the International Society for Optical Engineering; v. 2624. Variant Series: EurOpt series SPIE proceedings series; v. 2624 LC Classification: R857.L37 P7414 1996 Dewey Class No.: 610/.28 21

Proceedings of laser-tissue interaction II: 21-23 January 1991, Los Angeles, California / Steven L. Jacques, chair/editor; sponsored and published by SPIE--the International Society for Optical Engineering. Published/Created: Bellingham, Wash., USA: SPIE, c1991. Related Authors: Jacques, Steven L. Society of Photo-optical Instrumentation Engineers. Description: ix, 415 p.: ill.; 28 cm. ISBN: 0819405175 Notes: One of four conferences held as part of the Program on Laser-Tissue Science of Biomedical Optics '91. Includes bibliographical references and index. Subjects: Lasers in medicine--Congresses. Lasers in biology--Congresses. Series: Progress in biomedical optics Proceedings of SPIE--the International Society for Optical Engineering; v. 1427. Variant Series: SPIE proceedings series; v. 1427 LC Classification: R857.L37 P77 1991 Dewey Class No.: 610/.28 20

Proceedings of laser-tissue interaction, tissue optics, and laser welding III: 5-8 September 1997, San Remo, Italy / Guy P. Delacrétaz ... [et al.], chairs/editors; sponsored by SILCM--Società Italiana di Laser Chirurgia e Medicina ... [et al]. Published/Created: Bellingham, Wash., USA: SPIE--the International Society for Optical Engineering, c1998. Related Authors: Delacrétez, Guy P. Società italiana di laser chirurgia e medicina. Society of Photo-optical Instrumentation Engineers. Description: ix, 348 p.: ill.; 28 cm. ISBN: 081942627X Notes: Includes bibliographical references and index. Subjects: Lasers in medicine--Congresses.

Proceedings of laser-tissue interaction: January 15-17 1990, Los Angeles, California / Steven L. Jacques, chair/editor; sponsored by SPIE--the International Society for Optical Engineering. Published/Created: Bellingham, Wash., USA: SPIE, c1990. Related Authors: Jacques, Steven L. Description: vii, 343 p.: ill.; 28 cm. ISBN: 0819402435 Notes: "Part of a four-conference SPIE Symposium on Biomedical Optics held at OE/LASE '90, 14-19-January 1990, Los Angeles, California"--P. vi. Includes bibliographical references and index. Subjects: Lasers in medicine--Lasers in biology--Congresses. Series: Progress in biomedical optics Proceedings of SPIE--the International Society for Optical Engineering; v. 1202. Variant Series: SPIE proceedings series; v. 1202 LC Classification: R857.L37 P76 1990 Dewey Class No.: 610/.28 20

Proceedings of low-energy laser effects on biological systems: 19-20 January 1993, Los Angeles, California / Michal Schwartz,

Michael Belkin, chairs-editors. Published/Created: Bellingham, Wash.: The Society of Photo-Optical Instrumentation Engineers, c1993. Related Authors: Schwartz, Michal. Belkin, Michael. Description: vii, 138 p.: ill.; 28 cm. ISBN: 0819411108 Notes: "Sponsored ... by SPIE--the International Society for Optical Engineering; cosponsored by BIOS--Biomedical Optics Society." Includes bibliographical references and index. Subjects: Lasers--Physiological effect--Congresses. Series: Progress in biomedical optics Proceedings of SPIE--the International Society for Optical Engineering; v. 1883. Variant Series: SPIE proceedings series; v. 1883 LC Classification: QP82.2.L3 P76 1993 Dewey Class No.: 574.19/15 20

Proceedings of medical applications of lasers II: 6-10 September 1994, Lille, France / Stephen G. Brown ... [et al.], chairs/editors; sponsored by The Commission of the European Communities, Directorate General for Science, Research, and Development ... [et al.] Published/Created: Bellingham, Wash.,: SPIE, 1994. Related Authors: Brown, Stephen G. Commission of the European Communities. Directorate-General for Science, Research, and Development. Society of Photo-optical Instrumentation Engineers. Description: xi, 412 p.: ill.; 28 cm. ISBN: 0819416606 Notes: Includes bibliographical references and index. Subjects: Lasers in medicine--Congresses. Series: Progress in biomedical optics Proceedings EurOpt series Proceedings of SPIE--the International Society for Optical Engineering; v. 2327. Variant Series: EurOpt series Proceedings / SPIE--the International Society for Optical Engineering; v. 2327 LC Classification: R857.L37 P7463 1994 Dewey Class No.: 610/.28 20

Proceedings of medical applications of lasers III: 12-16 September 1995, Barcelona, Spain / Stephen G. Bown ... [et al.], chairs/editors; sponsored by ELA, the European Laser Association ... [et al.]. Published/Created: Bellingham, Wash., USA: SPIE--The International Society for Optical Engineering, [1995] Related Authors: Bown, Stephen G. European Laser Association. Society of Photo-optical Instrumentation Engineers. Description: xxi, 556 p.: ill.; 28 cm. ISBN: 0819419877 Notes: Includes bibliographical references and index. Subjects: Lasers in medicine--Congresses. Lasers in dentistry--Congresses. Series: Progress in biomedical optics; v. 2623 Proceedings EurOpt series. Proceedings of SPIE--the International Society for Optical Engineering; v. 2623. Variant Series: EurOpto series SPIE proceedings series; v. 2623 LC Classification: R857.L37 P7463 1995 Dewey Class No.: 610/.28 21

Proceedings of medical applications of lasers in dermatology, cardiology, ophthalmology, and dentistry II: 11-12 September 1998, Stockholm, Sweden / Gregory B. Altshuler ... [et al.], chairs/editors; sponsored by EOS--the European Optical Society, SPIE--the International Society for Optical Engineering, [and] ELA--the European Laser Association; cosponsored by SSL--Scandinavian Society for Laser Therapy ... [et al.]. Published/Created: Bellingham, Wash., USA: SPIE, c1999. Related Authors: Altshuler, Grigori B. Description: vii, 252 p.: ill.; 28 cm. ISBN: 0819430269 Notes: Includes bibliographical references and index. Subjects: Lasers in medicine--Lasers in dentistry--Lasers in ophthalmology--Lasers--Therapeutic use--Congresses. Series: Progress in biomedical optics Proceedings of SPIE--the International Society for Optical Engineering; v. 3564. Proceedings EurOpt series. Variant Series: SPIE proceedings series; v. 3564 EurOpt series LC Classification: R857.L37 P7465 1999 Dewey Class No.: 610/.28 21

Proceedings of medical applications of lasers in dermatology, ophthalmology, dentistry, and endoscopy: 4-7 September 1997, San Remo, Italy / Gregory B. Altshuler ... [et al.], chairs/editors; sponsored by SILCM--Società Italiana di Laser Chirurgia e Medicina ... [et al.]. Published/Created: Bellingham, Wash., USA: SPIE--the International Society for Optical

Engineering, c1997. Related Authors: Altshuler, Grigori B. Description: ix, 296 p.: ill. (some col.); 28 cm. ISBN: 0819426245 Notes: Includes bibliographical references and index. Subjects: Lasers in medicine--Congresses. Lasers in dentistry--Congresses. Lasers--Therapeutic use--Congresses. Series: Progress in biomedical optics Proceedings of SPIE--the International Society for Optical Engineering; v. 3192. Proceedings EurOpt series. Variant Series: SPIE proceedings series; v. 3192 EurOpt series LC Classification: R857.L37 P7466 1997 Dewey Class No.: 610/.28 21

Proceedings of medical applications of lasers: 4-5 September 1993, Budapest, Hungary / Kazuhiko Atsumi ... [et al.], chairs/editors; sponsored by BiOS--Biomedical Optics Society, European Optical Society, SPIE--the International Society for Optical Engineering; under the patronage of Domokos Kosáry, Miklos Réthelyi; hosted by Hungarian Medical Laser and Medical Optics Society, HUNGOPTIKA--SPIE Hungary Chapter, Semmelweis University Laser Center. Published/Created: Bellingham, Wash., USA: SPIE, c1994. Related Authors: Atsumi, Kazuhiko, 1928- Biomedical Optics Society. European Optical Society. Society of Photo-optical Instrumentation Engineers. Description: ix, 426 p.: ill.; 28 cm. ISBN: 0819413534 (pbk.) Notes: Spine Title - Medical applications of lasers. Includes bibliographical references and index. Subjects: Lasers in medicine--Congresses. Series: Progress in biomedical optics Proceedings EurOpt series. Proceedings of SPIE--the International Society for Optical Engineering; v. 2086. Variant Series: EurOpt series SPIE proceedings series; v. 2086 LC Classification: R857.L37 P746 1994 Dewey Class No.: 610/.28 20

Proceedings of medical lasers and systems II: 19-20 January 1993, Los Angeles, California / David M. Harris, C. Murray Penney, chairs-editors. Published/Created: Bellingham, Wash.: Society of Photo-Optical Instrumentation Engineers, c1993. Related Authors: Harris, David M. Penney, C. Murray. Society of Photo-optical Instrumentation Engineers. Biomedical Optics Society. Laser Institute of America. Description: ix, 212 p.: ill.; 28 cm. ISBN: 0819411191 (pbk.) Notes: "Sponsored ... by SPIE--the International Society for Optical Engineering; cosponsored by BIOS--Biomedical Optics Society; cooperating organization, Laser Institute of America." Includes bibliographical references and index. Subjects: Lasers in medicine--Congresses. Series: Progress in biomedical optics Proceedings of SPIE--the International Society for Optical Engineering; v. 1892. Variant Series: SPIE proceedings series; v. 1892 LC Classification: R857.L37 P75 1993 Dewey Class No.: 610/.28 20

Proceedings of medical lasers and systems: 23-24 January 1992, Los Angeles, California / David M. Harris, Stuart Harman, chair/editors; sponsored and published by SPIE--the International Society for Optical Engineering; cosponsored by Laser Institute of America. Published/Created: Bellingham, Wash., USA: SPIE, c1992. Related Authors: Harris, David M. Harman, Stuart. Description: ix, 159 p.: ill.; 28 cm. ISBN: 0819407968 (pbk.) Notes: Includes bibliographical references and index. Subjects: Lasers in medicine--Congresses. Series: Progress in biomedical optics Proceedings of SPIE--the International Society for Optical Engineering; v. 1650. Variant Series: SPIE proceedings series; v. 1650 LC Classification: R857.L37 P75 1992 Dewey Class No.: 610/.28 20

Proceedings of ophthalmic technologies. Published/Created: Bellingham, Wash.: SPIE, c1991- Related Authors: Society of Photo-optical Instrumentation Engineers. Description: v.: ill.; 28 cm. Vol. for 1991 lacks numeric designation but constitutes 1. 21-22 Jan. 1991- Ceased with: 9 (1999). Current Frequency: Annual ISSN: 1089-8786 Cancel/Invalid LCCN: sn 95037178 Notes: Beginning with the 2000 conference, issues are cataloged separately. SERBIB/SERLOC merged record Subjects: Lasers in ophthalmology--

Periodicals. Ophthalmology--Technological innovations--Periodicals. Series: Progress in biomedical optics Proceedings of SPIE--the International Society for Optical Engineering. Variant Series: SPIE proceedings series LC Classification: RE86 .P759 RE86 .P76 Dewey Class No.: 617.7/0028 21

Proceedings of optical and imaging techniques for biomonitoring II: 9-10 September 1996, Vienna, Austria / Hans-Jochen Foth, Renato Marchesini, Halina Podbielska, chairs/editors; sponsored by ... ELA--the European Laser Association ... [et al.]. Published/Created: Bellingham, Wash., USA: SPIE, c1996. Related Authors: Foth, Hans-Jochen. Marchesini, R. (Renato) Podbielska, Halina. Description: vii, 228 p.: ill.; 28 cm. ISBN: 0819423297 Notes: Includes bibliographical references and index. Subjects: Holography in medicine--Holographic interferometry--Lasers in medicine--Medical microscopy--Imaging systems in medicine--Congresses. Series: Progress in biomedical optics Proceedings EurOpt series. Proceedings of SPIE--the International Society for Optical Engineering; v. 2927. Variant Series: SPIE proceedings series; v. 2927 EurOpt series LC Classification: R857.H64 P766 1996 Dewey Class No.: 610/.28 21

Proceedings of optical and imaging techniques for biomonitoring III: 6-8 September 1997, San Remo, Italy / Hans-Jochen Foth, Renato Marchesini, Halina Podbielska, chairs/editors; sponsored by ... SILCM--Società italiana di laser chirurgia e medicina ... [et al.]. Published/Created: Bellingham, Wash., USA: SPIE, c1998. Related Authors: Foth, Hans-Jochen. Marchesini, R. (Renato) Podbielska, Halina. Society of Photo-optical Instrumentation Engineers. Società italiana di laser chirurgia e medicina. Description: v, 238 p.: ill.; 28 cm. ISBN: 0819426288 Notes: Includes bibliographical references and index. Subjects: Holography in medicine--Holographic interferometry--Lasers in medicine--Medical microscopy--Imaging systems in medicine--Congresses.

Proceedings of optical and imaging techniques for biomonitoring: 14-16 September 1995, Barcelona, Spain / Hans-Jochen Foth ... [et al.], chairs/editors; sponsored by ELA--the European Laser Association ... [et al.]. Published/Created: Bellingham, Wash., USA: SPIE, c1996. Related Authors: Foth, Hans-Jochen. Description: xix, 390 p.: ill.; 28 cm. ISBN: 0819419923 (pbk.) Notes: Includes bibliographical references and index. Subjects: Imaging systems in medicine--Congresses. Lasers in medicine--Congresses. Series: Progress in biomedical optics (Unnumbered) Proceedings EurOpt series Proceedings of SPIE--the International Society for Optical Engineering; v.2628. Variant Series: Progress in biomedical optics EurOpto series SPIE proceedings series; v. 2628 LC Classification: R857.O6 P774 1996 Dewey Class No.: 616.07/54 21

Pulsed single-frequency lasers: technology and applications / William K. Bischel, Larry A. Rahn, chairs/editors; sponsored by SPIE--the International Society for Optical Engineering; cooperating organizations, American Academy of Otolaryngology, Head and Neck Surgery ... [et al.]. Published/Created: Bellingham, Wash., USA: The Society, c1988. Related Authors: Bischel, William K. Rahn, Larry A. Society of Photo-optical Instrumentation Engineers. Description: viii, 239 p.: ill.; 28 cm. ISBN: 0892529474 (pbk.) Notes: Includes bibliographies and index. Subjects: Solid-state lasers--Congresses. Laser spectroscopy--Congresses. Series: Proceedings of SPIE--the International Society for Optical Engineering; v. 912 LC Classification: TA1705 .P95 1988 Dewey Class No.: 621.36/61 19

Quantum dot devices and computing: 21 January 2002, San Jose, USA / James A. Lott ... [et al.]; sponsored ... by SPIE--the International Society for Optical Engineering. Published/Created: Bellingham, Wash., USA: SPIE, c2002. Related Authors: Lott, James Anthony. Society of Photo-optical Instrumentation Engineers. Description: v, 108 p.: ill.; 28

cm. ISBN: 0819443956 Notes: Includes bibliographical references and index. Subjects: Quantum dots--Congresses. Quantum computers--Congresses. Semiconductor lasers--Congresses. Series: Proceedings of SPIE--the International Society for Optical Engineering; v. 4656. Variant Series: SPIE proceedings series, 0277-786X; v. 4656

Quantum Electronics and Laser Science Conference (2001: Baltimore, Maryland) Quantum Electronics and Laser Science Conference: technical digest: summaries of papers presented at the Quantum Electronics and Laser Science Conference: QELS 2001: Baltimore Convention Center, Baltimore, Maryland, May 6-11, 2001 / sponsored by APS/Division of Laser Science, IEEE/Lasers and Electro-Optics Society, OSA-Optical Society of America. Edition Information: Conference edition. Published/Created: Washington, D.C.: Optical Society of America, c2001. Related Authors: American Physical Society. Division of Laser Science. Lasers and Electro-optics Society (Institute of Electrical and Electronics Engineers) Optical Society of America. Description: [xv], 283, [31] p.: ill.; 28 cm. ISBN: 155752677X (meeting edition) 155752663X (postconference ed.) 078036595X (microfiche) Notes: "Postconference Technical Digest"--cover. Includes postdeadline papers. "Catalog number 01CH37172"--verso of T.p. Includes bibliographic references and author indexes. Subjects: Quantum electronics--Lasers--Laser spectroscopy--Photochemistry--Photobiology--Laser cooling--Quantum optics--Congresses. Nonlinear optics--Congresses. Series: OSA trends in optics and photonics; v. 57

Quantum Electronics and Laser Science Conference (2nd: 1991: Baltimore, Md.) Conference on Quantum Electronics Laser Science: summaries of papers presented at the Conference on Quantum Electronics Laser Science, May 12-17, 1991, Baltimore, Maryland / sponsored by American Physical Society, IEEE/Lasers and Electro-Optics Society, Optical Society of America, in cooperation with Quantum Electronics Division of the European Physical Society, Japanese Quantum Electronics Joint Group. Edition Information: Postconference ed. Published/Created: Washington, DC: Optical Society of America, c1991. Description: vi, 339 p.: ill.; 29 cm. ISBN: 1557521913 (hardcover) Notes: Cover Title - Quantum electronics and laser science. ""IEEE catalog number 91CH2946-2"--T.p. verso. Includes bibliographical references and indexes. Subjects: Lasers--Congresses. Quantum electronics--Congresses. Series: Technical digest series (Optical Society of America); 1991, v. 11. Variant Series: 1991 technical digest series; v. 11 LC Classification: TA1673 .Q36 1991 Dewey Class No.: 621.36/6 20

Quantum Electronics and Laser Science Conference (2nd: 1991: Baltimore, Md.) Conference on Quantum Electronics Laser Science: summaries of papers presented at the Conference on Quantum Electronics Laser Science, May 12-17, 1991, Baltimore, Maryland / sponsored by American Physical Society, IEEE/Lasers and Electro-Optics Society, Optical Society of America, in cooperation with Quantum Electronic Division of the European Physical Society, Japanese Quantum Electronics Joint Group. Edition Information: Conference ed. Published/Created: Washington, D.C.: Optical Society of America, c1991. Description: vi, 290 p.: ill.; 28 cm. ISBN: 1557521905 (softcover) Notes: Cover Title - Quantum electronics laser science. "IEEE catalog number: 91CH2946-2"--T.p. verso. Includes bibliographical references and index. Subjects: Lasers--Quantum electronics--Congresses. Series: Technical digest series (Optical Society of America) (Conference ed.); 1991, v. 11. Variant Series: 1991 technical digest series; v. 11 LC Classification: TA1673 .Q36 1991 Dewey Class No.: 621.36/6 20

Quantum Electronics and Laser Science Conference (4th: 1993: Baltimore, Md.) Quantum Electronics and Laser Science

Conference: summaries of papers presented at the Quantum Electronics and Laser Science Conference, May 2-7, 1993, Baltimore, Maryland / sponsored by Optical Society of America, IEEE/Lasers and Electro-Optics Society, Laser Science Topical Group of the American Physical Society in cooperation with Quantum Electronics Division of the European Physical Society, Japanese Quantum Electronics Joint Group. Edition Information: Conference ed. Published/Created: Washington, DC: Optical Society of America, c1993. Related Authors: Optical Society of America. Lasers and Electro-Optics Society (Institute of Electrical and Electronics Engineers) American Physical Sjociety. Laser Science Topical Group. Description: xviii, 309 p.: ill.; 28 cm. ISBN: 1557523010 Notes: "Catalog number 93CH3322-5"--T.p. verso. Includes bibliographical references and index. Subjects: Quantum electronics--Congresses. Lasers--Congresses. Series: Technical digest series (Optical Society of America); 1993, v. 12. Variant Series: 1993 technical digest series, v. 12 LC Classification: QC685 .Q36 1993a Dewey Class No.: 621.36/6 20

Quantum Electronics and Laser Science Conference (4th: 1993: Baltimore, Md.) Quantum Electronics and Laser Science Conference: summaries of papers presented at the Quantum Electronics and Laser Science Conference, May 2-7, 1993, Baltimore, Maryland / sponsored by Optical Society of America, IEEE/Lasers and Electro-Optics Society, Laser Science Topical Group of the American Physical Society in cooperation with Quantum Electronics Division of the European Physical Society, Japanese Quantum Electronics Joint Group. Edition Information: Postconference ed. Published/Created: Washington, DC: Optical Society of America, c1993. Related Authors: Optical Society of America. Lasers and Electro-Optics Society (Institute of Electrical and Electronics Engineers) American Physical Sjociety. Laser Science Topical Group. Description: xviii, 364 p.: ill.; 28 cm. ISBN: 1557523029 (pbk.) Notes: "Catalog number 93CH3322-5"--T.p. verso. Includes bibliographical references and index. Subjects: Quantum electronics--Congresses. Lasers--Congresses. Series: Technical digest series (Optical Society of America); 1993, v. 12. Variant Series: 1993 technical digest series, v. 12 LC Classification: QC685 .Q36 1993

Quantum Electronics and Laser Science Conference (6th: 1996: Anaheim, California) QELS '96: summaries of papers presented at the Quantum Electronics and Laser Science Conference, June 2-7, 1996, Anaheim Convention Center, Anaheim, California / sponsored by Optical Society of America, IEEE/Lasers and Electro-Optics Society, Division of Laser Science of the American Physical Society; in cooperation with Quantum Electronics Division of the European Physical Society, Japanese Quantum Electronics Joint Group. Edition Information: Conference ed. Published/Created: Washington, D.C.: Optical Society of America, c1996. Related Authors: European Physical Society. Quantum Electronics and Optics Division. Optical Society of America. Lasers and Electro-optics Society (Institute of Electrical and Electronics Engineers) American Physical Society. Laser Science Topical Group. Japanese Quantum Electronics Joint Group. Description: v, 256 p.: ill.; 28 cm. ISBN: 1557524440 Notes: "Catalog number 96CH35902"--T.p. verso. Includes bibliographical references and author index. Subjects: Quantum electronics--Lasers--Laser spectroscopy--Photochemistry--Photobiology--Light sources--Quantum optics--Nonlinear optics--Congresses. Series: Technical digest series (Optical Society of America); 1996, v. 9. Variant Series: 1996 technical digest series; v. 9 LC Classification: QC685 .Q36 1996 Dewey Class No.: 537.5 21

Quantum Electronics and Laser Science Conference (8th: (1999: Baltimore, Md.) Technical digest: summaries of papers presented at the Quantum Electronics and

Laser Science Conference: Baltimore Convention Center, Baltimore, Maryland, May 23-28, 1999. Edition Information: Postconference ed. Published/Created: Washington, DC: Optical Society of America, c1999. Description: 1 v. (various pagings): ill.; 27 cm. ISBN: 155752596X (acid-free paper) Notes: "QELS '99 sponsored by APS/Division of Laser Science, IEEE/Lasers and Electro-Optics Society, OSA-Optical Society of America." Includes bibliographical references and index. Subjects: Quantum electronics--Congresses. Lasers--Congresses. Series: Technical digest series (Optical Society of America); 1999. Variant Series: 1999 technical digest series LC Classification: QC685 .Q36 1999 Dewey Class No.: 537.5 21

Quantum Optoelectronics Topical Meeting (1991: Salt Lake City, Utah) Quantum optoelectronics: summaries of papers presented at the Quantum Optoelectronics Topical Meeting: March 11-13, 1991, Salt Lake City Utah / cosponsored by Optical Society of America, IEEE/Lasers and Electro-Optics Society in cooperation with Japan Society of Applied Physics. Edition Information: Postconference ed. Published/Created: Washington, DC: OSA, c1991. Description: xv, 315 p.: ill.; 29 cm. ISBN: 1557521751 Notes: Includes bibliographical references. Subjects: Lasers--Congresses. Optoelectronics--Congresses. Quantum electronics--Congresses. Series: Technical digest series (Optical Society of America); 1991, v. 7. Variant Series: 1991 technical digest series; v. 7 LC Classification: TA1673 .Q38 1991 Dewey Class No.: 621.36/6 20

Quantum Optoelectronics Topical Meeting (1993: Palm Springs, Calif.) Quantum optoelectronics: summaries of papers presented at the Quantum Optoelectronics Topical Meeting, March 17-19, 1993, Palm Springs, California / sponsosred by Optical Society of America; technical cosponsor IEEE/Lasers and Electro-Optics Society. Edition Information: Postconference ed. Published/Created: Washington, DC: The Society, c1993. Related Authors: Optical Society of America Description: viii, 141 p.: ill.; 28 cm. ISBN: 1557522928 (pbk.) Notes: Includes bibliographical references and index. Subjects: Lasers--Optoelectronics--Quantum electronics--Congresses. Series: Technical digest series (Optical Society of America); 1993, v.8 Variant Series: 1993 technical digest series; v. 8 LC Classification: TA1673 .Q38 1993 Dewey Class No.: 621.381/045 20

Quantum optoelectronics: March 19-21, 1997, Hyatt Regency Lake Tahoe, Incline Village, Nevada / sponsored and managed by Optical Society of America. Edition Information: Postconference ed. Published/Created: Washington, DC: The Society, c1997. Description: x, 152 p.: ill.; 28 cm. ISBN: 1557524939 (Postconference ed.) 1557524858 (1997 Technical Digest Series) Notes: Includes bibliographical references. Subjects: Optoelectronic devices--Quantum electronics--Quantum electrodynamics--Semiconductors--Lasers--Congresses. Series: Technical digest series (Optical Society of America); 1997, v. 9. Variant Series: 1997 technical digest series; v. 9 LC Classification: TA1750 .Q34 1997 Dewey Class No.: 621.382/045 21

Quantum optoelectronics: summaries of the papers presented at the topical meeting, March 15-17, 1995, Dana Point, California / sponsored by Optical Society of America; cosponsored by IEEE/Lasers and Electro-optics Society, IEEE/Electron Devices Society. Edition Information: Postconference ed. Published/Created: Washington, DC: Optical Society of America, c1995. Description: x, 214 p.: ill.; 28 cm. ISBN: 1557523967 Notes: Includes bibliographical references and index. Subjects: Optoelectronic devices--Optoelectronics--Materials--Quantum electronics--Lasers--Congresses. Series: Technical digest series (Optical Society of America); 1995, v. 14. Variant Series: Technical digest series; 1995, v. 14 LC Classification: TA1750 .Q35 1995 Dewey Class No.: 621.381/045 20

Quantum well lasers / edited by Peter S. Zory, Jr. Published/Created: Boston: Academic Press, c1993. Related Authors: Zory, Peter S., 1936- Description: xvi, 504 p.: ill.; 24 cm. ISBN: 0127818901 (alk. paper) Notes: Includes bibliographical references and index. Subjects: Semiconductor lasers. Quantum electronics. Series: Quantum electronics--principles and applications LC Classification: TA1700 .Q36 1993 Dewey Class No.: 621.36/6 20

Quantum Wells for Optics and Optoelectronics Topical Meeting (1989: Salt Lake City, Utah) Quantum wells for optics and optoelectronics: summaries of papers presented at the Quantum Wells for Optics and Optoelectrinics Topical Meeting, March 6-8, 1989, Salt Lake City, Utah / cosponsored by the Air Force Office of Scientific Research, Lasers and Electro-Optics Society of IEEE, [and] Optical Society of America, in cooperation with Quantum Electronics Group of the Japan Society of Applied Physics. Edition Information: Postconference ed. Published/Created: Washington, D.C. (1816 Jefferson Place, N.W., Washington 20036): Optical Society of America, c1989. Related Authors: United States. Air Force. Office of Scientific Research. Lasers and Electro-optics Society (Institute of Electrical and Electronics Engineers) Optical Society of America. Description: xii, 312 p.: ill.; 29 cm. ISBN: 1557520844 Notes: Cover Title - Quantum wells for optics & optoelectronics. Includes bibliographical references. Subjects: Quantum wells--Congresses. Optics--Congresses. Optoelectronics--Congresses. Series: Technical digest series (Optical Society of America); 1989, v. 10. Variant Series: 1989 technical digest series; v. 10 LC Classification: QC176.8.E4 Q385 1989 Dewey Class No.: 621.381/045 20

Rapid prototyping and flexible manufacturing: 16 June 1997, Munich, FRG / Rolf-Jürgen Ahlers, Gunther Reinhart, chairs/editors; sponsored by EOS--The European Optical Society, SPIE--the International Society for Optical Engineering, [and] The Commission of the European Communities, Directorate General for Science, Research, and Development. Published/Created: Bellingham, Wash., USA: SPIE, c1997. Related Authors: Ahlers, R.-J. (Rolf-Jürgen) Reinhart, Gunther. Society of Photo-optical Instrumentation Engineers. European Optical Society. Commission of the European Communities. Directorate-General for Science, Research, and Development. Description: vii, 152 p.: ill.; 28 cm. ISBN: 0819425222 Notes: Includes bibliographical references and index. Subjects: Flexible manufacturing systems--Congresses. Rapid prototyping--Congresses. Lasers in engineering--Congresses. Manufacturing processes--Technological innovations Congresses. Series: Proceedings of SPIE--the International Society for Optical Engineering; v. 3102. Proceedings EurOpt series. Variant Series: EurOpt series SPIE proceedings series; v. 3102 LC Classification: TS155.65 .R38 1997 Dewey Class No.: 670.42/7 21

Rare earth doped fiber lasers and amplifiers / edited by Michel J.F. Digonnet. Published/Created: New York: Marcel Dekker, c1993. Related Authors: Digonnet, Michel J. F. Description: xv, 659 p.: ill.; 24 cm. ISBN: 0824787854 (acid-free paper) Notes: Includes bibliographical references and index. Subjects: Rare earth lasers. Light amplifiers. Optical fibers. Series: Optical engineering (Marcel Dekker, Inc.); v. 37. Variant Series: Optical engineering; 37 LC Classification: TA1677 .R37 1993 Dewey Class No.: 621.36/6 20

Rare-earth-doped devices II: 26-27 January 1998, San Jose, California / Seppo Honkanen, Shibin Jiang, chairs/editors; sponsored and published by SPIE--the International Society for Optical Engineering. Published/Created: Bellingham, Wash.: SPIE, c1998. Related Authors: Honkanen, Seppo. Jiang, Shibin. Society of Photo-optical Instrumentation Engineers. Description: vii, 162 p.: ill.; 28 cm. ISBN: 0819427195 Notes: Includes bibliographical references and index. Subjects: Lasers--Materials--Congresses.

Rare earth metal alloys--Congresses. Optical amplifiers--Materials--Congresses. Optical wave guides--Materials--Congresses. Rare earth lasers--Congresses. Series: Proceedings of SPIE--the International Society for Optical Engineering; v. 3280. Variant Series: Proceedings of SPIE; v. 3280 LC Classification: TA1673 .R372 1998 Dewey Class No.: 621.36/6 21

Rare-earth-doped devices: 10-11 February, 1997, San Jose, California / Seppo Honkanen, chair/editor; sponsored and published by SPIE--the International Society for Optical Engineering; cooperating organization, DARPA--Defense Advanced Research Projects Agency. Published/Created: Bellingham, Wash.: SPIE, c1997. Related Authors: Honkanen, Seppo. Society of Photo-optical Instrumentation Engineers. United States. Defense Advanced Research Projects Agency. Description: ix, 214 p.: ill.; 28 cm. ISBN: 0819424072 Notes: Includes bibliographic references and author index. Subjects: Lasers--Materials--Congresses. Rare earth metal alloys--Congresses. Optical amplifiers--Materials--Congresses. Optical wave guides--Materials--Congresses. Series: Proceedings of SPIE--the International Society for Optical Engineering; v. 2996. Variant Series: Proceedings / SPIE--the International Society for Optical Engineering; v. 2996 LC Classification: TA1673 .R37 1997 Dewey Class No.: 621.36/6 21

Rare-earth-doped fiber lasers and amplifiers / edited by Michel J.F. Digonnet. Edition Information: 2nd ed., rev. and expanded. Published/Created: New York: Marcel Dekker, 2001. Related Authors: Digonnet, Michel J. F. Description: xii, 777 p.: ill.; 27 cm. ISBN: 0824704584 (alk. paper) Notes: Includes bibliographical references and index. Subjects: Rare earth lasers. Light amplifiers. Optical fibers. Series: Optical engineering (Marcel Dekker, Inc.); v. 71. Variant Series: Optical engineering; v. 71 LC Classification: TA1677 .R37 2001 Dewey Class No.: 621.36/3 21

Rare-earth-doped materials and devices III: 27-28 January 1999, San Jose, California / Shibin Jiang, Seppo Honkanen, chairs/editors; sponsored by SPIE--the International Society for Optical Engineering; cooperating organization, DARPA--Defense Advanced Research Projects Agency. Published/Created: Bellingham, Wash.: SPIE, c1999. Related Authors: Jiang, Shibin. Honkanen, Seppo. Society of Photo-optical Instrumentation Engineers. United States. Defense Advanced Research Projects Agency. Society of Photo-optical Instrumentation Engineers. Description: vi, 190 p.: ill.; 28 cm. ISBN: 0819430927 Notes: Includes bibliographical references and index. Subjects: Lasers--Materials--Congresses. Rare earth metal alloys--Congresses. Optical glass--Congresses. Optical wave guides--Materials--Congresses. Optical amplifiers--Materials--Congresses. Series: Proceedings of SPIE--the International Society for Optical Engineering; v. 3622. Variant Series: Proceedings / SPIE--the International Society for Optical Engineering; v. 3622 LC Classification: TA1673 .R374 1999 Dewey Class No.: 621.36/6 21

Rare-earth-doped materials and devices V: 22-23 January, 2001, San Jose, [California] USA / Shibin Jiang, chair/editor; sponsored and published by SPIE--the International Society for Optical Engineering. Published/Created: Bellingham, Washington: SPIE, c2001. Related Authors: Jiang, Shibin. Description: xxxii, 270 p.: ill.; 28 cm. ISBN: 0819439606 Notes: First and second conferences have Rare-earth-doped devices. Includes bibliographic references and author index. Subjects: Lasers--Rare earth metal alloys--Optical amplifiers--Optical wave guides--Materials--Congresses. Rare earth lasers--Congresses. Series: Proceedings of SPIE--the International Society for Optical Engineering; v. 4282. Variant Series: SPIE proceedings series; v. 4282 LC Classification: TA1673 .R3743 2001 Dewey Class No.: 621.36/6 21

Recent advances in the uses of light in physics, chemistry, engineering, and medicine: 19-21 June 1991, the City College of New York / Daniel L. Akins, Robert R. Alfano, chairs/editors; sponsored by the Center for Analysis of Structures and Interfaces (CASI), the Institute for Ultrafast Spectroscopy and Lasers (IUSL); supported by Allied-Signal, Inc. ... [et al.]. Published/Created: Bellingham, Wash.: SPIE--the International Society for Optical Engineering, c1992. Related Authors: Akins, Daniel L. Alfano, R. R. Description: xii, 349 p.: ill.; 28 cm. ISBN: 0819407305 Notes: Includes bibliographical references and index. Subjects: Optics--Congresses. Optics--Industrial applications--Congresses. Semiconductors--Congresses. Lasers in medicine--Congresses. Series: Proceedings of SPIE--the International Society for Optical Engineering; v. 1599. Variant Series: Proceedings / SPIE--the International Society for Optical Engineering; v. 1599 LC Classification: QC350 .R38 1992

Recent trends in physics: (crystal growth and laser applications) / editor, Francis P. Xavier. Published/Created: Madras, India: Loyola College, 1994. Related Authors: Xavier, Francis P. Loyola College (Madras, India). Dept. of Physics. Description: vii, 121 p.: ill.; 25 cm. Notes: Papers originally presented at the symposia, 'Recent Trends in Crystal Growth' and 'Recent Trends in Laser Applications' sponsored by the Physics Dept., Loyola College, Madras, India. "March 1994." Includes bibliographical references. Subjects: Crystal growth--Lasers--Congresses. Series: Loyola College publication; no. 7 LC Classification: QD921 .R433 1994 Dewey Class No.: 548/.5 20

Replication and molding of optical components: 13-14 January 1988, Los Angeles, California / Max J. Riedl, chair/editor; sponsored by SPIE--the International Society for Optical Engineering; cooperating organizations, American Academy of Otolaryngology--Head and Neck Surgery ... [et al.]. Published/Created: Bellingham, Wash., USA: SPIE, c1988. Related Authors: Riedl, Max J. Description: viii, 176 p.: ill.; 28 cm. ISBN: 0892529318 Notes: "One of nineteen conferences comprising the Symposium on Lasers and Optics at SPIE's O-E LASE '88, 10-17 January 1988, Los Angeles, California"--P. vii. Includes bibliographies and index. Subjects: Optical instruments--Lenses--Design and construction--Congresses. Series: Proceedings of SPIE--the International Society for Optical Engineering; v. 896 LC Classification: TS510 .R46 1988 Dewey Class No.: 681/.4 19

Research on laser theory / edited by A.N. Orayevskiy; translated by Kevin S. Hendzel. Published/Created: Commack: Nova Science Publishers, c1988. Related Authors: Oraevskii, A. N. (Anatolii Nikolaevich) Hendzel, Kevin S. Description: vii, 288 p.: ill.; 25 cm. ISBN: 0941743063: Notes: Translation of: Issledovaniia po teorii lazerov. Includes bibliographies and index. Subjects: Lasers--Quantum electronics--Congresses. Series: Trudy Fizicheskogo instituta. English; v. 171. Variant Series: Proceedings of the Lebedev Physics Institute of the Academy of Sciences of the USSR; v. 171 LC Classification: QC1 .A4114 Vol. 171 QC658 Dewey Class No.: 530 s 535.5/8 19

Saratov fall meeting 2000: coherent optics of ordered and random media: 3-6 October 2000, Saratov, Russia / Dmitry A. Zimnyakov, chair/editor; organized by Saratov State University (Russia) ... [et al.]; in cooperation with Ministry of Education of the Russian Federation ... [et al.]; sponsored by SPIE Russia Chapter. Published/Created: Bellingham, Wash., USA: SPIE, c2001. Related Authors: Zimnyakov, Dmitry A. Society of Photo-optical Instrumentation Engineers. Russian Chapter. Society of Photo-optical Instrumentation Engineers. International Workshop and Fall School for Young Scientists and Students on Optics, Laser Physics, and Biophysics (2000: Saratov,

Russia) Description: x, 320 p.: ill.; 28 cm. ISBN: 0819439207 Notes: "International Workshop and Fall School for Young Scientists and Students on Optics, Laser Physics, and Biophysics"--Cover. Includes bibliographical references and index. Subjects: Lasers--Industrial applications--Lasers in biophysics--Light--Scattering--Coherence (Optics)--Congresses. Series: Proceedings of SPIE--the International Society for Optical Engineering; v. 4242. Variant Series: SPIE proceedings series, 0277-786X; v. 4242

Scanning probe microscopies: 20-22 January 1992, Los Angeles, California / Srinivas Manne. Published/Created: Bellingham, Wash.: SPIE--the Society of Photo-optical Instrumentation Engineers, c1992. Related Authors: Manne, Srinivas. Description: ix, 218 p.: ill.; 28 cm. ISBN: 0819407852 Notes: "Conference 1639, Scanning probe microscopies, was part of a four-conference program on laser spectroscopy held in SPIE's OE/LASE '92 Lasers, Sensors & Spectroscopy Symposium, 19-25 January 1992, in Los Angeles"--P. vii. Includes bibliographical references and index. Subjects: Scanning probe microscopy--Congresses. Series: Proceedings of SPIE--the International Society for Optical Engineering; v. 1639. Variant Series: SPIE proceeding series; v. 1639 LC Classification: QH212.S33 S375 1992 Dewey Class No.: 502/.8/25 20

Selected papers on apodization--coherent optical systems / editors, James P. Mills, Brian J. Thompson. Published/Created: Bellingham, Wash., USA: SPIE Optical Engineering Press, c1996. Related Authors: Mills, James Patrick, 1946- Thompson, Brian J. Description: xiv, 531 p.: ill.; 29 cm. ISBN: 0819421502 (alk. paper) Notes: Includes bibliographical references and indexes. Subjects: Imaging systems. Coherence (Optics) Lasers. Series: SPIE milestone series; v. MS 119 LC Classification: TK8315 .S45 1996 Dewey Class No.: 621.36/7 20

Selected papers on CO2 lasers / James D. Evans, editor. Published/Created: Bellingham, Wash., USA: SPIE Optical Engineering Press, c1990. Related Authors: Evans, James D. (James David), 1942- Description: xii, 547 p.: ill.; 28 cm. ISBN: 0819404926 0819404934 (pbk.) Notes: Includes bibliographical references and index. Subjects: Carbon dioxide lasers. Series: SPIE milestone series; v. MS 22 LC Classification: TA1695 .S45 1990 Dewey Class No.: 621.36/63 20

Selected papers on dye lasers / F.J. Duarte. Published/Created: Bellingham, Wash., USA: SPIE Optical Engineering Press, c1992. Related Authors: Duarte, F. J. (Frank J.) Description: xxii, 660 p.: ill.; 29 cm. ISBN: 0819408840 (hardbound) 0819408859 (softbound) Notes: Includes bibliographical references and indexes. Subjects: Dye lasers. Series: SPIE milestone series; v. MS 45 LC Classification: TA1690 .S45 1992 Dewey Class No.: 621.36/64 20

Selected papers on fundamentals of lasers / William T. Silfvast, editor. Published/Created: Bellingham, Wash.: SPIE Optical Engineering Press, c1993. Related Authors: Silfvast, William Thomas, 1937- Description: xviii, 686 p.: ill.; 29 cm. ISBN: 0819412120 0819412112 (soft) Notes: Includes bibliographical references and indexes. Subjects: Lasers. Masers. Series: SPIE milestone series; v. MS 70 LC Classification: QC689 .S45 1993 Dewey Class No.: 621.36/6 20

Selected papers on gas laser technology edior, J. Gary Eden. Published/Created: Bellingham, Wash.: SPIE Optical Engineering Press, c2000. Related Authors: Eden, J. G. Description: xviii, 714 p.: ill.; 29 cm. ISBN: 0819435198 Notes: Includes bibliographical references and index. Subjects: Gas lasers. Series: SPIE milestone series; v. MS 159 LC Classification: TA1695 .S454 2000 Dewey Class No.: 621.36/63 21

Selected papers on high power lasers / John M. Soures, editor. Published/Created: Bellingham, Wash., USA: SPIE--the

International Society for Optical Engineering, c1991. Related Authors: Soures, John M., 1943- Description: xvi, 711 p.: ill.; 28 cm. ISBN: 0819407992 (hard) 081940800X (soft) Notes: Includes bibliographical references and index. Subjects: High power lasers. Series: SPIE milestone series; v. MS 43 LC Classification: TA1677 .S414 1991 Dewey Class No.: 621.36/6 20

Selected papers on laser beam diagnostics / editors, Robert N. Hindy, Jeffrey H. Hunt. Published/Created: Bellingham, Wash.: SPIE Optical Engineering Press, c1996. Related Authors: Hindy, Robert N. Hunt, Jeffrey H., 1957- Description: xvii, 553 p.: ill.; 29 cm. ISBN: 0819422835 (alk. paper) Notes: Includes bibliographical references and index. Subjects: Lasers--Industrial applications. Laser Doppler velocimeter. Fluid dynamic measurements. Optical radar. Lasers in medicine. Series: SPIE milestone series; v. MS 126 LC Classification: TA1677 .S4145 1996 Dewey Class No.: 621.36/6 20

Selected papers on laser crystal growth / editor, Robert Uhrin. Published/Created: Bellingham, Wash.: SPIE Optical Engineering Press, 2000. Related Authors: Uhrin, Robert, 1945- Description: xv, 565 p.: ill.; 29 cm. ISBN: 0819438111 Notes: Includes bibliographical references and index. Subjects: Solid-state lasers--Materials. Crystals. Crystal growth. Series: SPIE milestone series; v. MS 164 LC Classification: TA1705 .S43 2000 Dewey Class No.: 621.36/6 21

Selected papers on laser design / Hugo Weichel, editor. Published/Created: Bellingham, Wash., USA: SPIE Optical Engineering Press, c1991. Related Authors: Weichel, Hugo, 1937- Description: xvi, 700 p.: ill.; 28 cm. ISBN: 0819406252 (softbound) 0819406244 (hardbound) Notes: "A reprint collection of outstanding papers from the world literature on optical and optoelectronic science, engineering, and technology"--Cover. Includes bibliographical references and indexes. Subjects: Lasers--Design and construction. Series: SPIE milestone series; v. MS 29 LC Classification: TA1677 .S415 1991 Dewey Class No.: 621.36/6 20

Selected papers on laser distance measurements / editors, Thierry Bosch, Marc Lescure. Published/Created: Bellingham, Wash.: SPIE Optical Engineering Press, c1995. Related Authors: Bosch, Thierry, 1965- Lescure, Marc, 1945- Description: xvi, 719 p.: ill.; 29 cm. ISBN: 0819420107 (alk. paper) Notes: Includes bibliographical references and indexes. Subjects: Distances--Measurement. Lasers--Industrial applications. Series: SPIE milestone series; v. MS 115 LC Classification: TA601 .S42 1995 Dewey Class No.: 681/.2 20

Selected papers on laser isotope separation--science and technology / Jeff W. Eerkens, editor. Published/Created: Bellingham, Wash., USA: SPIE Optical Engineering Press, c1995. Related Authors: Eerkens, Jeff W., 1931- Description: xxiv, 703 p.: ill.; 29 cm. ISBN: 0819419982 (alk. paper) Notes: Includes bibliographical references and indexes. Subjects: Lasers in isotope separation. Series: SPIE milestone series; v. MS 113 LC Classification: TP156.I7 S45 1995 Dewey Class No.: 660/.29884 20

Selected papers on laser safety / David H. Sliney, editor. Published/Created: Bellingham, Wash., USA: SPIE Optical Engineering Press, c1995. Related Authors: Sliney, David H. Description: xx, 708 p.: ill.; 29 cm. ISBN: 081942014X (alk. paper) Notes: Includes bibliographical references and indexes. Subjects: Retina--Effect of radiation on. Lasers--Safety measures. Eye--Protection. Lasers--Health aspects. Series: SPIE milestone series; v. MS 117 LC Classification: RE551 .S45 1995 Dewey Class No.: 617.7 20

Selected papers on optical chaos / editors, F.T. Arecchi, R.G. Harrison; Brian J.Thompson, general editor. Published/Created: Bellingham, Wash., USA: SPIE Optical Engineering Press, c1994. Related Authors: Arecchi, F. T. Harrison, R. G. (Robert G.), 1944-

Thompson, Brian J. Description: xvi, 719 p.: ill.; 29 cm. ISBN: 0819412171 (hard) 0819412163 (soft) Notes: "Bibliography" p. 671-711. Includes bibliographical references and indexes. Subjects: Quantum optics. Masers. Chaotic behavior in systems. Series: SPIE milestone series; v. MS 75 LC Classification: QC446.2 .S444 1994 Dewey Class No.: 621.36/6 20

Selected papers on optical fibers in medicine / Abraham Katzir, editor. Published/Created: Bellingham, Wash., USA: SPIE Optical Engineering Press, c1990. Related Authors: Katzir, Abraham. Description: xvii, 715 p.: ill.; 28 cm. ISBN: 0819403687 (hardbound) 0819403695 (softbound) Notes: "A publication of SPIE--the International Society for Optical Engineering." Includes bibliographical references (p. [701]-708) and indexes. Subjects: Optical fibers in medicine. Endoscopy--methods--collected works. Fiber Optics--collected works. Laser Surgery--collected works. Lasers--therapeutic use. Series: SPIE milestone series; v. MS 11 LC Classification: R857.O59 S45 1990 Dewey Class No.: 610/.28 20

Selected papers on optical parametric oscillators and amplifiers and their applications / Jeffrey H. Hunt, editor. Published/Created: Bellingham, Wash., USA: SPIE Optical Engineering Press, c1997. Related Authors: Hunt, Jeffrey H., 1957- Description: xvii, 460 p.: ill.; 29 cm. ISBN: 0819426768 (alk. paper) Notes: Includes bibliographical references and indexes. Subjects: Lasers. Parametric amplifiers. Optical amplifiers. Series: SPIE milestone series; v. MS 140 LC Classification: TA1677 .S4155 1997 Dewey Class No.: 621.36/6 21

Selected papers on rare-earth-doped fiber laser sources and amplifiers / Michel J.F. Digonnet, editor. Published/Created: Bellingham, Wash.: SPIE Optical Engineering Press, c1992. Related Authors: Digonnet, Michel J. F. Description: xxiii, 694 p.: ill.; 28 cm. ISBN: 0819407356 (softbound) 0819407348 (hardbound) Notes: Includes bibliographical references and indexes. Series: SPIE milestone series; v. MS 37 LC Classification: TA1677 .S416 1992 Dewey Class No.: 621.36/6 20

Selected papers on semiconductor diode lasers / James J. Coleman, editor. Published/Created: Bellingham, Wash., USA: SPIE Optical Engineering Press, c1992. Related Authors: Coleman, James J., 1950- Description: xvii, 332 p.: ill.; 28 cm. ISBN: 0819408921 (hardbound) 081940893X (softbound) Notes: Includes bibliographical references and indexes. Subjects: Semiconductor lasers. Series: SPIE milestone series; v. MS 50 LC Classification: TA1700 .S43 1992 Dewey Class No.: 621.36/61 20

Selected papers on solid state lasers / Richard C. Powell, editor. Published/Created: Bellingham, Wash., USA: SPIE Optical Engineering Press, c1991. Related Authors: Powell, Richard C. (Richard Conger), 1939- Description: xvi, 476 p.: ill.; 28 cm. ISBN: 0819406295 (softbound) 0819406287 (hardbound) Notes: Includes bibliographical references and indexes. Subjects: Solid-state lasers. Series: SPIE milestone series; v. MS 31 LC Classification: TA1705 .S44 1991 Dewey Class No.: 621.36/61 20

Selected papers on tissue optics: applications in medical diagnostics and therapy / Valery V. Tuchin, editor. Published/Created: Bellingham, Wash.: SPIE Optical Engineering Press, c1994. Related Authors: Tuchin, V. V. (Valeri Viktorovich) Description: xxix, 670 p.: ill.; 29 cm. ISBN: 0819416959 (hardbound) 0819416940 (softbound) Notes: "A publication of SPIE--the International Society for Optical Engineering." Includes bibliographical references and indexes. Subjects: Tissues--Optical properties--Congresses. Scattering, Radiation--Light--Lasers--Diagnostic Imaging--collected works. Series: SPIE milestone series; v. MS 102 LC Classification: QH642 .S45 1994 Dewey Class No.: 611/.018 20

Selected papers on tunable solid-state lasers / editor, Valerii Ter-Mikirtychev. Published/Created: Bellingham, WA: SPIE Optical Engineering Press, 2002. Projected Pub. Date: 0207 Related Authors: Ter-Mikirtychev, Valerii, 1966- Description: p. cm. ISBN: 0819446556 Notes: Includes index. Subjects: Solid-state lasers. Tunable lasers. Series: SPIE milestone series; v. MS 173 LC Classification: TA1705 .S45 2002 Dewey Class No.: 621.36/61 21

Selected papers on ultrafast laser technology / Timothy R. Gosnell, Antoinette J. Taylor, editors. Published/Created: Bellingham, Wash., USA: SPIE Optical Engineering Press, c1991. Related Authors: Gosnell, Timothy R., 1957- Taylor, Antoinette J., 1956- Description: xxi, 680 p.: ill.; 28 cm. ISBN: 0819408301 081940831X (pbk.) Notes: Includes bibliographical references and indexes. Subjects: Lasers. Laser pulses, Ultrashort. Series: SPIE milestone series; v. MS 44 LC Classification: TA1677 .S418 1991 Dewey Class No.: 621.36/6 20

Selected papers on upconversion lasers / editor, Timothy R. Gosnell. Published/Created: Bellingham, Wash.: SPIE Optical Engineering Press, c2000. Related Authors: Gosnell, Timothy R., 1957- Description: xx, 470 p.: ill.; 29 cm. ISBN: 081943793X Notes: Includes bibliographical references and index. Subjects: Solid-state lasers. Optical pumping. Far infrared lasers. Multiphoton processes. Laser photochemistry. Series: SPIE milestone series; v. MS 161 LC Classification: TA1705 .S46 2000 Dewey Class No.: 621.36/61 21

Selected papers on UV, VUV, and X-ray lasers / Ronald W. Waynant, Marwood N. Ediger. Published/Created: Bellingham, Wash.: SPIE Optical Engineering Press, c1993. Related Authors: Waynant, Ronald W. Ediger, Marwood N., 1958- Description: xv, 596 p.: ill.; 28 cm. ISBN: 0819411256 0819411264 (pbk.) Notes: Includes bibliographical references and index. Subjects: X-ray lasers. Ultraviolet radiation. Gas lasers. Excimer lasers. Series: SPIE milestone series; v. MS 71 LC Classification: TA1707 .S45 1993 Dewey Class No.: 621.36/6 20

Self-organization in optical systems and applications in information technology / Mikhail A. Vorontsov, Walter B. Miller (eds.). Edition Information: 2nd ed. Published/Created: Berlin; New York: Springer, c1998. Related Authors: Vorontsov, M. A. (Mikhail Alekseevich) Miller, Walter B. (Walter Blaine), 1933- Description: xv, 247 p.: ill.; 24 cm. ISBN: 3540641254 (pbk.: alk. paper) Notes: Includes bibliographical references and index. Subjects: Self-organizing systems. Lasers. Nonlinear optics. Series: Springer series in synergetics (Unnumbered) Variant Series: Springer series in synergetics LC Classification: Q325 .S46 1998 Dewey Class No.: 003/.71 21

Self-organization in optical systems and applications in information technology / Mikhail A. Vorontsov, Walter B. Miller, eds. Published/Created: Berlin; New York: Springer, c1995. Related Authors: Vorontsov, M. A. (Mikhail Alekseevich) Miller, Walter B. (Walter Blaine), 1933- Description: xv, 247 p.: ill.; 25 cm. ISBN: 3540570861 (Berlin: acid-free paper) Notes: Includes bibliographical references and index. Subjects: Self-organizing systems. Lasers. Nonlinear optics. Series: Springer series in synergetics; v. 66. Variant Series: Springer series in synergetics; 66 LC Classification: Q325 .S46 1995 Dewey Class No.: 535/.2 20

Semiconductor diode lasers / edited by William Streifer, Michael Ettenberg. Published/Created: New York: IEEE Press, c1991- Related Authors: Streifer, William. Ettenberg, Michael. Description: v. <1: ill.; 29 cm. ISBN: 0879422610 (v. 1) Notes: Includes bibliographical references and indexes. Subjects: Semiconductor lasers. Series: Progress in lasers and electro-optics LC Classification: TA1700 .S44 1991 Dewey Class No.: 621.36/6 20

Semiconductor lasers / edited by Eli Kapon. Published/Created: San Diego: Academic Press, c1999. Related Authors: Kapon, Eli. Description: 2 v.: ill.; 24 cm. ISBN: 0123976308 (v. 1) 0123976316 (v. 2) Contents: v. 1. Fundamentals -- v. 2. Materials and structures. Notes: Includes bibliographical references and indexes. Subjects: Semiconductor lasers. Series: Optics and photonics LC Classification: TA1700 .S4522 1999 Dewey Class No.: 621.36/6 21

Semiconductor lasers and optical communication: Laser Optics 2000: 26-30 June, 2000, St. Petersburg, Russia / Serguei A. Gurevich, Nikolay N. Rosanov, editors; organized by Institute for Laser Physics (Russia) ... [et al.]; supported by Ministry of Science and Technical Policy of the Russian Federation ... [et al.]; published by SPIE--the International Society for Optical Engineering. Published/Created: Bellingham, Washington: SPIE, c2001. Related Authors: Gurevich, Sergei A., 1949- Rosanov, Nikolay N. Vserossiiskii nauchnyi tsentr "Gosudarstvennyi opticheskii institut im. S.I. Vavilova." Institute for Laser Physics. Russia (Federation). Ministerstvo nauki i tekhnologii. Society of Photo-optical Instrumentation Engineers. Laser Optics 2000 (2000: Saint Petersburg, Russia) Description: vi, 204 p.: ill.; 28 cm. ISBN: 0819440442 Notes: Includes bibliographic references and author index. Subjects: Semiconductor lasers--Congresses. Optical communications--Congresses. Series: Proceedings of SPIE--the International Society for Optical Engineering; v. 4354. Variant Series: SPIE proceedings series; v. 4354

Semiconductor lasers for lightwave communication systems: 21-22 August 2001, Denver, USA / Carmen S. Menoni, Richard P. Mirin, chairs/editors; sponsored ... by SPIE--the International Society for Optical Engineering; cooperating organization, Colorado Photonics Industry Association (USA). Published/Created: Bellingham, Wash., USA: SPIE, c2001. Related Authors: Menoni, Carmen S. Mirin, Richard Paul, 1967- Society of Photo-optical Instrumentation Engineers. Colorado Photonics Industry Association. Description: vii, 92 p.: ill.; 28 cm. ISBN: 0819442577 Notes: Includes ssssbibliographical references and index. Subjects: Semiconductor lasers--Congresses. Laser communication systems--Congresses. Series: Proceedings of SPIE--the International Society for Optical Engineering; v. 4533. Variant Series: SPIE proceedingss series; v. 4533

Semiconductor lasers II: 6-7 November 1996, Beijing, China / Siamak Forouhar, Qiming Wang, chairs/editors; sponsored by SPIE--the International Society for Optical Engineering, COEMA--China Optics & Optoelectronic Manufacturers Association, COS--Chinese Optical Society; cooperating organizations, National Natural Science Foundation of China ... [et al.]; published by, SPIE--the International Society for Optical Engineering. Published/Created: Bellingham, Wash., USA: SPIE, c1996. Related Authors: Forouhar, Siamak, 1950- Wang, Qiming, 1933- China Optics & Optoelectronic Manufacturers Association. Zhongguo guang xue xue hui. Guo jia zi ran ke xue ji jin wei yuan hui (China) Society of Photo-optical Instrumentation Engineers. Description: xi, 358 p.: ill.; 28 cm. ISBN: 0819422878 Notes: Includes bibliographical references and author index. Subjects: Semiconductor lasers--Congresses. Series: Proceedings of SPIE--the International Society for Optical Engineering; v. 2886. Variant Series: SPIE proceeding series; v. 2886 LC Classification: TA1700 .S463 1996 Dewey Class No.: 621.36/6 21

Semiconductor lasers III: 16-18 September, 1998, Beijing, China / Qiming Wang, Lawrence J. Davis, Siamak Forouhar, chairs/editors; sponsored by SPIE--the International Society for Optical Engineering, COEMA--China Optics & Optoelectronic Manufacturers Association, COS--Chinese Optical Society; cooperating organizations, National Natural Science Foundation of China ... [et al.]; published by, SPIE--the International Society for Optical Engineering. Published/Created: Bellingham, Washington: SPIE, c1998. Related Authors: Wang, Qiming, 1933- Davis, Lawrence J. Forouhar, Siamak, 1950- China Optics & Optoelectronic Manufacturers Association. Zhongguo guang xue xue hui. Guo jia zi ran ke xue ji jin wei yuan hui (China) Society of Photo-optical Instrumentation Engineers. Description: ix, 404 p.: ill.; 28 cm. ISBN: 0819430080 Notes: Includes bibliographical references and author index. Subjects: Semiconductor lasers--Congresses. Series: Proceedings of SPIE--the International Society for Optical Engineering; v. 3547. Variant Series: SPIE proceeding series; v. 3547 LC Classification: TA1700 .S4523 1998 Dewey Class No.: 621.36/6 21

Semiconductor lasers. Edition Information: Conference ed. Published/Created: Washington, DC: Optical Society of America, 1995. Description: p. cm. ISBN: 1557524092 (pbk.) Series: 1995 technical digest series; v. 20 LC Classification: 9508

Semiconductor lasers: advanced devices and applications :summaries of papers presented at the topical meeting, August 21-23, 1995, Keystone, Colorado / cosponsored by Optical Society of America, IEEE/Lasers and Electro-optics Society. Edition Information: Postconference ed. Published/Created: Washington, D.C.: Optical Society of America, 1995. Description: xi, 209 p.: ill.; 29 cm. ISBN: 1557524084 Notes: Includes bibliographical references and indexes. Subjects: Semiconductor lasers--Congresses. Semiconductor lasers. Injection lasers. Conferences. Series: Technical digest series (Optical Society of America); 1995, v. 20. Variant Series: 1995 technical digest series; v. 20 LC Classification: TA1700 .S452 1995 Dewey Class No.: 621.36/6 21

Semiconductor lasers: past, present, and future / editor, Govind P. Agrawal. Published/Created: Woodbury, N.Y.: AIP Press/American Institute of Physics, c1995. Related Authors: Agrawal, G. P. (Govind P.), 1951- Description: xx, 365 p.: ill.; 25 cm. ISBN: 156396211X (acid-free paper) Notes: Includes bibliographical references and index. Subjects: Semiconductor lasers. Series: AIP series in theoretical and applied optics LC Classification: TA1700 .S46 1995 Dewey Class No.: 621.36/6 20

Semiconductor science and technology / V. Stefan and N.G. Basov, editors. Edition Information: 2nd ed. Published/Created: La Jolla, CA: Stefan University Press, 2002. Projected Pub. Date: 0202 Related Authors: Stefan, V. Basov, N. G. (Nikolai Gennadievich), 1922- Description: v. cm. ISBN: 1889545112 (v. 1: acid-free paper) 1889545120 (v. 2: acid-free paper) Contents: v. 1. Semiconductor lasers -- v. 2. Quantum dots and quantum wells. Notes: Includes bibliographical references and indexes. Subjects: Semiconductors. Series: The Stefan University Press series on frontiers in science and technology LC Classification: QC611 .S46 2002 Dewey Class No.: 537.6/22 21

Short-pulse high-intensity lasers and applications II: 21-22 January 1993, Los Angeles, California / Hector A. Baldis, chair/editor; sponsored and published by SPIE--the International Society for Optical Engineering. Published/Created: Bellingham, Wash: SPIE , c1993. Related Authors: Baldis, Hector A. Society of Photo-optical Instrumentation Engineers. Description: vii, 234 p.: ill.; 28 cm. ISBN: 081941087X Notes: Includes bibliographical references and index. Subjects: High power lasers--Laser pulses, Ultrashort--X-ray lasers--Laser-plasma interactions--Congresses. Series: Proceedings of SPIE--the International Society for Optical Engineering; v. 1860. Variant Series: Proceedings / SPIE--the International Society for Optical Engineering; v. 1860 LC Classification: TA1673 .S52 1993 Dewey Class No.: 621.36/6 20

Short-pulse high-intensity lasers and applications: 22-23 January 1991, Los

Angeles, California / Hector A. Baldis, chair/editor; sponsored and published by SPIE--the International Society for Optical Engineering. Published/Created: Bellingham, Wash., USA: SPIE, c1991. Related Authors: Baldis, Hector. Society of Photo-optical Instrumentation Engineers. Description: vii, 145 p.: ill.; 28 cm. ISBN: 0819405035 Notes: "Part of a four-conference program ... held at SPIE's Symposium on High-Power Lasers, a part of OE/LASE '91, 20-25-January 1991"--P. v. Includes bibliographical references and index. Subjects: High power lasers--Picosecond pulses--Laser-plasma interactions--Congresses. Series: Proceedings of SPIE--the International Society for Optical Engineering; v. 1413. Variant Series: Proceedings / SPIE--the International Society for Optical Engineering; v. 1413 LC Classification: TA1673 .S53 1991 Dewey Class No.: 621.36/6 20

Short-wavelength lasers and their applications: proceedings of an international symposium, Osaka, Japan, November 11-13, 1987 / editor, C. Yamanaka. Published/Created: Berlin; New York: Springer-Verlag, c1988. Related Authors: Yamanaka, Chiyoe, 1923- Description: xiv, 410 p.: ill.; 25 cm. ISBN: 0387503110 (U.S.) Notes: "International Symposium on Short Wavelength Lasers and Their Applications ... coordinated by the MOE (Ministry of Education, Science, and Culture) and the Institute of Laser Engineering, Osaka University"--Pref. Includes bibliographies and index. Subjects: X-ray lasers--Congresses. Free electron lasers--Congresses. Excimer lasers--Congresses. Laser fusion--Congresses. Series: Springer proceedings in physics; v. 30 LC Classification: TA1673 .S54 1988 Dewey Class No.: 621.36/63 19

Short-wavelength radiation sources: 24-25 July 1991, San Diego, California / Phillip Sprangle, chair/editor; sponsored and published by SPIE--the International Society for Optical Engineering. Published/Created: Bellingham, Wash.: SPIE, c1991. Related Authors: Sprangle, P. (Phillip) Society of Photo-optical Instrumentation Engineers. Description: ix, 298 p.: ill.; 28 cm. ISBN: 0819406805 Notes: "Part of a two-conference program ... held at SPIE's 1991 International Symposium on Optical Applied Science and Engineering, 21-26 July 1991"--P. vii. Includes bibliographical references and index. Subjects: Free electron lasers--Radiation sources--Quantum electronics--Congresses. Series: Proceedings of SPIE--the International Society for Optical Engineering; v. 1552. Variant Series: Proceedings / SPIE--the International Society for Optical Engineering; v. 1552 LC Classification: QC689.5.L37 S56 1991 Dewey Class No.: 621.36/6 20

Soft X-ray lasers and applications II: 28-29 July, 1997, San Diego, California / Jorge J. Rocca, Luiz B. Da Silva, chairs/editors; sponsored and published by SPIE--the International Society for Optical Engineering. Published/Created: Bellingham, Washington: SPIE, c1997. Related Authors: Rocca, Jorge J. Da Silva, Luiz B. Society of Photo-optical Instrumentation Engineers. Description: ix, 346 p.: ill.; 28 cm. ISBN: 0819425788 Notes: Includes bibliographic references and author index. Subjects: X-ray lasers--Congresses. Grenz rays--Congresses. Series: Proceedings of SPIE--the International Society for Optical Engineering; v. 3156. Variant Series: Proceedings / SPIE--the International Society for Optical Engineering; v. 3156 LC Classification: TA1707 .S64 1997 Dewey Class No.: 621.36/6 21

Soft X-ray lasers and applications III: 19-20 July 1999, Denver, Colorado / Jorge J. Rocca, Luiz B. Da Silva, chairs/editors; sponsored and published by SPIE--the International Society for Optical Engineering. Published/Created: Bellingham, Wash.: SPIE, c1999. Related Authors: Rocca, Jorge J. Da Silva, Luiz B. Society of Photo-optical Instrumentation Engineers. Description: ix, 314 p.: ill.; 28 cm. ISBN: 0819432628 Notes: Includes bibliographical references and index.

Subjects: X-ray lasers--Congresses. Grenz rays--Congresses. Series: Proceedings of SPIE--the International Society for Optical Engineering; v. 3776. Variant Series: SPIE proceedings series, 0277-786X; v. 3776 LC Classification: TA1707 .S643 1999 Dewey Class No.: 621.36/6 21

Soft X-ray lasers and applications IV: 1-3 August, 2001, San Diego, [California] USA / Ernst E. Fill, Jorge J.G. Rocca, chairs/editors; sponsored and published by SPIE--the International Society for Optical Engineering. Published/Created: Bellingham, Washington: SPIE, c2001. Related Authors: Fill, E. (Ernst), 1940- Rocca, Jorge J. Society of Photo-optical Instrumentation Engineers. Description: xi, 246 p.: ill.; 28 cm. ISBN: 0819442194 Notes: Includes bibliographical references and author index. Subjects: X-ray lasers--Congresses. Grenz rays--Congresses. Series: Proceedings of SPIE--the International Society for Optical Engineering; v. 4505. Variant Series: SPIE proceedings series; v. 4505

Soft X-ray lasers and applications: 10-11 July, 1995, San Diego, California / Jorge J. Rocca, Peter L. Hagelstein, chairs/editors; sponsored and published by SPIE--the International Society for Optical Engineering. Published/Created: Bellingham, Wash., USA: SPIE, c1995. Related Authors: Rocca, Jorge J. Hagelstein, Peter L. Society of Photo-optical Instrumentation Engineers. Description: xi, 390 p.: ill.; 28 cm. ISBN: 081941879X Notes: Includes bibliographic references and author index. Subjects: X-ray lasers--Congresses. Series: Proceedings of SPIE--the International Society for Optical Engineering; v. 2520. Variant Series: Proceedings / SPIE--the International Society for Optical Engineering; v. 2520 LC Classification: TA1673 .S67 1995 Dewey Class No.: 621.36/6 21

Solid freeform and additive fabrication, 2000: symposium held April 24-26, 2000, San Francisco, U.S.A. / editors, Stephen C. Danforth, Duane Dimos, Fritz B. Prinz. Published/Created: Warrendale, Pa.: Materials Research Society, 2000. Related Authors: Danforth, Stephen C. Dimos, Duane. Prinz, Fritz. Description: ix, 220 p.: ill.; 24 cm. ISBN: 1558995331 Notes: Includes bibliographical references and indexes. Subjects: Manufacturing processes--Solid freeform fabrication--Composite materials--Ceramic materials--Lasers--Industrial applications--Congresses. Series: Materials Research Society symposia proceedings; v. 625. Variant Series: Materials Research Society symposium proceedings, 0272-9172; v. 625 LC Classification: TS183 .S658 2000 Dewey Class No.: 670.42/7 21

Solid freeform fabrication: a new direction in manufacturing: with research and applications in thermal laser processing / by Joseph J. Beaman ... [et al.]. Published/Created: Dordrecht; Boston: Kluwer Academic Publishers, c1997. Related Authors: Beaman, Joseph J. Description: 330 p.: ill.; 24 cm. ISBN: 0792398343 Notes: Includes bibliographical references and index. Subjects: CAD/CAM systems. Solid freeform fabrication. Prototypes, Engineering--Computer simulation. Lasers--Industrial applications. LC Classification: TS155.6 .S6373 1997 Dewey Class No.: 670.42/7 21

Solid state lasers / sponsored by SPIE--the International Society for Optical Engineering. Published/Created: Bellingham, Wash., USA: SPIE, c1990- Related Authors: Society of Photo-optical Instrumentation Engineers. Description: v.: ill.; 28 cm. Vols. for 1991-<1997 also numbered: 2-<6 No. issues published in 1994 or 1995. 15-17 Jan. 1990- Current Frequency: Annual Cancel/Invalid LCCN: sn 93037115 Notes: SERBIB/SERLOC merged record Subjects: Solid-state lasers--Congresses. Series: Proceedings of SPIE--the International Society for Optical Engineering. Variant Series: Proceedings / SPI

Solid state lasers and nonlinear crystals / sponsored and published by SPIE--the

International Society for Optical Engineering. Published/Created: Bellingham, Wash.: SPIE, c1995- Related Authors: Society of Photo-optical Instrumentation Engineers. Description: v.: ill.; 28 cm. 5-7 Feb. 1995- Current Frequency: Annual ISSN: 1083-3358 Notes: SERBIB/SERLOC merged record Subjects: Solid-state lasers--Congresses. Crystals--Congresses. Nonlinear optics--Congresses. Series: Proceedings of SPIE--the International Society for Optical Engineering. Variant Series: Proceedings / SPIE--the International Society for Optical Engineering LC Classification: TA1671 .S65 Dewey Class No.: 621.36/61/05 20

Solid state lasers IX: 25-26 January, 2000, San Jose, California / Richard Scheps, chair/editor; sponsored and published by SPIE--the International Society for Optical Engineering. Published/Created: Bellingham, Washington: SPIE, c2000. Related Authors: Scheps, Richard, 1946- Society of Photo-optical Instrumentation Engineers. Description: ix, 354 p.: ill.; 28 cm. ISBN: 0819435465 Notes: Includes bibliographic references and author index. Subjects: Solid-state lasers--Congresses. Series: Proceedings of SPIE--the International Society for Optical Engineering; v. 3929. Variant Series: SPIE proceedings series; v. 3929

Summaries of papers presented at the Conference on Lasers and Electro-optics. Edition Information: Conference ed. Published/Created: Washington, DC: Optical Society of America, c1988- Description: v.: ill.; 28 cm. [8th] (25-29 Apr. 1988)- Current Frequency: Annual Continues in part: Conference on Lasers and Electro-optics. Digest of technical papers (DLC) 87640834 (OCoLC)7601607 ISSN: 1054-0385 Cancel/Invalid LCCN: sn 89041476 95644381 Notes: Sponsored by the Lasers and Electro-optics Society and Optical Society of America in cooperation with the Quantum Electronics Division of the European Physical Society and Japanese Quantum Electronic Joint Group. SERBIB/SERLOC merged record Additional Form Avail.: Beginning with issue for 1997 also available by subscription, in PDF format, via the World Wide Web. Subjects: Lasers--Electrooptics--Optoelectronic devices--Congresses. Series: Technical digest series (Optical Society of America) (Conference ed.) Variant Series: Technical digest series LC Classification: TA1673 .C664c Dewey Class No.: 621.36/6 20

Svelto, Orazio. Principles of lasers / Orazio Svelto; translated from Italian and edited by David C. Hanna. Edition Information: 3rd ed. Published/Created: New York: Plenum, c1989. Related Authors: Hanna, D. C. (David C.), 1941- Description: xiii, 494 p.: ill.; 24 cm. ISBN: 0306429675 Notes: Translation of: Principi dei laser. Includes bibliographies and index. Subjects: Lasers. LC Classification: QC688 .S913 1989 Dewey Class No.: 535.5/8 19

Symposium B on Laser, Lamp, and Synchrotron Assisted Materials Surface Processing (1992: Strasbourg, France) Materials surface processing: proceedings of Symposium B on Laser, Lamp and Synchrotron Assisted Materials Surface Processing of the 1992 E-MRS Spring Conference, Strasbourg, France, June 2-5 1992 / edited by M. Stuke, E.E. Marinero, I. Nishiyama. Published/Created: Amsterdam; New York: North-Holland, 1993. Related Authors: Stuke, M. (Michael) Marinero, Ernesto E. Nishiyama, Isao. Description: xiv, 450 p.: ill.; 28 cm. ISBN: 0444899065 Notes: "Reprinted from Applied surface science 69"--T.p. verso. Includes bibliographical references and indexes. Subjects: Surfaces (Technology)--Congresses. Lasers--Industrial applications--Congresses. Plasma etching--Congresses. Synchrotron radiation--Congresses. Series: European Materials Research Society symposia proceedings; v. 32 LC Classification: TA418.7 .S947 1992 Dewey Class No.: 620/.44 20

Symposium B on Photon-Assisted Processing of Surfaces and Thin Films (1994: Strasbourg, France) Photon-assisted processing of surfaces and thin films: proceedings of Symposium B on Photon-Assisted Processing of Surfaces and Thin Films of the 1994 E-MRS Spring Conference, Strasbourg, France, May 24-27, 1994 / edited by J. Dieleman, U.K.P. Biermann, P. Hess. Published/Created: Amsterdam; New York: Elsevier, 1995. Related Authors: Dieleman, J. Biermann, U. K. P. (Udo K. P.) Hess, P. (Peter) Description: xvi, 632 p.: ill.; 27 cm. ISBN: 0444821627 (acid-free paper) Notes: "Reprinted from Applied surface science 86 (1-4)"--T.p. verso. Includes bibliographical references and indexes. Subjects: Surfaces (Technology)--Lasers--Industrial applications--Photon beams--Industrial applications--Plasma etching--Plasma-enhanced chemical vapor deposition--Congresses. Series: European Materials Research Society symposia proceedings; v. 47 LC Classification: TA418.7 .S948 1994 Dewey Class No.: 620/.44 20

Symposium E on Laser Surface Processing and Characterization (1991: Strasbourg, France) Laser surface processing and characterization: proceedings of Symposium E on Laser Surface Processing and Characterization of the 1991 E-MRS Spring Conference, Strasbourg, France, May 28-31, 1991 / edited by I.W. Boyd. Published/Created: Amsterdam; New York: North-Holland, 1992. Related Authors: Boyd, Ian W., 1958- Description: xv, 535 p.: ill.; 28 cm. ISBN: 0444894195 Notes: Includes bibliographical references and indexes. Subjects: Thin films--Surfaces--Congresses. Photochemistry--Congresses. Lasers in physics--Congresses. Series: European Materials Research Society symposia proceedings; v. 24 LC Classification: QC176.84.S93 S96 1991 Dewey Class No.: 620/.44 20

Symposium E on Surface Processing and Laser Assisted Chemistry (1990: Strasbourg, France) Surface processing and laser assisted chemistry: proceedings of Symposium E on Surface Processing and Laser Assisted Chemistry of the 1990 E-MRS spring conference, Strasbourg, France, 29 May-1 June 1990 / edited by I.W. Boyd, E. Fogarassy, M. Stuke. Published/Created: Amsterdam; New York: North-Holland; New York, NY, USA: Sole distributors for the USA and Canada, Elsevier Science Pub. Co., 1990. Related Authors: Boyd, Ian W., 1958- Fogarassy, E. (Eric) Stuke, M. (Michael) Description: xv, 476 p.: ill.; 28 cm. ISBN: 0444889477 (alk. paper) Notes: Includes bibliographical references and indexes. Subjects: Surfaces (Technology)--Congresses. Lasers in chemistry--Congresses. Series: European Materials Research Society symposia proceedings; v. 18 LC Classification: TA418.7 .S955 1990 Dewey Class No.: 620/.44 20

Symposium G on Surface Processing: Laser, Lamp, Plasma (1998: Strasbourg, France) Surface processing: laser, lamp, plasma: proceedings of Symposium G on Surface Processing: Laser, Lamp, Plasma of the E-MRS Spring Conference, Strasbourg, France, 16-19 June 1998 / edited by I.W. Boyd, J. Perrière, M. Stuke. Published/Created: Amsterdam; New York: Elsevier, 1999. Related Authors: Boyd, Ian W., 1958- Perrière, J. (Jacques) Stuke, M. (Michael) European Materials Research Society. Meeting (1998: Strasbourg, France) Description: xiv, 658 p.: ill.; 29 cm. ISBN: 0080436102 Notes: "Reprinted from Applied surface science, vol. 138-139".--T.p. verso. Includes bibliographical references. Subjects: Surfaces (Technology)--Effect of radiation on--Congresses. Lasers--Industrial applications--Congresses. Sputtering (Physics)--Congresses. Laser ablation--Congresses. Series: European Materials Research Society symposia proceedings; v. 82 LC Classification: TA418.7 .S956 1998 Dewey Class No.: 620/.44 21

Symposium H on Laser Processing of Surfaces and Thin Films (1996: Strasbourg, France) Laser processing of surfaces and thin films: proceedings of Symposium H on Laser Processing of Surfaces and Thin Films of the 1996 E-MRS Spring Conference, Strasbourg, France, June 4-7, 1996 / edited by C.N. Afonso, E. Matthias, T. Szörényi.

Published/Created: Amsterdam; New York: Elsevier, c1997. Related Authors: Afonso, C. N. (Carmen N.) Matthias, E. (Eckart) Szörényi, T. (Tamás) Description: xvi, 654 p.: ill.; 26 cm. ISBN: 0444205055 Notes: "Reprinted from Applied surface science, vols. 109 and 110 (1997)"--T.p. verso. Includes bibliographical references and indexes. Subjects: Lasers--Industrial applications--Congresses. Thin films--Congresses. Surfaces (Technology)--Congresses. Series: European Materials Research Society symposia proceedings; v. 64 LC Classification: TA1673 .S94 1996 Dewey Class No.: 621.36/6 21

Symposium on Advanced Photon Research (1st: 1999: Kyoto, Japan) Proceedings of the First Symposium on Advanced Photon Research: November 8-9, 1999, Keihanna Plaza, Advanced Photo Research Center, Kyoto, Japan / Kansai Research Establishment, Japan Atomic Energy Research Institute. Published/Created: Tokai-mura, Naka-gun, Ibaraki-ken, Japan: Japan Atomic Energy Research Institute, c2000. Related Authors: Nihon Genshiryoku Kenky¯ujo. Description: xix, 339 p., [1] leaf of plates: ill. (some col.); 30 cm. Notes: "(Received February 9, 2000)." "March 2000"--Cover. "JAERI-Conf 2000-0006." Includes bibliographical references. Text in English and Japanese. Subjects: Photons--Congresses. Laser beams--Congresses. Free electron lasers--Congresses. LC Classification: MLCM 2001/02487

Symposium on Laser Processes for Microelectronic Applications (1987: Honolulu, Hawaii) Proceedings of the Symposium on Laser Processes for Microelectronic Applications / edited by J.J. Ritsko, D.J. Ehrlich, M. Kashiwagi. Published/Created: Pennington, NJ (10 S. Main St., Pennington 08534-2896): Electrochemical Society, c1988. Related Authors: Ritsko, J. J. Ehrlich, Daniel J. Kashiwagi, M. Electrochemical Society. Dielectrics and Insulation Division. Electrochemical Society. Electronics Division. Description: vii, 251 p.: ill.; 23 cm. Notes: Spine Title - Laser processes for microelectronic applications. "Dielectrics and Insulation and Electronics Divisions." Includes bibliographies and index. Subjects: Microelectronics--Congresses. Lasers--Industrial applications--Congresses. Series: Proceedings (Electrochemical Society); v. 88-10. Variant Series: Proceedings / Electrochemical Society; v. 88-10 LC Classification: TK7874 .S935 1987 Dewey Class No.: 621.381/7 19

Symposium on Optical Fiber Measurements (1992: Boulder, Colo.) Technical digest, Symposium on Optical Fiber Measurements, 1992: digest of a symposium sponsored by the National Institute of Standards and Technology in cooperation with the IEEE Lasers and Electro-optics Society and the Optical Society of America, September 15-17, 1992, National Institue of Standards and Technology, Boulder, Colorado / edited by G.W. Day, D.L. Franzen. Published/Created: Boulder, Colo.: NIST; Washington: For sale by the Supt. of Docs., U.S. G.P.O., [1992] Related Authors: Day, G. W. Franzen, Douglas L. National Institute of Standards and Technology (U.S.) Lasers and Electro-optics Society (Institute of Electrican and Electronics Engineers) Optical Society of America. Description: viii, 237 p.: ill.; 28 cm. Notes: "September 1992." Includes bibliographical references and index. Subjects: Optical fibers--Measurement--Congresses. Series: NIST special publication; 839 LC Classification: QC100 .U57 no. 839 TA1800 Dewey Class No.: 602/.18 s 621.382/75 20

Symposium on Optical Fiber Measurements (1994: Boulder, Colo.) Technical digest, Symposium on Optical Fiber Measurements, 1994: digest of a symposium sponsored by the National Institute of Standards and Technology in cooperation with the IEEE Lasers and Electro-optics Society and the Optical Society of America, September 13-15, 1994, National Institue of Standards and Technology, Boulder, Colorado / edited by G.W. Day, D.L. Franzen, R.K. Hickernell.

Published/Created: Boulder, Colo.: NIST; Washington: For sale by the Supt. of Docs., U.S. G.P.O., 1994. Related Authors: Day, G. W. Franzen, D. L. Hickernell, R. K. National Institute of Standards and Technology (U.S.) Lasers and Electro-optics Society (Institute of Electrican and Electronics Engineers) Optical Society of America. Description: viii, 219 p.: ill.; 28 cm. Notes: "September 1994." Includes bibliographical references and index. Subjects: Optical fibers--Measurement--Congresses. Series: NIST special publication; 864 LC Classification: QC100 .U57 no. 864 TA1800 Dewey Class No.: 602/.18 s 621.36/92/0287 20

Symposium on Optical Fiber Measurements (1996: Boulder, Colo.) Technical digest, Symposium on Optical Fiber Measurements, 1996: digest of symposium sponsored by the National Institute of Standards and Technology in cooperation with the IEEE Lasers and Electro-Optics Society and Optical Society of America / edited by G.W. Day, D.L. Franzen, P.A. Williams. Published/Created: Boulder, Colo.: U.S. Dept. of Commerce, National Institute of Standards and Technology, 1996. Related Authors: Day, G. W. Franzen, Douglas L. Williams, P. A. (Paul Andrew), 1965- National Institute of Standards and Technology (U.S.) Lasers and Electro-optics Society (Institute of Electrical and Electronics Engineers) Optical Society of America. Description: viii, 215 p.: ill.; 28 cm. Notes: "October 1996." Includes bibliographical references and index. Subjects: Optical fibers--Measurement--Congresses. Series: NIST special publication; 905 LC Classification: QC100 .U57 no. 905 TA1800 Dewey Class No.: 602/.18 s 621.36/92/0287 21

Symposium on Optoelectronics (6th: 1999: Bucharest, Romania) SIOEL '99: Sixth Symposium on Optoelectronics: 22-24 September 1999, Bucharest, Romania / Teodor Necsoiu, Maria Robu, Dan C. Dumitras, editors; sponsored by National Agency for Science, Technology and Innovation (Romania) ... [et al.]; organized by IOEL-SA--Institute of Optoelectronics (Romania) ... [et al.]. Published/Created: Bellingham, Wash., USA: SPIE, c2000. Related Authors: Necsoiu, Teodor. Robu, Maria. Dumitras, Dan C. Description: xvi, 846 p.: ill.; 28 cm. ISBN: 0819437050 Notes: Includes bibliographical references and index. Subjects: Optoelectronics--Materials--Lasers--Industrial applications--Laser materials--Optoelectronic devices--Design and construction Congresses. Series: Proceedings of SPIE--the International Society for Optical Engineering; v. 4068. Variant Series: SPIE proceedings series; v. 4068

Sympozjum Techniki Laserowej (3rd: 1990: ´Swinouj´scie, Poland) Abstracts: III-rd Symposium on Laser Technology / [editors, Wieslaw Woli´nski, Bohdan Wolczak, Danuta Gajda]. Published/Created: [Szczecin: s.n.], 1990. Related Authors: Woli´nski, Wieslaw. Wolczak, Bohdan. Gajda, Danuta Description: 138 p.; 24 cm. Notes: At head of Title - Polish Academy of Sciences. Electronics and Telecommunication Committee ... Includes bibliographical references and index. Subjects: Lasers--Congresses. LC Classification: TA1673 .S97 1990 Dewey Class No.: 621.36/6 20

Sympozjum Techniki Laserowej (4th: 1993: Szczecin, Poland and ´Swinouj´scie, Poland) Abstracts: IV-th Symposium on Laser Technology, 26-30 September 1993, Szczecin-´Swinouj´scie / [editors, Danuta Gajda ... et al.]. Published/Created: [Szczecin: s.n., 1993] Related Authors: Gajda, Danuta. escription: 124 p.: ill.; 24 cm. Notes: At head of Title - Polish Academy of Sciences, Committee of Electronics and Telecommunications ... Includes bibliographical references and index. Subjects: Lasers--Industrial applications--Congresses. LC Classification: TA1677 .S96 1993b Dewey Class No.: 621.36/6 20

Takahashi, N. Shinichi, 1949- A bibliography of doctoral theses on semiconductor lasers / compiled by N. Shinichi Takahashi. Published/Created: Yokohama, Japan: Keio University, c1994. Description: xxvi,

175 p.: ill.; 26 cm. Notes: Includes bibliographical references (p. x-xiv) and index. Subjects: Semiconductor lasers--Dissertations, Academic--Bibliography. LC Classification: QC689.55.S45 T35 1994 Z5838.L3 Dewey Class No.: 016.62136/6 20

Tang, C. L. (Chung Liang), 1934- Fundamentals of optical parametric processes and oscillators / C.L. Tang and L.K. Cheng. Published/Created: Amsterdam: Harwood Academic Publishers, c1995. Related Authors: Cheng, L. K. (Lap Kin), 1960- Description: vii, 130 p.: ill. (1 col.); 23 cm. ISBN: 3718658186 (pbk.) Notes: Includes bibliographical references and index. Subjects: Tunable lasers. Parametric devices. Optical amplifiers. Crystal optics. Parametrons. Series: Laser science and technology, 0899-2711; v. 20 LC Classification: TA1706 .T36 1995 Dewey Class No.: 621.36/6 21

Taylor, Barbara, 1954- Light / Barbara Taylor. Published/Created: New York: Gloucester, 1992. Description: 32 p.: ill. (some col.), map; 30 cm. ISBN: 053117381X Summary: Explores the properties and phenomena of light and examines such topics as rainbows and lasers. Includes art projects and language activities. Notes: Includes index. Subjects: Light--Juvenile literature. Light. Series: Focus on (New York, N.Y.) Variant Series: Focus on LC Classification: QC360 .T375 1992 Dewey Class No.: 535 20

Taylor, Nick, 1945- Laser: the inventor, the Nobel laureate, the thirty-year patent war / Nick Taylor. Published/Created: New York: Simon & Schuster, c2000. Description: 304 p.: ill.; 25 cm. ISBN: 0684835150 Notes: Includes index. Subjects: Gould, Gordon, 1920- Physicists--United States--Biography. LC Classification: QC16.G63 T39 2000 Dewey Class No.: 621.36/6/092 B 21

The "Delfin" laser-thermonuclear installation: operational complex and future directions / edited by G.V. Sklizkov; translated by Kevin S. Hendzel. Published/Created: Commack, N.Y.: Nova Science Publishers, c1988. Related Authors: Sklizkov, G. V. Description: viii, 292 p.: ill.; 25 cm. ISBN: 0941743225 Notes: Translation of: Lazernaia termoiadernaia ustanovka "Del′fin"--deistvuiushchii kompleks i napravleniia razvitiia. Includes bibliographies and index. Subjects: Lasers. Laser-plasma interactions. Series: Trudy Fizicheskogo instituta. English; v. 178. Variant Series: Proceedings of the Lebedev Physics Institute, Academy of Sciences of the USSR, 0568-5508; v. 178 LC Classification: QC1 .A4114 vol. 178 QC685 Dewey Class No.: 530 s 535.5/8 19

The Authorized collection of holusion art: how and why it works. Published/Created: Irving, Tex.: NVision Grafix, c1994. Related Authors: NVision Grafix. Description: 36 p.: col. ill.; 32 cm. ISBN: 0964092301 Subjects: Lasers in art. Art and holography. Optical illusions. LC Classification: N6494.L3 A9 1994 Dewey Class No.: 760 20

The CO2 laser in otolaryngology and head to neck surgery / editors, V.H. Oswal, H.K. Kashima, L.M. Flood. Published/Created: London; Boston: Wright, 1988. Related Authors: Oswal, V. H. Kashima, H. K. Flood, L. M. Description: xxi, 200 p.: ill.; 24 cm. ISBN: 0723605874: Notes: Includes bibliographies and index. Subjects: Lasers in otolaryngology. Head--Surgery. Neck--Surgery. Carbon dioxide lasers--Therapeutic use. LC Classification: RF51.5 .C63 1988 Dewey Class No.: 617/.51059 20

The French-Israeli Workshop on Apatites and Lasers: November 25-26, 1996, Jerusalem International Convention Center, Jerusalem, Israel: Scientific program and workshop abstracts. Published/Created: Jerusalem: Ministry of Science, State of Israel; Ministry of Foreign Affairs, Republic of France, [199]6. Description: 1 v. LC Classification: IN PROCESS

The Industrial laser handbook. Published/Created: New York: Springer-

Verlag, c1992- Description: v.: ill.; 29 cm. 1992-1993 ed.- Current Frequency: Biennial Continues: Industrial laser annual handbook 0886-0106 (OCoLC)12790114 (DLC) 82640984 ISSN: 0941-4185 Notes: SERBIB/SERLOC merged record Subjects: Lasers--Industrial applications--Periodicals. Laser industry--Directories. LC Classification: TA1671 .I53 Dewey Class No.: 621.366/05 19

The Laser focus world report on the U.S. government laser and electro-optics market: a review and forecast of federal lightwave technology programs and budgets. Published/Created: Westford, MA: PennWell Pub., c1990- Related Authors: Foresight Science and Technology, Inc. Description: v.; 28 cm. First vol. lacks designation. [No. 1]- Current Frequency: Biennial ISSN: 1061-4907 Notes: "A Laser focus world/PennWell publication." Published in conjunction with Foresight Science and Technology, Inc. SERBIB/SERLOC merged record Subjects: Government purchasing--Public contracts--United States--Directories. Lasers--United States--Periodicals. Optoelectronic devices--Laser industry--Optoelectronics industry--Periodicals. LC Classification: JK1677.L37 L37 Dewey Class No.: 353.0071/2/025 20

The Physics and technology of laser resonators / edited by D.R. Hall and P.E. Jackson. Published/Created: Bristol; New York: A. Hilger, c1989. Related Authors: Hall, D. R. (Denis R.) Jackson, P. E. (Paul E.) Description: xiv, 253 p.: ill.; 24 cm. ISBN: 0852741170 Nsotes: Includes bibliographical references and index. Subjects: Lasers. Lasers--Resonators. LC Classification: QC688 .P479 1989 Dewey Class No.: 621.36/6 20

Thomas, Jens. The noble gases / by Jens Thomas. Published/Created: Tarrytown, N.Y.: Benchmark Books, c2003. Projected Pub. Date: 0204 Description: v. cm. ISBN: 0761414622 Notes: Includes index. 1. What are the noble gases? -- 2. Where are the noble gases found? -- 3. How were the noble gases discovered? -- 4. How do we get hold of the noble gases? -- 5. Special characteristics -- 6. How do the noble gases react? -- 7. Liquid helium -- 8. Lighting up our lives -- 9. Lasers -- 10. Unreactive atmospheres -- 11. Helium underwater -- 12. Radon in medicine -- 13. Chemical reactions. Subjects: Gases, Rare--Juvenile literature. Gases, Rare. Series: Elements (Benchmark Books) Variant Series: The elements LC Classification: QD162 .T48 2003 Dewey Class No.: 546/.75 21

Tillman, Dick, 1936- Laser sailing for the 1990s / Dick Tillman; with foreword by Bruce Kirby. Published/Created: Camden, Me.: International Marine Pub., c1991. Related Authors: Tillman, Dick, 1936- New laser sailing. Description: xv, 175 p.: ill.; 23 cm. ISBN: 087742294X: Notes: Rev. ed. of: The new laser sailing / Dick Tillman and Dave Powlison. c1983. Subjects: Sailing. Lasers (Sailboats) LC Classification: GV811 .T535 1991 Dewey Class No.: 797.1/24 20

Tillman, Dick, 1936- The complete book of laser sailing / Dick Tillman. Published/Created: Camden, Me.: International Marine/McGraw-Hill, c2000. Related Authors: Tillman, Dick, 1936-. Laser sailing for the 1990s. Description: x, 150 p.: ill.; 24 cm. ISBN: 0071357882 (alk. paper) Notes: Rev. ed. of: Laser sailing for the 1990s. c1991. Includes index. Subjects: Sailing. Lasers (Sailboats) LC Classification: GV811 .T535 2000 Dewey Class No.: 797.1/24 21

Topical Meeting on Advanced Solid State Lasers (1998: Coeur d'Alene, Idaho) Advanced solid state lasers: from the Topical Meeting [sic] Advanced Solid State Lasers, February 2-4, 1998, Coeur d'Alene, Idaho / edited by Walter R. Bosenberg, Martin M. Fejer; sponsored by Optical Society of America; technical co-sponsor, IEEE/Lasers and Electro-Optics Society. Published/Created: Washington, DC: Optical Society of America, c1998. Related Authors: Bosenberg, Walter R. Fejer, Martin Michael. Optical Society of America. Lasers and Electro-optics Society

(Institute of Electrical and Electronics Engineers) Description: xv, 611 p.: ill. (some col.); 28 cm. ISBN: 1557525234 Notes: Includes bibliographical references and indexes. Subjects: Solid-state lasers--Congresses. Series: OSA trends in optics and photonics; v. 19. Variant Series: Trends in optics and photonics series, 1094-5695; vol. 19 LC Classification: TA1705 .T67 1998 Dewey Class No.: 621.36/61 21

Topical Meeting on Advanced Solid-State Lasers (1999: Boston, Mass.) Advanced solid-state lasers: from the Topical Meeting, January 31-February 3, 1999, Boston, Massachusetts / edited by Martin M. Fejer, Hagop Injeyan, and Ursula Keller; sponsored by Optical Society of America; technical co-sponsor, IEEE/Lasers and Electro-Optics Society. Published/Created: Washington, DC: Optical Society of America, c1999. Related Authors: Fejer, Martin M. (Martin Michael) Injeyan, Hagop, 1952- Keller, Ursula. Optical Society of America. Lasers and Electro-optics Society (Institute of Electrical and Electronics Engineers) Description: xvi, 755 p.: ill.; 28 cm. ISBN: 1557525838 (tops: acid-free paper) Notes: Includes bibliographical references and index. Subjects: Solid-state lasers--Congresses. Series: OSA trends in optics and photonics; v. 26. Variant Series: Trends in optics and photonics series, 1094-5695; vol. 26 LC Classification: TA1705 .T67 1999 Dewey Class No.: 621.36/6 21

Topical Meeting on Integrated and Guided Wave Optics (1988: Santa Fe, N.M.) Integrated and guided-wave optics: summaries of papers presented at the Integrated and Guided-Wave Optics Topical Meeting, March 28-30, 1988, Santa Fe, New Mexico / cosponsored by Optical Society of America and Lasers and Electro-Optics Society of the Institute of Electrical and Electronics Engineers. Edition Information: Postconference ed. Published/Created: Washington, D.C.: OSA, c1988. Related Authors: Optical Society of America. Lasers and Electro-Optics Society (Institute of Electrical and Electronics Engineers) Description: xv, 428 p.: ill.; 28 cm. ISBN: 1557520305 Notes: Includes bibliographical references. Subjects: Integrated optics--Congresses. Optical wave guides--Congresses. Series: Technical digest series (Optical Society of America); 1988, v. 5. Variant Series: 1988 technical digest series; v. 5 LC Classification: TA1660 .T66 1988 Dewey Class No.: 621.36/93 20

Topical Meeting on Integrated and Guided Wave Optics (1989: Houston, Tex.) Integrated and guided-wave optics: summaries of papers presented at the Integrated and Guided-wave Optics Topical Meeting, February 6-8, 1989, Houston, Texas / cosponsored by Optical Society of America and Lasers and Electro-optics Society of the Institute of Electrical and Electronics Engineers. Edition Information: Postconference ed. Published/Created: Washington, D.C.: Optical Society of America, c1989. Related Authors: Optical Society of America. Lasers and Electro-optics Society (Institute of Electrical and Electronics Engineers) Description: ix, 293 p.: ill.; 29 cm. ISBN: 1557520712 Notes: Cover Title - Integrated & guided-wave optics. Includes bibliographical references. Subjects: Integrated optics--Congresses. Optical wave guides--Congresses. Lasers--Congresses. Optical communications--Congresses. Series: Technical digest series (Optical Society of America); 1989, v. 4. Variant Series: 1989 technical digest series; v. 4 LC Classification: TA1660 .T66 1989 Dewey Class No.: 621.36/93 20

Topical Meeting on Laser Applications to Chemical Analysis (1990: Incline Village, Nev.) Laser applications to chemical analysis: summaries of papers presented at the Laser Applications to Chemical Analysis Topical Meeting, February 5-8, 1990, Incline Village, Nevada / cosponsored by the Air Force Office of Scientific Research ... [et al.]. Edition Information: Postconference ed. Published/Created: Washington, DC: Optical Society of America, c1990.

Description: x, 159 p.: ill.; 29 cm. ISBN: 1557521158 (hardcover) Notes: Includes bibliographical references. Subjects: Laser spectroscopy--Congresses. Lasers in chemistry--Congresses. Series: Technical digest series (Optical Society of America); 1990, v. 2. Variant Series: 1990 technical digest series; v. 2 LC Classification: QD96.L3 T66 1990a Dewey Class No.: 543/.0858 20

Topical Meeting on Laser Applications to Chemical Analysis (1990: Incline Village, Nev.) Laser applications to chemical analysis: summaries of papers presented at the Laser Applications to Chemical Analysis Topical Meeting, February 5-8, 1990, Incline Village, Nevada / cosponsored by the Air Force Office of Scientific Research ... [et al.]. Edition Information: Conference ed. Published/Created: Washington, D.C.: Optical Society of America, c1990. Related Authors: United States. Air Force. Office of Scientific Research. Description: x, 142 p.: ill.; 28 cm. ISBN: 155752114X (softcover) 1557521158 (hardcover: Postconference ed., includes Postdeadline papers) Notes: "Postdeadline papers" (p. 144-159) inserted. Includes bibliographical references and index. Subjects: Laser spectroscopy--Congresses. Lasers in chemistry--Congresses. Series: Technical digest series (Optical Society of America); 1990, v. 2. Variant Series: 1990 technical digest series; v. 2 LC Classification: QD96.L3 T66 1990 Dewey Class No.: 543/.0858 20

Topical Meeting on Laser Applications to Chemical Analysis (1992: Salt Lake City, Utah) Laser applications to chemical analysis: summaries of papers presented at the Laser Applications to Chemical Analysis Topical Meeting, January 27-30, 1992, Salt Lake City, Utah / sponsored by Optical Society of America. Edition Information: Postconference ed. Published/Created: Washington, DC: The Society, c1992. Description: ix, 185 p.: ill.; 28 cm. ISBN: 1557522146 Notes: Includes bibliographical references and indexes. Subjects: Laser spectroscopy--Congresses. Lasers in chemistry--Congresses. Series: Technical digest series (Optical Society of America); 1992, v. 2. Variant Series: 1992 technical digest series; v. 3 [i.e. v. 2] LC Classification: QD96.L3 T66 1992 Dewey Class No.: 543/.0858 20

Topical Meeting on Laser Applications to Chemical Analysis (1994: Jackson Hole, Wyo.) Laser applications to chemical analysis: summaries of papers presented at the Laser Applications to Chemical Analysis Topical Meeting, March 8-11, 1994, Jackson Hole, Wyoming / sponsored by Optical Society of America. Edition Information: Postconference ed. Published/Created: Washington, DC: The Society, c1994. Description: xi, 274 p.: ill.; 28 cm. ISBN: 1557523339 Notes: Includes bibliographical references. Subjects: Laser spectroscopy--Congresses. Lasers in chemistry--Congresses. Series: Technical digest series (Optical Society of America); 1994, v. 5. Variant Series: 1994 technical digest series: v. 5 LC Classification: QD96.L3 T66 1994 Dewey Class No.: 543/.0858 20

Topical Meeting on Optical Data Storage (13th: 1997: Tucson, Ariz.) 1997 Optical Data Storage Topical Meeting: conference digest, 7-9 April 1997, Omni Tucson National Golf Resort & Spa, Tucson, Arizona, USA / sponsored by IEEE/Lasers and Electro-Optics Society, Optical Society of America, SPIE, the International Society for Optical Engineering. Published/Created: [New York]: Institute of Electrical and Electronics Engineers, c1997. Related Authors: Lasers and Electro-optics Society (Institute of Electrical and Electronics Engineers) Optical Society of America. Society of Photo-optical Instrumentation Engineers. Description: vii, 109 p.: ill.; 28 cm. ISBN: 0780338855 (softbound) 0780338863 (microfiche) Notes: "IEEE catalog number: 97TH8273." Includes bibliographical references and index. Subjects: Optical storage devices--Congresses. LC Classification: TA1635 .T66 1997 Dewey Class No.: 621.39/767 21

Topical Meeting on Optical Data Storage (13th: 1997: Tucson, Ariz.) Optical Data Storage'97: 7-9 April, 1997, Tucson, Arizona / Henryk Birecki, James Z. Kwiecien, chairs/editors; sponsored by IEEE/Lasers and Electro-Optics Society; cosponsored by OSA--Optical Society of America, SPIE--the International Society for Optical Engineering; published by SPIE--the International Society for Optical Engineering. Published/Created: Bellingham, Washington: SPIE, c1997. Related Authors: Birecki, Henryk. Kwiecien, James Z. Society of Photo-optical Instrumentation Engineers. Optical Society of America. Lasers and Electro-Optics Society (Institute of Electrical and Electronics Engineers) Description: ix, 252 p.: ill.; 28 cm. ISBN: 0819425303 Notes: "Thirteenth Topical Meeting on Optical Data Storage was held 7-9 April 1997"--P. ix. Includes bibliographic references and author index. Subjects: Optical storage devices--Computer storage devices--Magnetooptical devices--Congresses. Series: Proceedings of SPIE--the International Society for Optical Engineering; v. 3109. Variant Series: Proceedings / SPIE--the International Society for Optical Engineering; v. 3109 LC Classification: TA1635 .T66 1997b Dewey Class No.: 621.39/767 21

Topical Meeting on Optical Data Storage (14th: 1998: Aspen, Colo.) Optical Data Storage '98: 10-13 May, 1998, Aspen, Colorado / Shigeo Kubota, Tom D. Milster, Paul J. Wehrenberg, chairs/editors; sponsored by OSA--Optical Society of America; cosponsored by IEEE/Lasers and Electro-Optics Society, SPIE--the International Society for Optical Engineering; published by SPIE--the International Society for Optical Engineering. Published/Created: Bellingham, Washington: SPIE, c1998. Related Authors: Kubota, Shigeo. Milster, Tom D. Wehrenberg, Paul J. Society of Photo-optical Instrumentation Engineers. Optical Society of America. Lasers and Electro-Optics Society (Institute of Electrical and Electronics Engineers) Description: ix, 292 p.: ill.; 28 cm. ISBN: 0819428515 Notes: Includes bibliographical references and author index. Subjects: Computer storage devices--Congresses. Optical storage devices--Congresses. Magnetooptical devices--Congresses. Series: Proceedings of SPIE--the International Society for Optical Engineering; v. 3401. Variant Series: Proceedings / SPIE--the International Society for Optical Engineering; v. 3401 LC Classification: TK7895.M4 T59 1998 Dewey Class No.: 621.39/767 21

Topical Meeting on Optical Data Storage (1989: Los Angeles, Calif.) Optical data storage: summaries of papers presented at the Optical Data Storage Topical Meeting, January 17-19, 1989, Los Angeles California / sponsored by Lasers and Electro-optics Society of IEEE, Optical Society of America, SPIE, the International Society for Optical Engineering. Edition Information: Postconference ed. Published/Created: Washington, D.C.: Optical Society of America, 1989. Related Authors: Optical Society of America. Description: ix, 205 p.: ill.; 29 cm. ISBN: 1557520658 Notes: Includes bibliographical references. Subjects: Optical storage devices--Congresses. Series: Technical digest series (Optical Society of America); 1989, v. 1. Variant Series: Technical digest series; 1989, v. 1 LC Classification: TA1635 .T66 1989 Dewey Class No.: 621.39/767 20

Topical Meeting on Optical Data Storage (1989: Los Angeles, Calif.) Optical Data Storage Topical Meeting: 17-19 January 1989, Los Angeles, California / Gordon R. Knight, Clark N. Kurtz, chairs/editors; cosponsored by OSA--Optical Society of America, SPIE--the International Society for Optical Engineering, LEOS/IEEE--Lasers and Electro-Optics Society of IEEE. Published/Created: Bellingham, Wash., USA: The Society, c1989. Related Authors: Knight, Gordon R. Kurtz, Clark N. Optical Society of America. Society of Photo-optical Instrumentation Engineers. Lasers and Electro-optics Society (Institute of Electrical and Electronics Engineers) Description: viii, 338 p.: ill.; 28 cm. ISBN:

0819401137 (pbk.) Notes: Includes bibliographical references. Subjects: Optical storage devices--Congresses. Series: Proceedings of SPIE--the International Society for Optical Engineering; v. 1078 LC Classification: TA1635 .T66 1989a Dewey Class No.: 621.39/767 20

Topical Meeting on Optical Data Storage (1991: Colorado Springs, Colo.) Optical Data Storage Topical Meeting: summaries of papers / presented at the Optical Data Storage Topical Meeting, February 25-27, 1991, Colorado Springs, Colorado; cosponsored by Optical Society of America, SPIE-the International Society for Optical Engineering, IEEE/Lasers and Electro-optics Society. Edition Information: Postconference ed. Published/Created: Washington, DC: Optical Society of America, c1991. Related Authors: Optical Society of America. Society of Photo-optical Instrumentation Engineers. Lasers and Electro-optics Society (Institute of Electrical and Electronics Engineers) Description: x, 259 p.: ill.; 29 cm. ISBN: 1557521697 (hardcover) 1557521689 (conference ed.: softcover) Notes: Cover Title - Optical data storage. Includes bibliographical references and index. Subjects: Optical storage devices--Congresses. Series: Technical digest series (Optical Society of America); 1991, v. 5. Variant Series: 1991 technical digest series; v. 5 LC Classification: TA1635 .T66 1991 Dewey Class No.: 621.39/767 20

Topical Meeting on Optical Data Storage (1994: Dana Point, Calif.) 1994 Topical Meeting on Optical Data Storage: 16-18 May 1994, Dana Point, California / David K. Campbell, Martin Chen, Koichi Ogawa, chairs/editors; sponsored by Optical Society of America; cosponsored by SPIE--the International Society for Optical Engineering, IEEE/Lasers and Electro-Optics Society. Published/Created: Bellingham, Wash.: SPIE--the International Society for Optical Engineering, c1994. Related Authors: Campbell, David K. Chen, M. (Martin) Ogawa, K¯oichi. Optical Society of America. Society of Photo-optical Instrumentation Engineers. Lasers and Electro-optics Society (Institute of Electrical and Electronics Engineers) Description: ix, 378 p.: ill.; 28 cm. ISBN: 0819416711 Notes: Includes bibliographical references and index. Subjects: Optical storage devices--Congresses. Series: Proceedings of SPIE--the International Society for Optical Engineering; v. 2338. Variant Series: Proceedings / SPIE--the International Society for Optical Engineering; v. 2338 LC Classification: TA1635 .T66 1994b Dewey Class No.: 621.39/767 20

Topical Meeting on Optical Data Storage (1994: Dana Point, Calif.) Optical data storage: summaries of papers presented at the Optical Data Storage Topical Meeting, May, 16-18, 1994, Dana Point, California / sponsored by Optical Society of America; cosponsored by SPIE--the International Society for Optical Engineering, IEEE/Lasers and Electo-optics Society. Edition Information: Postconference ed. Published/Created: Washington, DC: Optical Society of America, c1994. Related Authors: Optical Society of America. Society of Photo-optical Instrumentation Engineers. Lasers and Electro-optics Society (Institute of Electrical and Electronics Engineers) Description: xi, 186 p.: ill.; 28 cm. ISBN: 1557523452 Notes: Includes bibliographical references and index. Subjects: Optical storage devices--Congresses. Series: Technical digest series (Optical Society of America); 1994, v. 10. Variant Series: Technical digest series; 1994, v. 10 LC Classification: TA1635 .T66 1994 Dewey Class No.: 621.39/76 20

Topical Meeting on Optical Fiber Communication (2000: Baltimore, Md.) Optical Fiber Communication Conference, March 7-10, 2000, Baltimore Convention Center, Baltimore, Maryland / sponsored by IEEE/Communications Society, IEEE/Lasers and Electro-Optics Society, Optical Society of America. Edition

Information: Postconference ed. Published/Created: Washington, DC: Optical Society of America, c2000. Description: 4 v.: ill.; 28 cm. ISBN: 1557526303 Contents: v. 1. Presentations from Tuesday, March 7, 2000 -- v. 2. Presentations from Wednesday, March 8, 2000 -- v. 3. Presentations from Thursday, March 9, 2000 -- v. 4. Presentations from Friday, March 10, 2000 plus OFC postdeadline papers. Notes: Includes bibliographical references and index. Subjects: Fiber optics--Congresses. Optical communications--Congresses. Integrated optics--Congresses. Series: OSA trends in optics and photonics; v. 37 LC Classification: TA1800 .T67 2000 Dewey Class No.: 621.382/75 21

Topical Meeting on Ultrafast Electronics and Optoelectronics (1999: Snowmass, Colo.) Ultrafast electronics and optoelectronics: from the Topical Meeting on Ultrafast Electronics and Optoelectronics, April 14-16, 1999, Snowmass, Colorado / edited by John E. Bowers, Wayne H. Knox; sponsored by Optical Society of America; technically cosponsored by IEEE/Lasers and Electro-Optics Society. Published/Created: Washington, DC: Optical Society of America, c1999. Related Authors: Bowers, John E. Knox, Wayne H. (Wayne Harvey), 1957- Optical Society of America. Lasers and Electro-optics Society (Institute of Electrical and Electronics Engineers) Description: x, 240 p.: ill.; 28 cm. ISBN: 1557526044 Notes: Includes bibliographical references (p. 220-236) and indexes. Subjects: Optical communications--Congresses. Pulse techniques (Electronics)--Congresses. Optoelectronics--Congresses. Picosecond pulses--Congresses. Semiconductors--Congresses. Laser pulses, Ultrashort--Congresses. Quantum electronics--Congresses. Series: OSA trends in optics and photonics; v. 28. Variant Series: OSA trends in optics and photonics series; v. 28 LC Classification: TK5103.59 .T664 1999 Dewey Class No.: 621.381 21

Topical Symposium on Combined Optical-microwave Earth and Atmosphere Sensing (1993: Albuquerque, N.M.) Topical Symposium on Combined Optical-microwave Earth and Atmosphere Sensing: conference proceedings, March 22-25, 1993, Albuquerque, NM / sponsored by the IEEE Geoscience and Remote Sensing Society, the IEEE Lasers and Electro-Optics Society, and the IEEE Microwave Theory and Techniques Society. Published/Created: Piscataway, NJ: Institute of Electrical and Electronics Engineers, 1993. Related Authors: IEEE Geoscience and Remote Sensing Society. Lasers and Electro-optics Society (Institute of Electrical and Electronics Engineers) IEEE Microwave Theory and Techniques Society. Description: viii, 261 p.: ill.; 28 cm. ISBN: 0780309693 (pbk.) 0780309707 (microfiche ed.) Subjects: Remote sensing--Congresses. LC Classification: G70.39 .T67 1993

Topical Symposium on Combined Optical-microwave Earth and Atmosphere Sensing (2nd: 1995: Atlanta, Ga.) Conference proceedings Second Topical Symposium on Combined Optical-microwave Earth and Atmosphere Sensing: April 3-6, 1995, Atlanta Renaissance Hotel, Atlanta, GA / co-sponsored by the IEEE Lasers and Electro-Optics Society, the IEEE Geoscience and Remote Sensing Society, and the IEEE Microwave Theory and Techniques Society. Published/Created: Piscataway, NJ: Institute of Electrical and Electronics Engineers, c1995. Related Authors: Lasers and Electro-optics Society (Institute of Electrical and Electronics Engineers) IEEE Geoscience and Remote Sensing Society. IEEE Microwave Theory and Techniques Society. United States. National Aeronautics and Space Administration. Description: x, 230 p.: ill.; 28 cm. ISBN: 0780324021 (softbound) 078032403X microfiche) Notes: Support provided by the National Aeronautics and Space Administration ... et al. "IEEE catalog number 95TH8015"--T.p. verso. Includes bibliographical references and index. Subjects: Remote sensing--Congresses. LC Classification: G70.39 .T67 1995 Dewey Class No.: 621.36/78 21

Townes, Charles H. How the laser happened: adventures of a scientist / Charles H. Townes. Published/Created: New York: Oxford University Press, 1999. Description: 200 p.: ill.; 25 cm. ISBN: 0195122682 (alk. paper) Notes: Includes index. Subjects: Lasers--History. Masers--History. Science and state--United States--History. LC Classification: QC687.2 .T68 1999 Dewey Class No.: 621.36/6/09 21

Tropical College on Applied Physics (3rd: 1988: Kuala Lumpur, Malaysia) Laser and plasma technology: third Tropical College on Applied Physics, 30th May-18th June 1988, University of Malaya, Kuala Lumpur, Malaysia / editors, C.S. Wong ... [et al.]. Published/Created: Singapore; New Jersey: World Scientific, 1990. Related Authors: Wong, C. S. Description: ix, 498 p.: ill.; 23 cm. ISBN: 9810201680 Notes: Includes bibliographical references. Subjects: Lasers--Congresses. Plasma devices--Congresses. LC Classification: TA1673 .T76 1988 Dewey Class No.: 621.48/4 20

Turcu, I. C. E. X-rays from laser plasmas: generation and applications / I.C.E. Turcu and J.B. Dance. Published/Created: Chichester; New York: Wiley, c1999. Related Authors: Dance, J. B. Description: xviii, 312 p.: ill.; 26 cm. ISBN: 0471983977 (alk. paper) Notes: Includes bibliographical references and index. Subjects: X-rays. Excimer lasers. Laser beams. Laser plasmas. Grenz rays. LC Classification: QC481 .T87 1999 Dewey Class No.: 539.7/222 21

Udupa, D. V. The design, fabrication, and testing of an air spaced Fabry-Perot etalon for dye laser wavelength stabilization system [microform] / by D.V. Udupa, S. Thakur, and R.P. Shukla. Published/Created: Mumbai, India: Bhabha Atomic Research Centre, 1997. Description: ia-b, 12 p.: ill.; 29 cm. Notes: At head of Title - Government of India, Atomic Energy Commission. "BARC/1997/E/023." Includes bibliographical references (p. 5). Microfiche. New Delhi: Library of Congress Office; Washington, D.C.: Library of Congress Photoduplication Service, 1998. 1 microfiche. Master microform held by: DLC. Subjects: Fabry-Perot interferometers. Dye lasers. LC Classification: Microfiche 98/60435

Ultrafast electronics and optoelectronics: summaries of the papers presented at the topical meeting, March 13-15, 1995, Dana Point, California / sponsored by Optical Society of America; cosponsored by IEEE/Lasers and Electro-Optics Societssy, IEEE/Electron Devices Society. Edition Information: Postconference ed. Published/Created: Washington, DC: Optical Society of America, c1995. Description: x, 211 p.: ill.; 29 cm. Notes: Includes bibliographical references and index. Subjects: Very high speed integrated circuits--Optoelectronics--Laser pulses, Ultrashort--Quantum electronics--Semiconductors--Optical communications--Congresses. Series: Technical digest series (Optical Society of America); 1995, v. 13. Variant Series: 1995 technical digest series; v. 13 LC Classification: TK7874.7 .U48 1995 Dewey Class No.: 621.381 20

Ultrafast electronics and optoelectronics: technical digest, March 17-19, 1997, Hyatt Regency Lake Tahoe, Incline Village, Nevada / technical cosponsors, IEEE/Lasers and Electro-Optics Society, IEEE/Electron Devices Society, Institute of Electronics, Communication, and Information Engineers (IECIE); sponsored and managed by Optical Society of America. Published/Created: Washington, DC: Optical Society of America, c1997. Description: x, 202 p.: ill.; 28 cm. ISBN: 1557524955 Notes: Includes bibliographical references and index. Subjects: Optical communications--Congresses. Pulse techniques (Electronics)--Optoelectronics--Picosecond pulses--Congresses. Semiconductors--Congresses. LC Classification: TK5103.59 .U48 1997

Ultrafast lasers probe phenomena in semiconductors and superconductors: 24-25 March 1992, Somerset, New Jersey /

Robert R. Alfano, chair/editor; sponsored by SPIE--the International Society for Optical Engineering. Published/Created: Bellingham, Wash.: SPIE, c1992. Related Authors: Alfano, R. R. Society of Photo-optical Instrumentation Engineers. Description: ix, 273 p.: ill.; 28 cm. ISBN: 0819408387 (pbk.) Notes: Includes bibliographical references and index. Subjects: Semiconductors--Congresses. Superconductors--Congresses. Laser beams--Congresses. Picosecond pulses--Congresses. Hot carriers--Congresses. Quantum wells--Congresses. Series: Proceedings of SPIE--the International Society for Optical Engineering; v. 1677. Variant Series: Proceedings / SPIE--the International Society for Optical Engineering; v. 1677 LC Classification: QC610.9 .U49 1992 Dewey Class No.: 537.6/2 20

Ultrafast optics and superstrong laser fields: Laser Optics 2000: 26-30 June, 2000, St. Petersburg, Russia / Alexander A. Andreev, Vladimir E. Yashin, editors; organized by Institute for Laser Physics (Russia) ... [et al.]; supported by Ministry of Science and Technical Policy of the Russian Federation ... [et al.]; published by SPIE--the International Society for Optical Engineering. Published/Created: Bellingham, Washington: SPIE, c2001. Related Authors: Andreev, Alexander A. Yashin, Vladimir E. Vserossiiskii nauchnyi tsentr "Gosudarstvennyi opticheskii institut im. S.I. Vavilova." Institute for Laser Physics. Russia (Federation). Ministerstvo nauki i tekhnologii. Society of Photo-optical Instrumentation Engineers. Laser Optics 2000 (2000: Saint Petersburg, Russia) Description: viii, 270 p.: ill.; 28 cm. ISBN: 0819440426 Notes: Includes bibliographic references and author index. Subjects: Laser pulses, Ultrashort--Congresses. High power lasers--Congresses. Series: Proceedings of SPIE--the International Society for Optical Engineering; v. 4352. Variant Series: SPIE proceedings series; v. 4352

Ultrafast processes in chemistry and photobiology / edited by M.A. El-Sayed, I. Tanaka, Y. Molin. Published/Created: Oxford [England]; Cambridge, Mass.: Blackwell Scientific, 1995. Related Authors: El-Sayed, Mustafa. Tanaka, I. Molin, IU. N. (IUrii Nikolaevich), 1934- International Union of Pure and Applied Chemistry. Description: xiv, 306 p.: ill.; 29 cm. ISBN: 086542893X Notes: "International Union of Pure and Applied Chemistry." Includes bibliographical references and index. Subjects: Lasers in chemistry. Laser spectroscopy. Laser pulses, Ultrashort. Series: A "chemistry for the 21st century" monograph LC Classification: QD63.L3 U48 1995 Dewey Class No.: 543/.0858 20

Ultrafast pulse generation and spectroscopy: 18-19, 22 January 1993, Los Angeles, California / Timothy R. Gosnell ... [et al.], chairs/editors; sponsored and published by SPIE--the International Society for Optical Engineering. Published/Created: Bellingham, Wash., USA: SPIE, c1993. Related Authors: Gosnell, Timothy R., 1957- Society of Photo-optical Instrumentation Engineers. Description: vii, 378 p.: ill.; 28 cm. ISBN: 0819410888 (pbk.) Notes: Includes bibliographical references and author index. Subjects: Laser pulses, Ultrashort--Congresses. Laser spectroscopy--Congresses. Semiconductor lasers--Congresses. Series: Proceedings of SPIE--the International Society for Optical Engineering; v. 1861. Variant Series: Proceedings / SPIE--the International Society for Optical Engineering; v. 1861 LC Classification: TA1673 .U46 1993 Dewey Class No.: 621.36/6 20

Ultrashort wavelength lasers II: 12-13 July 1993, San Diego, California / Szymon Suckewer, chair/editor; sponsored and published by SPIE--the International Society for Optical Engineering. Published/Created: Bellingham, Wash., USA: SPIE, c1994. Related Authors: Suckewer, S. Society of Photo-optical Instrumentation Engineers. Description: x, 298 p.: ill.; 28 cm. ISBN: 0819412619 (pbk.) Notes: Includes bibliographical references and author index. Subjects: X-ray lasers--Congresses. Series: Proceedings of SPIE--the International Society for Optical Engineering; v. 2012. Variant Series: Proceedings / SPIE--the International Society for Optical Engineering; v. 2012 LC Classification: TA1707 .U45 1994 Dewey Class No.: 621.36/6 20

Ultrashort-wavelength lasers: 22-23 July 1991, San Diego, California / Szymon Suckewer, chair/editor; sponsored and published by SPIE--the International Society for Optical Engineering. Published/Created: Bellingham, Wash.: The Society, c1992. Related Authors: Suckewer, S. Society of Photo-optical Instrumentation Engineers. Description: x, 351 p.: ill.; 28 cm. ISBN: 0819406791 Notes: Includes bibliographical references and index. Subjects: X-ray lasers--Congresses. Series: Proceedings of SPIE--the International Society for Optical Engineering; v. 1551. Variant Series: Proceedings / SPIE--the International Society for Optical Engineering; v. 1551 LC Classification: TA1707 .U47 1992 Dewey Class No.: 621.36/6 20

Ultraviolet spectroscopy and UV lasers / edited by Prabhakar Misra, Mark A. Dubinskii. Published/Created: New York: Marcel Dekker, 2002. Projected Pub. Date: 0202 Related Authors: Misra, Prabhakar, 1955- Dubinskii, Mark A., 1948- Description: p. cm. ISBN: 0824706684 (acid-free paper) Notes: Includes bibliographical references and index. Subjects: Ultraviolet spectroscopy. Ultraviolet radiation. Laser beams. Series: Practical spectroscopy; v. 30 LC Classification: QD96.U4 U47 2002 Dewey Class No.: 535.8/44 21

United States. Congress. House. Committee on Armed Services. Subcommittee on Research and Development. Laser briefing for RDT&E budget request for fiscal year 1990: hearing before the Research and Development Subcommittee of the Committee on Armed Services, House of Representatives, One Hundred First Congress, first session, hearing held, March 8, 1989. Published/Created: Washington: U.S. G.P.O.: For sale by the Supt. of Docs., Congressional Sales Office, U.S. G.P.O., 1990. Description: iii, 43 p.: ill.; 24 cm. Notes: Distributed to some depository libraries in microfiche. Shipping list no.: 90-239-P. "H.A.S.C no. 101-34." Item 1012-A, 1012-B (MF) Subjects: Lasers--Military applications--Research--United States. LC Classification: KF27 .A7668 1989b Dewey Class No.: 355.8/246 20

United States. Congress. Senate. Committee on Energy and Natural Resources. Subcommittee on Energy Research and Development. Atomic vapor laser isotope separation program: hearing before the Subcommittee on Energy Research and Development of the Committee on Energy and Natural Resources, United States Senate, One Hundred Second Congress, first session, on the status of the Department of Energy's atomic vapor laser isotope separation program, September 24, 1991. Published/Created: Washington: U.S. G.P.O.: For sale by the U.S. G.P.O., Supt. of Docs., Congressional Sales Office, 1991. Description: iii, 66 p.; 24 cm. ISBN: 0160370418 Notes: Distributed to some depository libraries in microfiche. Shipping list no.: 92-075-P. Item 1040-A, 1040-B (MF) Subjects: United States. Dept. of Energy. Lasers in isotope separation--United States--Technological innovations. Uranium enrichment--United States--Technological innovations. Series: United States. Congress. Senate. S. hrg.; 102-318. Variant Series: S. hrg.; 102-318 LC Classification: KF26 .E554 1991d

UV and visible lasers and laser crystal growth: 7-9 February 1995, San Jose, California / Richard Scheps, Milan R. Kokta, chairs/editors; sponsored and published by SPIE--the International Society for Optical Engineering. Published/Created: Bellingham, Wash.: SPIE, c1995. Related Authors: Scheps, Richard, 1946- Kokta, Milan R. Society of Photo-optical Instrumentation Engineers. Description: ix, 360 p.: ill.; 28 cm. ISBN: 0819417270 Notes: Includes bibliographical references and author index. Subjects: Solid-state lasers--Congresses. Dye lasers--Congresses. Gas lasers--Congresses. Crystal growth--Congresses. Series: Proceedings of SPIE--the International Society for Optical Engineering; v. 2380. Variant Series: Proceedings / SPIE--the International Society for Optical Engineering; v. 2380 LC Classification: TA1673 .U8 1995 Dewey Class No.: 621.36/6 20

Van Hecke, Gerald R. A guide to lasers in chemistry / Gerlad R. Van Hecke, Kerry K. Karukstis. Published/Created: Boston: Jones and Bartlett, c1998. Related Authors: Karukstis, Kerry K. Description: xi, 252 p.: ill.; 29 cm. ISBN: 0763704121 Notes: Includes bibliographical references and index. Subjects: Lasers in chemistry. Laser spectroscopy. Laser photochemistry. LC Classification: QD63.L3 V36 1998 Dewey Class No.: 542/.8 21

Vasil′ev, Peter. Ultrafast diode lasers: fundamentals and applications / Peter Vasil′ev. Published/Created: Boston: Artech House, c1995. Description: xi, 271 p.: ill.; 24 cm. ISBN: 0890067368 Notes: Includes bibliographical references and index. Subjects: Semiconductor lasers. Laser pulses, Ultrashort. Series: Artech House optoelectronics library LC Classification: TA1700 .V37 1995 Dewey Class No.: 621.36/61 20

Verdeyen, Joseph Thomas. Laser electronics / Joseph T. Verdeyen. Edition Information: 3rd ed. Published/Created: Englewood Cliffs, N.J.: Prentice Hall, c1995. Description: xxvi, 778, 12 p.: ill.; 25 cm. ISBN: 013706666X Notes: Includes bibliographical references and index. Subjects: Lasers. Semiconductor lasers. Series: Prentice Hall series in solid state physical electronics LC Classification: TA1675 .V47 1995 Dewey Class No.: 621.36/61 20

Verdeyen, Joseph Thomas. Laser electronics / Joseph T. Verdeyen. Edition Information: 2nd ed. Published/Created: Englewood Cliffs, N.J.: Prentice Hall, c1989. Description: xvii, 622 p.: ill.; 24 cm. ISBN: 0135236304 Notes: Includes bibliographies and indexes. Subjects: Lasers. Semiconductor lasers. Series: Prentice-Hall series in solid state physical electronics LC Classification: TA1675 .V47 1989 Dewey Class No.: 621.36/61 19

Vertical-cavity surface-emitting laser arrays: 27-28 January 1994, Los Angeles, California / Jack L. Jewell, chair/editor; sponsored and published by SPIE--the International Society for Optical Engineering. Published/Created: Bellingham, Wash., USA: SPIE, c1994. Related Authors: Jewell, Jack L. Society of Photo-optical Instrumentation Engineers. Description: v, 152 p.: ill.; 28 cm. ISBN: 0819414425 (pbk.) Notes: Includes bibliographical references and author index. Subjects: Semiconductor lasers--Congresses. Series: Proceedings of SPIE--the International Society for Optical Engineering; v. 2147. Variant Series: Proceedings / SPIE--the International Society for Optical Engineering; v. 2147 LC Classification: TA1700 .V47 1994 Dewey Class No.: 621.36/6 20

Vertical-cavity surface-emitting laser devices / [edited by] H.E. Li, K. Iga. Published/Created: New York: Springer, 2002. Projected Pub. Date: 0201 Related Authors: Li, H. E. (Herbert E.), 1957- Iga, Ken'ichi, 1940- Description: p. cm. ISBN: 3540678514 (alk. paper) Notes: Includes bibliographical references and index. Subjects: Semiconductor lasers. Series: Springer series in photonics; v. 6 LC Classification: TA1770 .V4717 2002 Dewey Class No.: 621.36/6 21

Vertical-cavity surface-emitting lasers II: 28-29 January 1998, San Jose, California / Kent D. Choquette, Robert A. Morgan, chairs/editors; sponsored ... by SPIE--The International Society for Optical Engineering. Published/Created: Bellingham, Wash., USA: SPIE, c1998. Related Authors: Choquette, Kent D. Morgan, Robert A. Society of Photo-optical Instrumentation Engineers. Description: ix, 254 p.: ill.; 28 cm. ISBN: 081942725X Notes: Includes bibliographical references and index. Subjects: Semiconductor lasers--Congresses. Series: Proceedings of SPIE--the International Society for Optical Engineering; v. 3286. Variant Series: SPIE proceedings series; v. 3286 LC Classification: TA1700 .V472 1998 Dewey Class No.: 621.36/6 21

Vertical-cavity surface-emitting lasers III: 25-26 January, 1999, San Jose, California / Kent D. Choquette, Chun Lei, chairs/editors; sponsored and published by, SPIE--The International Society for Optical Engineering; cooperating organization, DARPA--Defense Advanced Research Projects Agency. Published/Created: Bellingham, Washington: SPIE, c1999. Related Authors: Choquette, Kent D. Lei, Chun. Society of Photo-optical Instrumentation Engineers. United States. Defense Advanced Research Projects Agency. Description: ix, 206 p.: ill.; 28 cm. ISBN: 0819430978 Notes: Includes bibliographic references and author index. Subjects: Semiconductor lasers--Congresses. Series: Proceedings of SPIE--the International Society for Optical Engineering; v. 3627. Variant Series: SPIE proceedings series; v. 3627 LC Classification: TA1673 .V47 1999 Dewey Class No.: 621.36/6 21 Other

Vertical-cavity surface-emitting lasers IV: 26-28 January 2000, San Jose, California / Kent D. Choquette, Chun Lei, chairs/editors; sponsored and published by, SPIE--The International Society for Optical Engineering. Published/Created: Bellingham, Wash., USA: SPIE, c2000. Related Authors: Choquette, Kent D. Lei, Zhun. Society of Photo-optical Instrumentation Engineers. Description: vii, 260 p.: ill.; 28 cm. ISBN: 0819435635 Notes: Includes bibliographic references and index. Subjects: Semiconductor lasers--Congresses. Series: Proceedings of SPIE--the International Society for Optical Engineering; v. 3946. Variant Series: SPIE proceedings series; v. 3946 LC Classification: TA1673 .V473 2000 Dewey Class No.: 621.36/6 21

Vertical-cavity surface-emitting lasers V: 24-25 January, 2001, San Jose, [California] USA / Kent D. Choquette, Chun Lei, chairs/editors; sponsored and published by, SPIE--The International Society for Optical Engineering. Published/Created: Bellingham, Washington: SPIE, c2001. Related Authors: Choquette, Kent D. Lei, Chun. Society of Photo-optical Instrumentation Engineers. Description: xxxiv, 234 p.: ill.; 28 cm. ISBN: 0819439649 Notes: Includes bibliographic references and author index. Subjects: Semiconductor lasers--Congresses. Series: Proceedings of SPIE--the International Society for Optical Engineering; v. 4286. Variant Series: SPIE proceedings series; v. 4286

Vertical-cavity surface-emitting lasers: 13-14 February, 1997, San Jose, California / Kent D. Choquette, Dennis G. Deppe, chairs/editors; sponsored and published by SPIE--the International Society for Optical Engineering; cooperating organization DARPA--Defense Advanced Research Projects Agency. Published/Created: Bellingham, Wash.: SPIE, c1996. Related Authors: Choquette, Kent D. Deppe, Dennis G. Description: ix, 202 p.: ill.; 28 cm. ISBN: 0819424145 Notes: Includes bibliographic references and author index. Subjects: Semiconductor lasers--Congresses. Optical interconnects--Congresses. Series: Proceedings of SPIE--the International Society for Optical Engineering; v. 3003 LC Classification: TA1700 .V473 1996 Dewey Class No.: 621.36/6 21

Vertical-cavity surface-emitting lasers: design, fabrication, characterization, and applications / edited by Carl W. Wilmsen, Henryk Temkin, and Larry A. Coldren. Published/Created: Cambridge; New York: Cambridge University Press, 1999. Related Authors: Wilmsen, Carl W. Temkin, H. Coldren, L. A. (Larry A.) Description: xvii, 455 p.: ill.; 26 cm. ISBN: 0521590221 Notes: Includes bibliographical references and index. Subjects: Semiconductor lasers. Series: Cambridge studies in modern optics (Unnumbered) Variant Series: Cambridge studies in modern optics LC Classification: TA1700 .V474 1999 Dewey Class No.: 621.36/6 21

Vertical-cavity surface-emitting lasers: technology and applications / edited by Julian Cheng and Niloy K. Dutta. Published/Created: [Amsterdam]: Gordon & Breach, 2000. Related Authors: Cheng, Julian. Dutta, N. K. (Niloy K.), 1953- Description: xiv, 323 p.: ill.; 24 cm. ISBN: 9056992635 Notes: Includes bibliographical references and index. Subjects: Semiconductor lasers. Optical interconnects. Lasers. Optical interconnects. Series: Optoelectronic properties of semiconductors and superlattices; v. 10 National Bib. No.: GB99-W2107

Visible and UV lasers: 25-26 January 1994, Los Angeles, California / Richard Scheps, chair/editor; sponsored and published by SPIE--the International Society for Optical Engineering. Published/Created: Bellingham, Wash., USA: SPIE, c1994. Related Authors: Scheps, Richard, 1946- Description: ix, 284 p.: ill.; 28 cm. ISBN: 0819414085 (pbk.) Notes: Includes bibliographical references and index. Subjects: Lasers--Solid-state lasers--Dye lasers--Gas lasers--Congresses. Series: Proceedings of SPIE--the International Society for Optical Engineering; v. 2115. Variant Series: Proceedings / SPIE--the International Society for Optical Engineering; v. 2115 LC Classification: TA1673 .V57 1994 Dewey Class No.: 621.36/6 20

Wakita, Koichi, 1944- Semiconductor optical modulators / by Koichi Wakita. Published/Created: Boston: Kluwer Academic Publishers, c1998. Description: xvi, 313 p.: ill.; 25 cm. ISBN: 0792380142 (alk. paper) Notes: Includes bibliographical references and index. Subjects: Semiconductor lasers. Quantum wells. Optoelectronics. LC Classification: TA1700 .W35 1998 Dewey Class No.: 621.36/61 21

Wavelength division multiplexing components: 29-31 January 1996, San Jose, California / Louis S. Lome, chair/editor; sponsored and published by SPIE--the International Society for Optical Engineering; cooperating organization, ARPA--Advanced Research Projects Agency. Published/Created: Bellingham, WA: SPIE, 1996. Related Authors: Lome, Louis S. Society of Photo-optical Instrumentation Engineers. United States. Advanced Research Projects Agency. Description: ix, 392 p.: ill.; 28 cm. ISBN: 0819420646 (pbk.) Notes: Includes bibliographical references and index. Subjects: Wavelength division multiplexing.--Congresses. Fiber optics--Congresses. Lasers--Congresses. Series: Proceedings of SPIE--the International Society for Optical Engineering; v. 2690. Variant Series: Proceedings / SPIE--the International Society for Optical Engineering; v. 2690 LC Classification: TK5103.59 .W38 1996 Dewey Class No.: 621.382/75 21

Weber, Marvin J., 1932- Handbook of lasers / Marvin J. Weber. Published/Created: Boca Raton: CRC Press, c2001. Description: 1198 p.: ill.; 26 cm. ISBN: 0849335094 (alk. paper) Notes: Includes bibliographical references and index. Subjects: Lasers--Handbooks, manuals, etc. Series: The CRC Press laser and optical science and technology series LC Classification: TA1683 .W44 2001 Dewey Class No.: 621.36/6 21

Weber, Marvin J., 1932- Handbook of optical materials / Marvin J. Weber. Published/Created: Boca Raton, FL: CRC Press, 2002. Projected Pub. Date: 0209 Description: p. cm. ISBN: 0849335124 (alk. paper) Notes: Includes bibliographical references and index. Subjects: Optical materials--Handbooks, manuals, etc. Lasers--Handbooks, manuals, etc. Electrooptics--Handbooks, manuals, etc. LC Classification: QC374 .W43 2002 Dewey Class No.: 621.36 21

Weber, Marvin John, 1932- Handbook of laser wavelengths / Marvin J. Weber. Published/Created: Boca Raton: CRC

Press, c1999. Description: 767 p.: ill.; 26 cm. ISBN: 0849335086 (alk. paper) Notes: Includes bibliographical references. Subjects: Lasers--Handbooks, manuals, etc. Laser materials--Handbooks, manuals, etc. Light--Wave-length--Handbooks, manuals, etc. Series: The CRC Press laser and optical science and technology series LC Classification: TA1683 .W43 1999 Dewey Class No.: 621.36/6 21

Weiss, C. O. Dynamics of lasers / C.O. Weiss, R. Vilaseca. Published/Created: Weinheim [Germany]; New York: VCH, c1991. Related Authors: Vilaseca, R. Description: xiii, 276 p.: ill.; 25 cm. ISBN: 3527265864 (Weinheim: acid-free paper) 0895739666 (New York: acid-free paper) Notes: Includes bibliographical references (p. 257-268) and index. Subjects: Lasers. Dynamics. Nonlinear theories. Series: Nonlinear systems; v. 1 LC Classification: QC688 .W45 1991 Dewey Class No.: 621.36/6 20

Westcott, Jeffrey P. The operational pyramid / by Jeffrey P. Westcott. Published/Created: Pittsburgh, Pa.: Dorrance Pub., c1995. Description: vii, 101 p.: ill.; 24 cm. ISBN: 0805935630 Notes: Includes bibliographical references (p. 101). Subjects: Great Pyramid (Egypt)--Miscellanea. Carbon dioxide lasers. LC Classification: DT63 .W43 1995 Dewey Class No.: 932 20

Wheeland, Ronald G. Lasers in skin disease / Ronald G. Wheeland. Published/Created: New York: Thieme Medical Publishers, 1988. Description: 142 p., [4] p. of plates: ill. (some col.); 29 cm. ISBN: 0865772711 Notes: Includes bibliographies and index. Subjects: Lasers--Therapeutic use. Skin--Diseases--Treatment. Laser Surgery. Skin Diseases--surgery. Series: American Academy of Facial Plastic and Reconstructive Surgery (Series) Variant Series: The American Academy of Facial Plastic and Reconstructive Surgery LC Classification: RL120.L37 W47 1988 Dewey Class No.: 616.5/0631 19

Wide-gap luminescent materials: theory and applications / edited by Stanley R. Rotman. Published/Created: Boston: Kluwer Academic Publishers, c1997. Related Authors: Rotman, Stanley R., 1958- Description: xiv, 368 p.: ill.; 25 cm. ISBN: 0792398378 (acid-free paper) Notes: Includes bibliographical references and index. Subjects: Phosphors. Wide gap semiconductors. Optoelectronics--Materials. Solid state lasers--Materials. Fiber optics--Materials. Scintillators. Series: Kluwer international series in--electronic materials, science and technology LC Classification: TK7871.15.P4 W53 1997 Dewey Class No.: 621.3815/2 21

Winburn, D. C. Practical laser safety / D.C. Winburn. Edition Information: 2nd ed., rev. and expanded. Published/Created: New York: M. Dekker, 1990. Description: x, 241 p.: ill.; 23 cm. ISBN: 0824782402 Notes: Includes bibliographical references. Subjects: Lasers--Safety measures. Series: Occupational safety and health (Marcel Dekker, Inc.); 11. Variant Series: Occupational safety and health; 11 LC Classification: TA1677 .W56 1990 Dewey Class No.: 621.36/6/0289 20

Windows on a new world: the third industrial revolution / edited by Joseph Finkelstein. Published/Created: New York: Greenwood Press, 1989. Related Authors: Finkelstein, Joseph, 1926- Description: xxi, 240 p.: ill.; 25 cm. ISBN: 0313263213 (lib. bdg.: alk. paper) Contents: Microelectronics / R.A. Powell -- Materials and modern technology / J.E. Burke -- Lasers / Joseph W. Haus and John Schroeder -- Biotechnology / Arnold E.S. Gussin -- Frontiers in biophysics / Jay Newman -- The grand system / Alan J. Scrime -- The revolution in manufacturing / I.M. Hymes -- Management during the third industrial revolution / Allan Doyle -- The third industrial revolution / Joseph Finkelstein and David Newman. Notes: Includes index. Bibliography: p. [233]-234. Subjects: Technological innovations--Economic aspects--History. Information technology--History. Microelectronics--History. Telecommunication--History.

Series: Contributions in economics and economic history, 0084-9235; no. 88 LC Classification: HC79.T4 W47 1989 Dewey Class No.: 338/.06 19

Witzigmann, Bernd, 1969- Design and implementation of a three-dimensional edge emitting quantum well laser simulator / Bernd Witzigmann. Published/Created: Konstanz: Hartung-Gorre, 2000. Description: x, 95 p.: ill.; 22 cm. ISBN: 3896496042 Notes: Abstract in English and German. Includes bibliographical references (p. 87-93). Subjects: Semiconductor lasers--Computer simulation. Quantum wells--Computer simulation. Series: Series in microelectronics; v. 102 LC Classification: TA1700 .W57 2000

Wood, David, 1957- Optoelectronic semiconductor devices / David Wood. Published/Created: New York: Prentice Hall, 1994. Description: xvii, 564 p.: ill.; 25 cm. ISBN: 0136387500 (pbk): Notes: Includes bibliographical references and index. Subjects: Semiconductors. Semiconductor lasers. Optoelectronics. Optics. Series: Prentice-Hall international series in optoelectronics LC Classification: TA1700 .W66 1994 Dewey Class No.: 621.3815/2 20

Wood, Leo. Lasers in the service of Australian industry: report of a workshop held at Macquarie University, 17-18 February 1992 / Leo Wood. Published/Created: [Canberra]: Dept. of Industry, Technology and Commerce, 1992. Related Authors: Australia. Dept. of Industry, Technology and Commerce. Description: x, 97 p.; 25 cm. ISBN: 0642180105 Subjects: Lasers--Australia--Industrial applications--Congresses. LC Classification: TA1673 .W66 1992 Dewey Class No.: 621.366 20

Workshop on Optronic Techniques in Diagnostic and Therapeutic Medicine (1990: Florence, Italy) Optronic techniques in diagnostic and therapeutic medicine / edited by Riccardo Pratesi. Published/Created: New York: Plenum Press, c1991. Related Authors: Pratesi, R. (Riccardo) Description: xvii, 309 p.: ill.; 26 cm. ISBN: 0306439387 Notes: "Based on the proceedings of a Workshop on Optronic Techniques in Diagnostic and Therapeutic Medicine, held March 26-27, 1990, in Florence, Italy"--T.p. verso. Includes bibliographical references and index. Subjects: Lasers in medicine--Congresses. Optoelectronics--Laser Surgery--Lasers--diagnostic use--therapeutic use--Congresses. Series: The Language of science LC Classification: R857.L37 W67 1990 Dewey Class No.: 617/.05 20

Workshop on Plasma and Laser Technology (2nd: 1990: Cairo, Egypt) Second Workshop on Plasma and Laser Technology, Cairo, February 21-28, 1990 / editor, E. Hintz. Published/Created: Julïch [Germany]: Forschungszentrum, Zentralbibliothek, c1990. Related Authors: Hintz, E. Description: 416 p.: ill.; 24 cm. ISBN: 3893360506 Notes: Cover Title - IInd Workshop on Plasma and Laser Technology. Includes bibliographical references. Subjects: Plasma (Ionized gases)--Plasma diagnostics--Lasers--Congresses. Series: Bilateral seminars of the International Bureau, 0938-7668; v. 2 LC Classification: QC717.6 .W66 1990

Worldwide markets for medical and dental lasers. Published/Created: Irvine, Calif.: Medical Data International, [c1998] Related Authors: Medical Data International, Inc. Description: 1 v. (various pagings); 30 cm. Notes: "August 1998." "#RP-771122." Subjects: Medical laser industry. Dental instruments and apparatus industry. Market surveys. LC Classification: HD9995.L372 W67 1998

Wormington, Charles M. Opthalmic lasers: [techniques and co-management] / Charles M. Wormington. Published/Created: Philadelphia, PA: Butterworth-Heinemann, 2003. Projected Pub. Date: 0211 Description: p. cm. ISBN: 0750695722 Subjects: Lasers in ophthalmology. LC Classification: RE86 .W675 2003 Dewey Class No.: 617.7/0028 21

Wright, V. Cecil. Laser surgery in gynecology: a clinical guide / V. Cecil Wright, John C. Fisher. Published/Created: Philadelphia: Saunders, c1993. Related Authors: Fisher, John C., 1922- Description: xix, 314 p.: ill. (some col.); 27 cm. ISBN: 0721640079 Notes: Includes bibliographical references and index. Subjects: Generative organs, Female--Laser surgery. Genital Diseases, Female--therapy. Genitalia, Female--surgery. Laser surgery. Lasers--therapeutic use. LC Classification: RG104 .W75 1993 Dewey Class No.: 618.1/059 20

X rays from laser plasmas: 19-21 August 1987, San Diego, California / Martin C. Richardson, chair/editor; sponsored by SPIE--the International Society for Optical Engineering; cooperating organizations, Applied Optics Laboratory, New Mexico State University ... [et al.]. Published/Created: Bellingham, Wash., USA: The Society, c1988. Related Authors: Richardson, Martin C. Society of Photo-optical Instrumentation Engineers. New Mexico State University. Applied Optics Laboratory. Description: viii, 324 p.: ill.; 28 cm. ISBN: 0892528664 Notes: Includes bibliographies and index. Subjects: Laser plasmas--Congresses. X-ray optics--Congresses. X-ray lasers--Congresses. Series: Proceedings of SPIE--the International Society for Optical Engineering; v. 831 LC Classification: TA1775 .X2 1988 Dewey Class No.: 621.36/6 20

X-ray FEL optics and instrumentation: 30-31 July, 2001, San Diego, [California] USA / Dennis M. Mills, Horst Schulte-Schrepping, John R. Arthur, chairs/editors; sponsored and published by, SPIE--the International Society for Optical Engineering. Published/Created: Bellingham, Washington: SPIE, c2001. Related Authors: Mills, Dennis M. Schulte-Schrepping, Horst. Arthur, John R. Society of Photo-optical Instrumentation Engineers. Description: v, 120 p.: ill.; 28 cm. ISBN: 0819437883 Notes: Includes bibliographic references and author index. Subjects: Free electron lasers--Congresses. X-ray optics--Congresses. Solid-state lasers--Congresses. Lasers--Congresses. Series: Proceedings of SPIE--the International Society for Optical Engineering; v. 4143. Variant Series: SPIE proceedings series; v. 4143

X-ray lasers 1990: proceedings of the 2nd international colloquium held at the University of York, 17-21 September 1990 / edited by G.J. Tallents. Published/Created: Bristol, England; Philadelphia: Institute of Physics, c1990. Related Authors: Tallents, G. J. International Colloquium on X-ray Lasers (2nd: 1990: University of York) Description: xii, 381 p.: ill.; 24 cm. ISBN: 085498044X Notes: "2nd International Colloquium on X-ray Lasers"--Pref. Includes bibliographical references and index. Subjects: X-ray lasers--Congresses. Series: Institute of Physics conference series; no. 116 LC Classification: TA1707 .X27 1990 Dewey Class No.: 621.36/6 20

X-ray lasers 1992: proceedings of the 3rd international colloquium held at Schliersee, Germany, 18-22 May 1992 / edited by E.E. Fill. Published/Created: Bristol [England]; Philadelphia: Institute of Physics, c1992. Related Authors: Fill, E. (Ernst), 1940- International Colloquium on X-ray Lasers (3rd: 1992: Schliersee, Germany) Description: xiv, 457 p.: ill.; 25 cm. ISBN: 0854984151 Notes: Papers presented at the Third International Colloquium on X-ray Lasers. Includes bibliographical references and index. Subjects: X-ray lasers--Congresses. Series: Institute of Physics conference series; no. 125 LC Classification: TA1707 .X28 1992 Dewey Class No.: 621.36/6 20

X-ray lasers 1994: fourth international colloquium / David C. Eder, Dennis L. Matthews. Published/Created: Woodbury, NY: American Institute of Physics, 1995. Description: p. cm. ISBN: 1563963752 Series: AIP conference proceedings; no. 332 LC Classification: 9505 BOOK NOT YET IN LC

Yariv, Amnon. Optical electronics / Amnon Yariv. Edition Information: 4th ed.

Published/Created: Philadelphia: Saunders College Pub., c1991. Description: xiii, 713 p.: ill.; 25 cm. ISBN: 0030474442 Notes: Includes bibliographical references and index. Subjects: Lasers. Fiber optics. Electrooptical devices. Acoustooptical devices. Optoelectronic devices. Series: The Holt, Rinehart, and Winston series in electrical engineering LC Classification: TA1675 .Y37 1991 Dewey Class No.: 621.36 20

Yariv, Amnon. Optical electronics in modern communications / Amnon Yariv. Edition Information: 5th ed. Published/Created: New York: Oxford University Press, 1997. Related Authors: Yariv, Amnon. Optical electronics. Description: xviii, 744 p.: ill.; 25 cm. ISBN: 0195106261 (cl) Notes: Rev. ed of: Optical electronics. 4th ed., c1991. Includes bibliographical references and index. Subjects: Lasers. Fiber optics. Electrooptical devices. Acoustooptical devices. Optoelectronic devices. Series: The Oxford series in electrical and computer engineering LC Classification: TA1675 .Y37 1997 Dewey Class No.: 621.382/7 20

Yariv, Amnon. Solutions manual for optical electronics in modern communications, 5th ed. / Amnon Yariv; with contributions from Huey-Daw Wu ... [et al.]. Published/Created: New York: Oxford University Press, 1997. Projected Pub. Date: 9702 Related Authors: Wu, Huey-Daw. Yariv, Amnon. Optical electronics in modern communications. Description: p. cm. ISBN: 019510627X (paper) Subjects: Lasers--Handbooks, manuals, etc. Fiber optics--Handbooks, manuals, etc. Electrooptical devices--Handbooks, manuals, etc. Acoustooptical devices--Handbooks, manuals, etc. Optoelectronic devices--Handbooks, manuals, etc. LC Classification: TA1675 .Y38 1997 Dewey Class No.: 621.382/7/076 21

Young, Matt, 1941- Optics and lasers: including fibers and optical waveguides / Matt Young. Edition Information: 5th completely rev. and enl. ed. Published/Created: Berlin; New York: Springer, c2000. Description: xix, 498 p.: ill.; 24 cm. ISBN: 354065741X (acid-free paper) Notes: Includes bibliographical references (p. [473]-480) and index. Subjects: Optics. Lasers. Fiber optics. Optical wave guides. Series: Advanced texts in physics, 1439-2674 LC Classification: QC335.2 .Y68 2000 Dewey Class No.: 621.36 21

Young, Matt, 1941- Optics and lasers: including fibers and optical waveguides / Matt Young. Edition Information: 4th rev. ed. Published/Created: Berlin; New York: Springer-Verlag, c1992. Description: xv, 343 p.: ill.; 25 cm. ISBN: 3540550100 (Berlin: alk. paper) 0387880100 (New York: alk. paper) Notes: Includes bibliographical references (p. [323]-327) and index. Subjects: Optics. Lasers. Fiber optics. Optical wave guides. LC Classification: QC355.2 .Y68 1992 Dewey Class No.: 621.36 20

Zhang, Jing-yuan. Optical parametric generation and amplification / Jing-yuan Zhang, Jung Y. Huang and Y.R. Shen. Published/Created: Australia; United States: Harwood Academic Publishers, c1995. Related Authors: Huang, Jung Y. Shen, Y. R. Description: vii, 70 p.: ill.; 23 cm. ISBN: 3718657430 Notes: Includes bibliographical references and index. Subjects: Tunable lasers. Parametric devices. Optical amplifiers. Series: Laser science and technology; v. 19

Zuev, V. S. Photochemical lasers / V.S. Zuev and L.D. Mikheev. Published/Created: Chur, Switzerland; Philadelphia: Harwood Academic, c1991. Related Authors: Mikheev, L. D. Description: x, 103 p.: ill.; 23 cm. Cancelled ISBN: 3718630622 Notes: Includes bibliographical references (p. 91-100) and index. Subjects: Chemical lasers. Series: Laser science and technology, 0899-2711; v. 11 LC Classification: TA1690 .Z84 1991 Dewey Class No.: 621.36/64 20

AUTHOR INDEX

A

B

C

D

E

F

G

H

I

M

N

O

P

R

S

T

U

SUBJECT INDEX

P

Q

R

S

T

U

V

W

X